CW01033619

Sacred Luxuries

Fragrance, Aromatherapy and
Cosmetics in Ancient Egypt

Sacred Luxuries

Fragrance, Aromatherapy and Cosmetics in Ancient Egypt

LISE MANNICHE

Photographs by

WERNER FORMAN

OPUS PUBLISHING LIMITED

LONDON

First published in 1999 by
Opus Publishing Limited
36 Camden Square
London NW1 9XA

Note: The recipes in this work have not been tested by the publisher and are not guaranteed for use.

A catalogue record of this book is available from the British Library

ISBN 0–9535546–0–0

Distributed by Art Books International Ltd
1 Stewart's Court, 220 Stewart's Road
London SW8 4UD

Printed in Italy by
Vincenzo Bona, s.r.l., Torino

Frontispiece The representation of Tutankhamun pouring scent into the queen's palm symbolised a climax of their union, and by extension belief in the renewal of life (see p. 97). One of the scenes on the gilded shrine which used to contain statuettes of the royal couple. 18th Dynasty, 1336-1327 BC. *Egyptian Museum, Cairo*

Contents

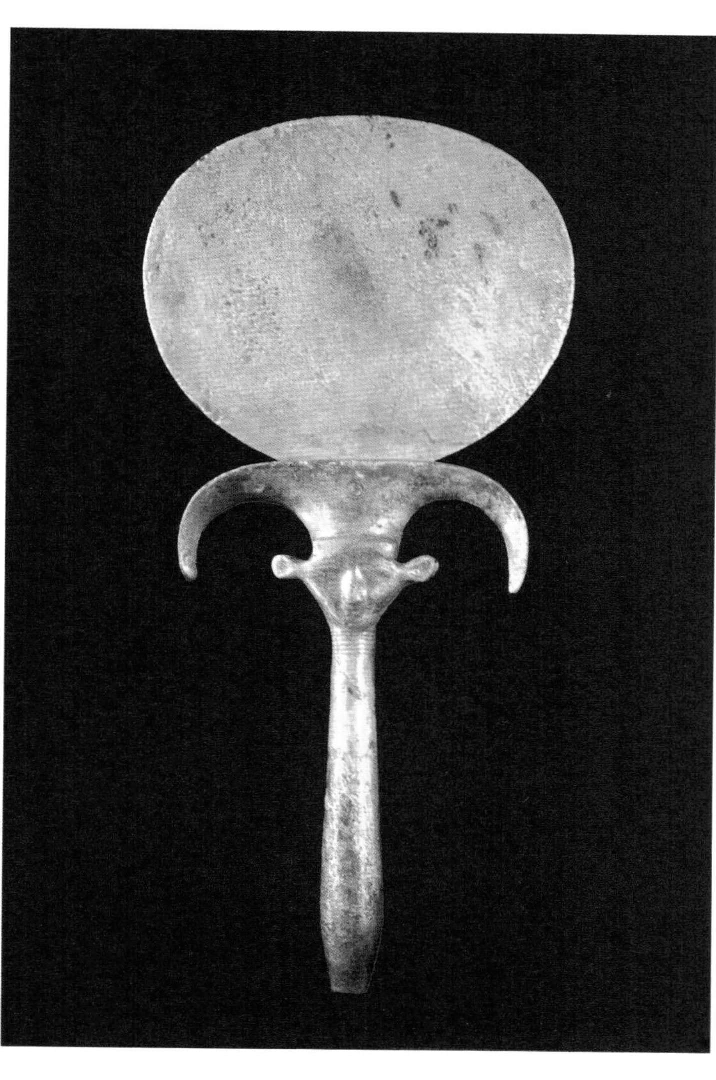

Polished bronze hand mirror with a handle in the form of a papyrus stem incorporating a double-sided image of the face of the goddess Hathor. Sheikh Abd el-Qurna. Height 32.2 cm. 18th Dynasty, c. 1550-1295 BC.
Egyptian Museum, Cairo

	Introduction	7
1	Ingredients	10
2	Scent in the Temple	33
3	Kyphi and Tiryac	47
4	Recipes for Luxury	61
5	Scent for Love and Rebirth	91
6	Fragrant Remedies	113
7	The Art of Cosmetics	127
	Epilogue	143
	Notes	146
	Bibliography	150
	Acknowledgments	151
	Ancient Egyptian Terms	152
	Index	153

Unguent jar in the form of a mother monkey holding its young. Inscribed with the name of king Merenra and a valediction. Alabaster, height 14 cm, 6th Dynasty, c. 2345-2181 BC. *Metropolitan Museum of Art, New York (30.8.34 – Theodore M. Davis Collection. Bequest of Theodore M. Davis, 1915)*

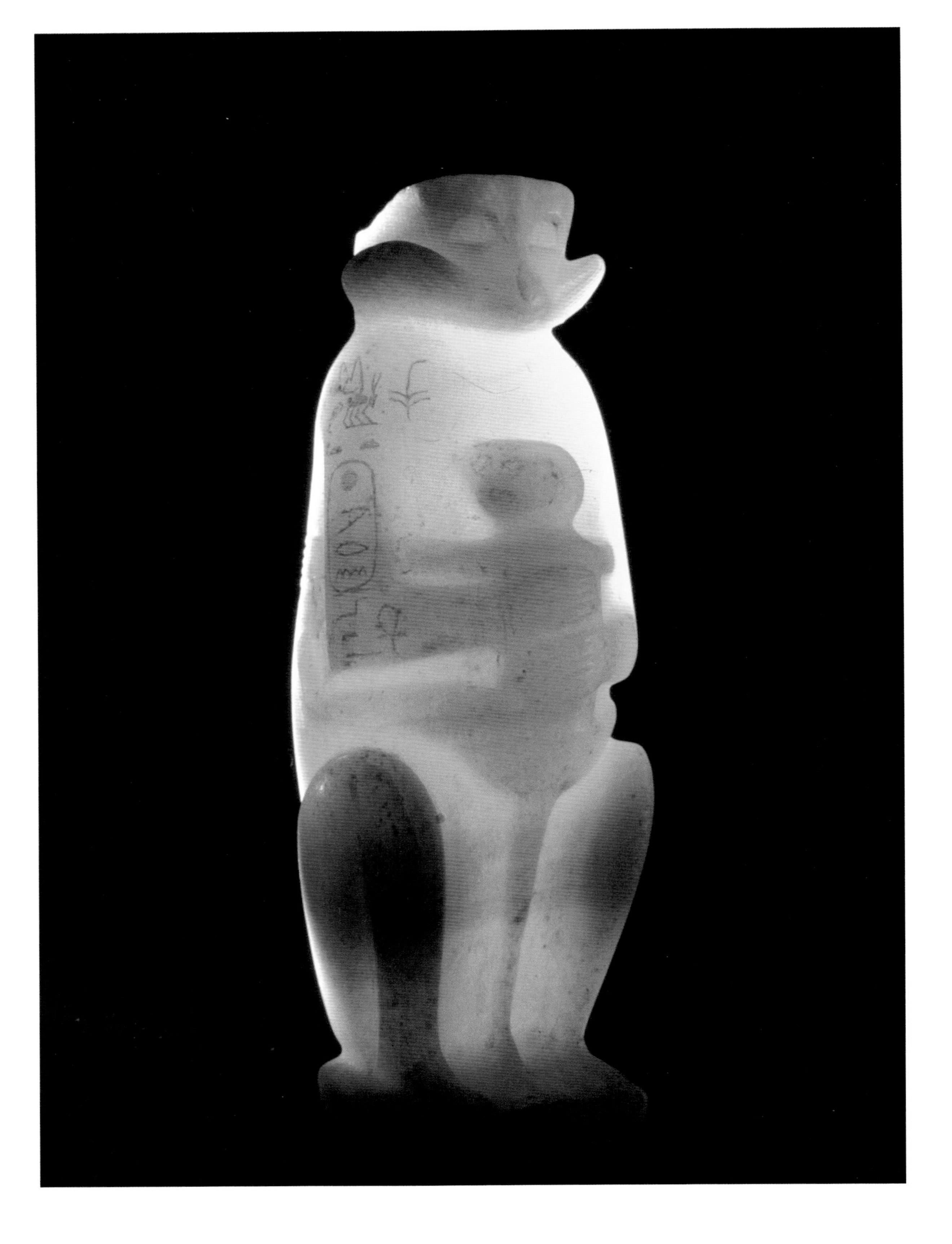

Introduction

The gods had favoured Egypt with a climate that was admirably suited for the production of floral fragrances. A regular supply of water and an abundance of sunshine assured good crops, whether the plants were cultivated or collected from the wilderness of the desert or the marshes of the River Nile. But in order to achieve fame the finished product had to have an aura of rarity, of exclusiveness and of the divine. The more exotic the ingredients, the more valued the commodity; the more exquisite its presentation, the greater the appeal. In this way, the visual and olfactory arts combined to make small objects of the greatest luxury appreciated not only in Egypt, but all over the ancient world.

Cosmetics had a largely mineral origin. In depictions of human beings in Egyptian art the prominence of the application of make-up is one of their chief characteristics, and among the earliest known artefacts are cosmetic palettes used to grind the substances made to enhance the appeal of gods, royalty and ordinary mortals.

In Egypt, the use of scented oils and incense had been known and developed from the earliest historical times. Funerary equipment includes containers for ointments and cosmetics, and ivory labels from the first dynasty were attached to jars containing 'Horus fragrance'. In the Old Kingdom specialists were in charge of the king's oils which were kept in an 'unguent chamber', and a selection of scented substances, usually seven in number, was provided for use in the Hereafter. Records are preserved of expeditions to the land of Punt, in later tradition equivalent to 'incense land'.

From the Middle Kingdom (c. 2000 BC) and on we begin to detect the existence of the fragrant routes to Egypt from other countries. Jars of ointment containing 'all good things' were delivered to the temple of Amun from the Levantine cities of Tunip, Tyre and Kedem among others. In the New Kingdom (ca. 1500 - 1000 BC) scented shipments from the Mycenean civilisation found their way to Egypt along with jars of drugs from Cyprus; merchandise arrived with bridal caravans from beyond the Euphrates; and jars of fragrant resin were carried on merchant ships that travelled around the ports of the Mediterranean.

Sweet ointment was enjoyed by pharaoh and mortals alike. At the court of Ramesses II in the Delta, we are told, the inhabitants dress in festive garments every day, their braided hair is drenched with sweet moringa oil, and they indulge in sweet ointment of the waters of a foreign locality called Segebyn. Moringa oil, which was admirably suited as a base oil for perfumes, was also distributed outside the palace for the enjoyment of the population of Thebes. One such happy event was depicted on a tomb wall around the reign of Tuthmosis III. Jars are piled up in the streets along with other goods. 'The people of Thebes are in jubilation, in joy and pleased at heart. "Ointment of sweet moringa oil, unguent of antiu resin" are the joyful words they say', the accompanying text informs us.

Sweet ointment was a remedy that even the gods would not want to be without. One of the most popular goddesses of all time, Isis, wife of Osiris who conceived her son Horus after his father's death, used it for medicinal

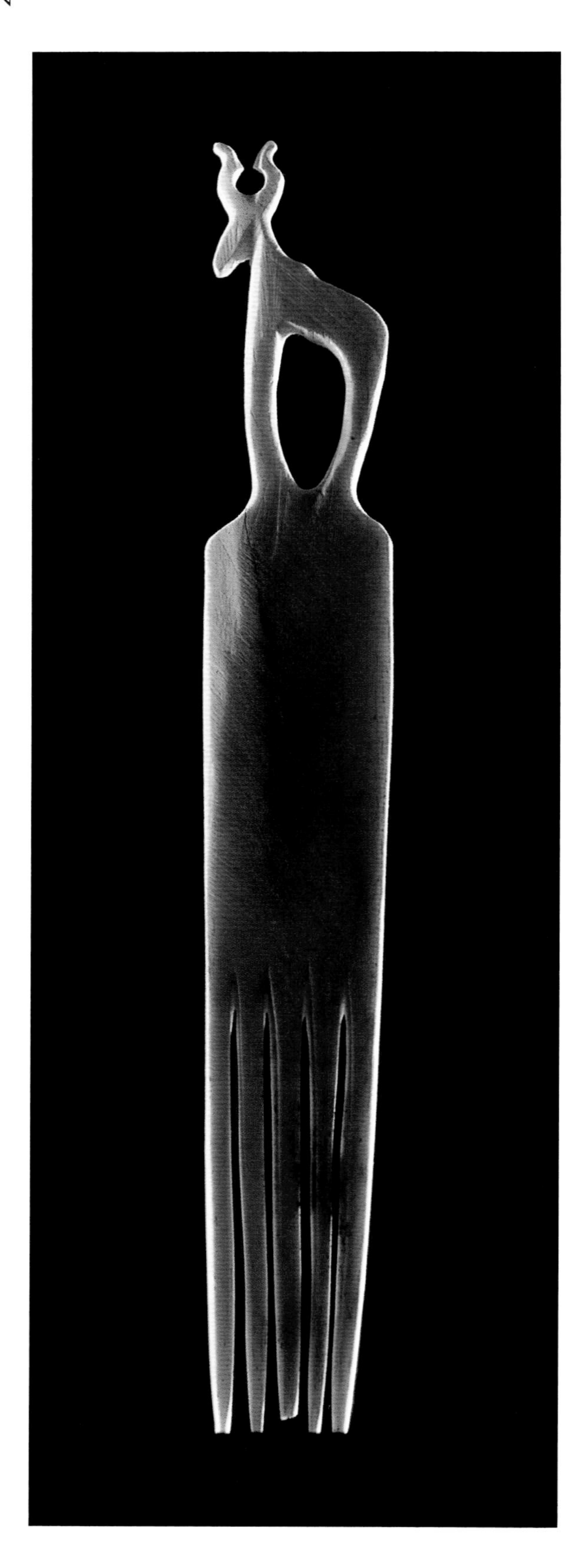

An exquisite bone comb embellished with a stylised representation of a gazelle or a similar horned animal.
Height 17 cm.
Predynastic, 3100 BC or earlier.
Ashmolean Museum, Oxford (1895.942)

purposes to heal a wound inflicted on her son's private parts. In the daily cult in the temple, ointment was presented to the deity along with cosmetics, food, clothing and ornaments, and during the rites performed at the initial steps in building a temple, alabaster jars with ointments were among the items included in the caches of foundation deposits. Works on the preparation of the substances, such as 'The magic book on how to prepare unguents' were kept in the temple library, with excerpts carved on the walls of the rooms in which the sacred material was stored. Oils were one of the necessities of life, which by the addition of scented matter were transformed into an item of luxury. Its use is well documented in literature as well as in art.

Anointing became a sign of distinction, a token of veneration towards a deity, an honour bestowed on an official. In a biblical context we are familiar with the episode that took place when Jesus sat in the house of Simon the leper and a woman entered with a flask of costly nard ointment and emptied it over his head. At the Egyptian court it was customary for the pharaoh to reward officials by presenting them with golden necklaces, gloves and other gifts. At the reward ceremony, when the official stood with his hands raised before his sovereign, an attendant would anoint his body and clothes with fragrance.

The sensible comments on plants by Theophrastus, the Greek botanist, relate not only to Athens in the 4th century AD, but also to foreign parts. It was around the same time that in between greater conquests Alexander the Great is said to have captured a chest of perfumes left in the camp of Dareios, king of the Persians, people well known for having commissioned perfumes that became famous all over the ancient world. According to Pliny, who recorded the incident at the beginning of Book 13 of his *Natural History*, the use of perfume was indeed due to the Persians.

When we reach the 1st century AD, information is forthcoming in the works of writers and medical men from the classical world. Athenaeus, Dioscorides, Pliny, and Galen all provide a wealth of details on plant material, much of which relates to scented matter, not only in the Graeco-Roman world, but in Egypt as well. The merchandise brought to Egypt was re-circulated when the finished product was exported to countries avid for scent from the land of the pharaohs.

This book owes its immediate inspiration to two visits to Egypt in 1990 and 1992, when I lectured to perfumers and people engaged in alternative medicine and related subjects. Our discussions while travelling down the Nile were most fruitful, and our visits to Egyptian manufacturers of essential oils and herb farms were enlightening.

I had occasion to read through many popular books on aromatherapy, where reference was frequently made to ancient Egyptian practices in both texts and illustrations. Much of the information was inexact, being based on secondary sources, if not on pure imagination. The art of aromatherapy at the present time is the most recent link in an unbroken chain of practices which originated in ancient civilisations such as the Egyptian, and the mere 'antiquity' of the concepts is as much part of the remedy now as it was to people in the ancient world, for they too looked to their ancestors for guidance.

The present work should go some way to demonstrate the contribution of the Egyptians. Recent (1998) analyses of the contents of cosmetic containers in the Louvre have shown that the manufacture of eyepaint was far more sophisticated than previously assumed. If more excavators and museum curators are encouraged to undertake an analysis of the contents of jars so often referred to in passing in the literature, the study of ancient scents will benefit greatly.

Much of the knowledge of the Greeks, and hence some of its original, ancient Egyptian source material, was transmitted by Arab scholars who added to the corpus of available medicinal writings their own knowledge of pharmacology. This tradition persisted and is alive and well in Islamic countries all over the world.

The popularity of scented and cosmetic material as on the one hand a luxury item and on the other as an ingredient in the daily cult of the gods gave rise to manufacture of a series of exquisite works of art in a variety of materials in the form of scent and cosmetic containers and dispensers. The best material for storing scent, according to Pliny, was alabaster, and a large amount of such little perfume bottles and kohl pots have been found in excavations. At one point jars of anhydrite or so-called 'blue marble', adorned with a figure of a monkey, were in vogue. Others were made of Egyptian faience, bone or wood. Perhaps the most widely distributed containers were polychrome glass flasks which have been found all over the Mediterranean countries.

Spoons for dispensing solid unguent or dry incense were often devised in the form of a swimming girl, pushing forward a duck, whose body formed the container. In the New Kingdom the creative skills of the craftsmen were particularly vivid, and especially the wood carvers indulged in depicting half-naked girls in a floral setting, often playing a musical instrument. Many of the most attractive examples of this delightful genre in Egyptian art are included in the present work.

1 The Ingredients

Opposite: Cosmetics and scented oils were the prerogative of the élite, here represented by the mother-in-law of Amenhotep III 'the Magnificent', in whose reign Egypt enjoyed a period of prosperity and artistic activity without precedent. Tuya's mummy mask is adorned with inlaid blue glass make-up. Gilded plaster on linen, semi-precious stones, glass. 18th Dynasty, c. 1390-1352 BC. *Egyptian Museum, Cairo*

Ancient perfumes were many things, but in one respect in particular they differed from our perfume as the term is generally understood. The basic principle of distillation had been invented by Aristotle in the fourth century BC, and it was further developed in the first and second centuries AD. But it was only in the 10th century that the technique was perfected by the Arabs and used to extract perfume. In antiquity, on the other hand, scent was based either on substances the fragrance of which was released by burning; it was produced by a mixture of a base oil with added scented ingredients; it was used by combining a fragrance with a fruited base; or it was enjoyed *au naturel* by sniffing fresh flowers, fruit or other aromatic substances.

The art of the perfumer consisted in making the fragrance last and in enhancing it, in knowing which fragrances to combine for a satisfying result, in being able to time carefully the preparation of the ingredients and in having the facilities for storing the finished product, or else his efforts would have been in vain. Sniffing the fragrance of fresh flowers was a simple pleasure, and the scent of frankincense and myrrh, as burnt in the temple, or at funerary ceremonies, involved nothing but the availability of the ingredients and hot coals in a censer. But it was in the intricate composite preparation of scented oils, fats or fruit pastes that the master craftsman revealed himself, and this is where we find the Egyptians excelling time and again.

Grasses that grew around the lakes of Syria, juniper from the slopes of Phoenicia, nard and spices from distant India, myrrh and frankincense from the land of Punt - these were some of the ingredients of the unguents that delighted the inhabitants of Egypt and the Mediterranean countries in antiquity. Although Egypt was, in the words of Pliny, 'of all the countries in the world the best adapted for the production of unguents'[1], exotic ingredients, brought from faraway places, were appreciated to convey that feel of luxury which is at the heart of perfumes.

In order to understand the nature of ancient scent we must discuss in some detail the ingredients that went into the various preparations. For this purpose any reference of ancient date, however brief, is of importance, for like taste, scent may be perceived differently at different times in different civilisations. What is appreciated in one place may be frowned upon elsewhere. Some items of food are treasured in one part of the world and abhorred in another. Hence it is not sufficient to sniff the plants today for comparison, if and when they can be identified and obtained. It is equally important to know how the ancients perceived the fragrance in their own time.

Identification of ingredients is a major task, especially in Egyptian texts. In the field of pharmacology, progress is constantly being made in narrowing down the nature of plant and other ingredients. The most detailed recipes for composite scented preparations date from the later days of Egyptian history when the doors to the classical world were wide open and Greek, Latin, as well as Egyptian, was understood. Recipes for a scented paste known under its Greek name of *kyphi*, for example, were written down not only in Greek, but also in Egyptian hieroglyphs.

Many of the Greek texts were later translated into Arabic, using designations which are in use to this day, and the herbs can therefore be identified with some degree of certainty, although one must be aware of the fact that approximate equivalents may have been employed for exotic items. Some ancient Egyptian words have survived in the Coptic language, which was spoken in Egypt during the first millennium AD. In order to assist translators and interpreters in those days, lists of words, the so-called 'scala', were compiled giving words in Coptic and Greek. Again the same reservations must be made about substituting terms for related plants when the original was not understood, or if a precise term did not exist.

Much of the Egyptian terminology can be traced further back to texts written down in the New Kingdom around 1500 BC, some even as far back as the so-called Pyramid Texts of the Old Kingdom ca. 2500 BC. But although few explicit recipes exist from such an early date, Egypt has sources other than the literature to be explored in an investigation of scented raw materials. Wall paintings, reliefs, arts and crafts depict flowers known for their scent, and actual remains of plants found in excavations provide solid evidence of the raw materials which were in fact available at the time.

Pliny, who lost his life during the eruption of Vesuvius in AD 79, is a valuable source of information concerning plant ingredients used in his day for perfume and other scented preparations. He often makes reference to Egypt, and in his *Natural History* he includes a lengthy section on plants used for unguents. Pliny relied largely on the older works by Theophrastus and Dioscorides. In addition to his major opus, *Enquiry into Plants*, Theophrastus (c. 372-287 BC) wrote an essay entitled 'On Odours'. In the former, he gave a list of twenty plants used for perfumes, including flowers, leaves, wood, resin and seeds, some of distant origin. Most of them are relevant to Egypt and are included in the survey that follows. In fact, he specifically states that iris is the only one of them that grows in Europe, and that the best and the most fragrant of the others are to be found in Asia and in the 'sunny regions'.[2] The book by Dioscorides, written in the 1st century AD, although entitled in its Latin translation *De Materia Medica*, contains paragraphs relevant to scent. In view of the extensive trade in luxury items his remarks on scented raw material in other parts of the ancient world have been taken into consideration, especially when these plants occurred in Egypt in antiquity, or still grow there.

Roots, barks and resins travelled easily and had a long lasting fragrance. Such were the items that were brought from far away to Egypt to be used in unguents which would then in turn travel further all over the Mediterranean. In contrast, the delicate scent of leaves and petals presented a problem. It first had to be captured in oil or fat, and therefore in all probability the Egyptian perfumers would have relied largely on their native flora. It is strange that the more exotic the ingredient, the better informed we are of its nature and use, for the mere rarity warranted an explanation of its habitat and nature. For example, it is obvious from representations that by far the most popular and significant scented plant in Egypt was the lotus. But it was so well known that the Egyptians apparently felt no need to put on record a detailed exposé of its properties.

In order to avoid giving a false impression of providing exact scientific identification of the plant ingredients, the major ancient fragrant materials are here listed alphabetically not in Latin, but under the name by which each is currently known, regardless of language. There are three main sections: Plants, Gums and Resins, Oils and Fats. An asterisk* denotes non-Egyptian origin and/or source.

The famous Greek herbalist Dioscorides recorded for posterity the ingredients and recipes used by Egyptian perfumers. He is represented in an Arabic translation of his great book. The manuscript from Mosul, Iraq, was written in Persian as well as in Arabic in the 13th century AD. *Persian MS No. 2127, Topkapi Palace Library, Istanbul*

Plants

*ASPALATHOS

An intriguing plant ingredient of this name is known from various sources. Theophrastus[3] includes it in his list of plants suitable for making perfume. Elsewhere[4] he refers to it as being 'sweet scented' and as astringent as 'kypeiron'. The translator of the Loeb edition of Theophrastus identifies it as thorny trefoil, *Calycotome villosa*.

Pliny[5] gives a lengthy description, adding the interesting piece of information that the plant grows in Egypt: 'In the same region [i.e. Egypt] grows aspalathos, a white thorn of the size of a moderate-sized tree, with the flower of a rose; the root is in demand for unguents. People say that any shrub over which a rainbow forms its arch gives out a scent as sweet as that of the aspalathos, but that if this happens in the case of an aspalathos a scent rises that is indescribably sweet. Some call this shrub "red sceptre" [*erysisceptrum*] and others "sceptre". The test of its genuineness lies in its fiery red colour, firmness to the touch and scent like that of beaver-oil. It is sold for 5 denarii a pound.' In a later chapter he adds: 'Throughout the Spains, many use [our common thorn] as an ingredient of ointments, calling it aspalathos. There is without doubt, as I have said, a wild thorn of this name in the East, white, and as big as an ordinary tree, but it is also the name of a shrub, lower in height but equally thorny, that grows in the islands Nisyrus and Rhodes, called by some erysisceptrum, by others sphagnos, and by the Syrians diaxylon. The best is that least like fennel-giant, of a red colour or inclining to purple when the bark has been removed. I have described its powerful scent when the rainbow rests extended over the shrub . . .'[6]

So the thorny shrub known by Pliny had a strongly scented root, which was red and firm. It had white rose-like flowers, and it grew in Egypt and/or Rhodes. The editor of the Loeb edition of Pliny identifies aspalathos in the above mentioned passages as camel's horn, *Alhagi maurorum*, adding that elsewhere the name may refer to thorny trefoil. *Alhagi maurorum* currently grows in many places in Egypt. Although being a thorny shrub with an elongated root, in other respects it differs from Pliny's description: its flowers are purple, and its main claim to fame is the treacly 'manna' collected on its leaves. In his *Flore pharaonique,* the French scholar V. Loret, on the other hand, was inclined to take aspalathos to be one of the shrubby *Convolvulus,* for example *C. scoparius*, the wood of which is used in perfumery under the name of *Bois de Rhodes*, or *Bois de roses.* The shrub occurs sporadically in Egypt.

Dioscorides includes a paragraph on aspalathos.[7] He, too equates it with the plant known as *erysisceptrum*. It is a shrub with prickly thorns, and it grows in Istrus, Nisyrus, Syria and Rhodes. The ointment makers use it to thicken their ointments, he says. It is used with the bark removed, by which time it should have a red or purple colour, odoriferous and bitter to the taste. His translator Goodyer identified it as broom. The Arabic translation gives *dar shishahan*, the Latin for this being *Cytisus lanigerus* (broom).

Some 1500 years after Pliny, Prospero Alpini, too, equates aspalathos with Arabic *darsisahan*.[8] The source of the herb in his days, he says, was Crete or Rhodes. It was imported as a root, long and hard and of a reddish yellowish colour, being very aromatic. The plant itself is a shrub with branches close together, with hard white thorns and leaves reminiscent of rue. The flowers are few and golden, similar to broom. They too, are very fragrant. When this plant is not available, it may be replaced by another, which is also erroneously called *darsisahan*. But this he 'suspects' is a kind of St. John's wort. Of this plant, however, the root is not generally used. Alpini's true aspalathos thus had a scented root, red and hard; it was a thorny shrub with broom-like golden flowers, and it was not native to Egypt.

Aspalathos is an ingredient in the three kyphi recipes written in Greek. In the recipes

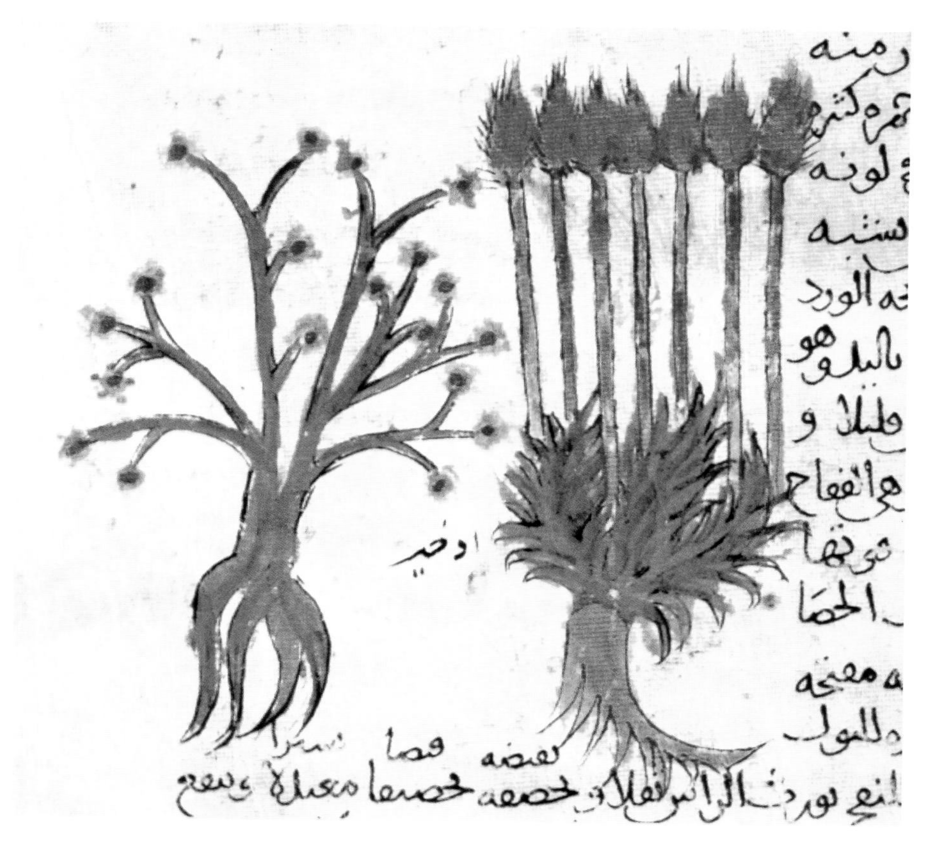

Camel grass.
An illustration from the Arabic translation of *De Materia Medica* by Dioscorides, copied in 11th century from the original completed in 990 AD by Abu Abd Allah el-Natili in Samarkand.
Universiteitsbibliothek, Leiden

carved on the walls of the temples of Edfu and Philae, the place is taken by a herb called *djeba*, with a synonym *djalem*. The older versions of kyphi include no such word. A medical papyrus, written in Demotic in the 2nd century AD, at the time when Galen wrote his works in Greek, prescribes for a stomach affliction a plant *djerem*, the Latin equivalent of which is given by the editor as the thorny trefoil which we saw in the Theophrastus edition. It is possible that djeba/djalem was not an exact equivalent name to aspalathos, but the name of a root used deliberately to adulterate the original which in spite of Pliny's information might have been unknown in Egypt, or possibly as an optional alternative.[9]

Pliny mentions that an oil was made from aspalathos by steeping it in oil and pressing out the juices.[10] The context indicates that this preparation was used for its scent rather than for medicinal reasons.

Apart from being an ingredient in kyphi, aspalathos appears in other contemporary recipes, namely for *medjat*, *hekenu* and the 'Hathor unguent' made at Edfu, and in a preparation of scented ox fat quoted by Dioscorides, all to be dealt with later.

*CAMEL GRASS

possibly *Andropogon schoenanthus* L.,
now known as *Cymbopogon citratus*
('lemon grass' or 'ginger grass')

In Greek versions of kyphi recipes, an identification of a herb called *schoinos* has been suggested with *Andropogon schoenanthus* L. It was not included in Theophrastus's list of herbs used in perfumery, but he does refer to it elsewhere as being an aromatic plant. He says that it grows east of Lebanon,[11] while Dioscorides claims that *schoinos* grows in Libya and Arabia (that of Libya being 'unprofitable'). It should be new, red and full of flowers; when cut or cleft it should incline to a purple colour, and when rubbed between the hands it should smell sweet like a rose . The flower, the reeds and the root of the plant are used.[12]

Pliny says that schoinos grows along with *acorus* and that it sells at 5 denarii a pound. He, too praises the Nabataean and Babylonian variety, claiming that the Libyan sort is useless. The best kind smells of roses and has a reddish colour.[13]

In the hieroglyphic recipes for kyphi, the equivalent for schoinos is given as *shut Nemti*, 'herb of Nemti'. But other parallel texts give a number of variant designations, some of which may be synonyms, others the names of interchangeable plants. It is interesting that the synonyms/replacements all have an exotic ring about them: 'Kushite [Nubian] herb', 'Nubian herb', 'rush of Asia', 'Syrian herb'.[14] From this it would seem that *schoenus* was not a plant that was native to Egypt.

Andropogon is now listed as occurring very rarely in the Isthmic desert, but not in other parts of Egypt. Since it grows both elsewhere in Africa, in Iran and in Arabia, it

Cardamom.
Illustration from the Arabic translation of *De Materia Medica* by Dioscorides.
11th century.
Universiteitsbibliothek, Leiden

remains a possibility that several, if not all, of the designations found in the hieroglyphic texts refer to *Andropogon schoenanthus.* The Arabic translation of Dioscorides has *idhkir*, Arabic for the plant known as andropogon. Whichever was the part of the original Egyptian recipe, the one known to the Greeks may well be our 'lemon grass'. The plant, which grows abundantly in India, has a scent which in modern times is compared to lemon; it is being used to adulterate lemon oil.

Schoinos was also known as *iuncus odoratus* in Latin. Theophrastus says that it has a more biting quality and is hotter than *kalamos* (sweet flag). Neither of the two, he remarks, are long-lasting and they soon get past their prime.[15]

In addition to its use in perfumery, lemon grass is nowadays prescribed to treat rheumatic pains, and it is diuretic, diaphoretic and vermifuge. Being scented, the root would have been suitable for travellers in ancient times. In Egypt in the late 19th century, powdered root was used in perfumery.

CARDAMOM

Elettaria cardamomum (L.) Maton

Cardamom is suggested as an alternative to cinnamon in Galen's version of kyphi and replaces cinnamon in Plutarch's version. The common provenance and sweet nature of these spices explain why they were interchangeable, however distinct they are to a modern palate. By the time that these two recipes were written down, cardamom would have been available from India along with other spices from that part of the world.[16] Dioscorides mentions that it was supplied from India and Arabia via the lands of the Eastern Mediterranean. He quotes its medicinal uses when mixed into water or wine and adds that it is used for thickening ointments. Its delicate flavour is not mentioned.[17]

The word for cardamom has not been identified in Egyptian texts.

CASSIA

Cinnamomum iners

Cassia is indicated in the kyphi recipe supplied by Galen, where the Egyptian original had pine resin. In this case the two interchangeable ingredients are quite distinct. But cassia resembles cinnamon in its nature and scent. In classical texts the two are often confused, and this may well have been the case in ancient Egypt as well.

The quills of the bark are similar to cinnamon, but are larger, and the flavour is hotter. It was included in Theophrastus's list of aromatic herbs originating in countries such as Arabia and India.[18] The branches, he says, they chop up into lengths of about two fingers' breadth and sew them up in raw hide. Little worms are engendered inside which eat the wood but not the bark, which is the part used for its bitter taste and pungent odour.

Dioscorides, too, places the source of cassia in Arabia. The merchants in Alexandria knew it under the name of *daphnitis* (referring to Greek laurel). A black, rose-scented kind

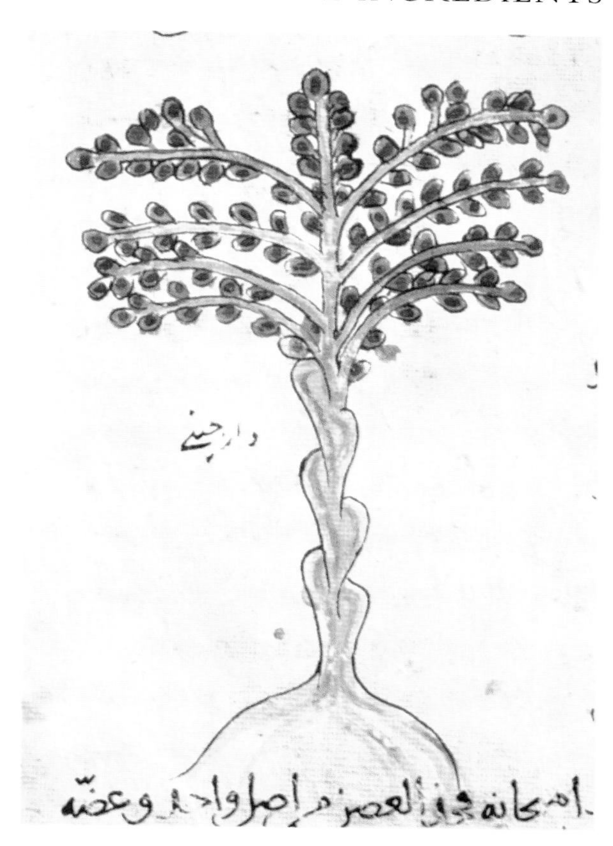

Right: Cinnamon. Illustration from the Arabic translation of *De Materia Medica* by Dioscorides. 11th century. *Universiteitsbibliotheek, Leiden*

was known as *gizir.* Its medicinal properties are such that two parts cassia will make up for one part cinnamon.[19] See further under cinnamon.

CINNAMON

Cinnamomum verum J. Presl

Cinnamon is indicated in many recipes supplied by the classical authors, including the Galen version for kyphi. In the Edfu versions the word *tisheps* appears to take its place, occasionally replaced by *khet nedjem,* literally 'sweet wood'.[20] Known from several other Egyptian contexts, it has long been taken to mean cinnamon, a commodity which was available in the Mediterranean at least from the 5th century BC, whatever the results of philological investigations may be. In the New Kingdom at least tisheps was the name of a precious commodity available in bundles. This much discussed item was once depicted on the wall of a tomb where it seems to consist of thin lengths of wood rather than quills.

In the days of Theophrastus, cinnamon originated in Arabia or India as did cassia (see above). Dioscorides says that there are many kinds of cinnamon, and he praises their medicinal properties, adding that cinnamon is also mixed with precious ointments.[21]

Cinnamomum verum J. Presl (*c. zeylanicum* Nees), or more recently *Cinnamomum camphora* (L.) J. Presl, native to East Africa, have been suggested as the ancient source of cinnamon. It has also been confused with cassia. In classical antiquity, with the spice roads to India opened, cinnamon was imported from the Far East. Egyptian sources of the New Kingdom mention tisheps as being imported from or via the land of Punt, generally thought to be located on the coast of Somalia. The merchandise came in the form of logs, bundles or 'measures'.

Cinnamon (or cassia) is the only spice specified in connection with mummification, when the body was treated with juniper ('cedar') oil, myrrh and cinnamon,[22] and mummies have been found with a smell of cinnamon or cassia still adhering to them. There is thus good reason to believe that the ancient Egyptians knew cinnamon, and that they made extensive use of it in perfumery.

CYPERUS GRASS (SEDGE)

Cyperus spp.

Greek versions of kyphi mention *kypeiros*, in fact *Cyperus longus* L., a herb which has been identified in plant remains from ancient Egypt dating as far back as the Old Kingdom. The corresponding place in the hieroglyphic version has '*giu* of the oases', or the synonym *sbebin.*[23] A word giu occurs as far back as in the medical papyri of ca. 1500 BC. Via an Arabic term *dasam* in the Coptic scala which gives for kypeiros the equivalent ⲁⲱⲓ ⲛⲥⲧⲟⲓ giu appears to describe the fattening properties of a herb, that is a descriptive term for the

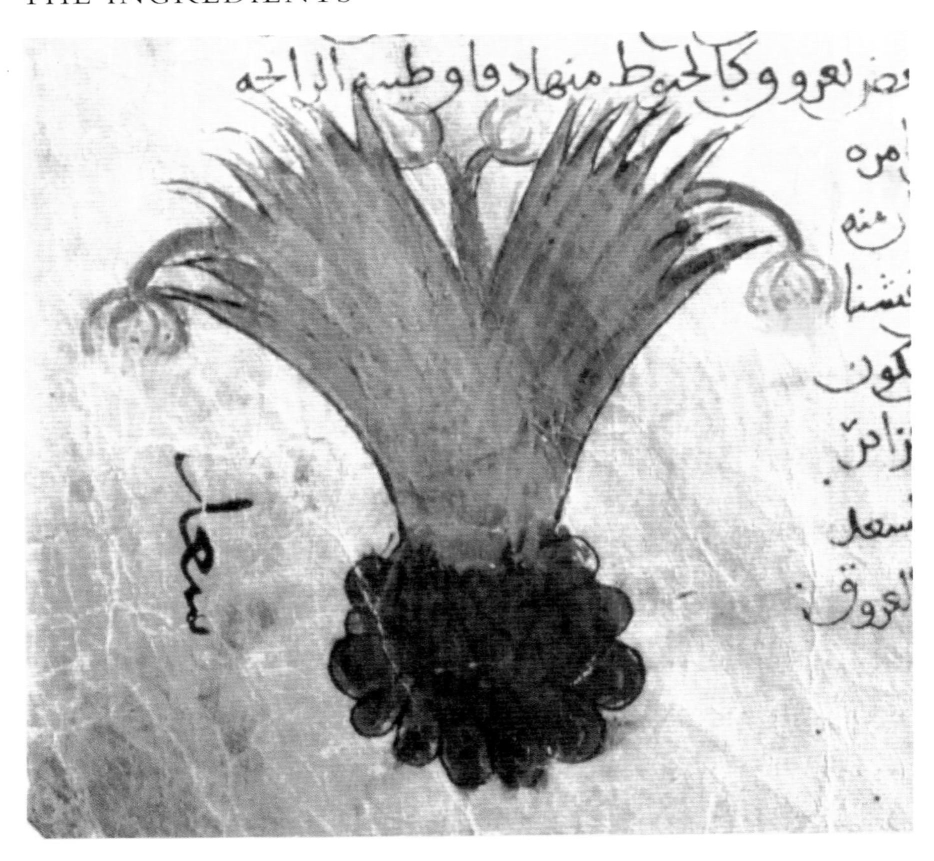

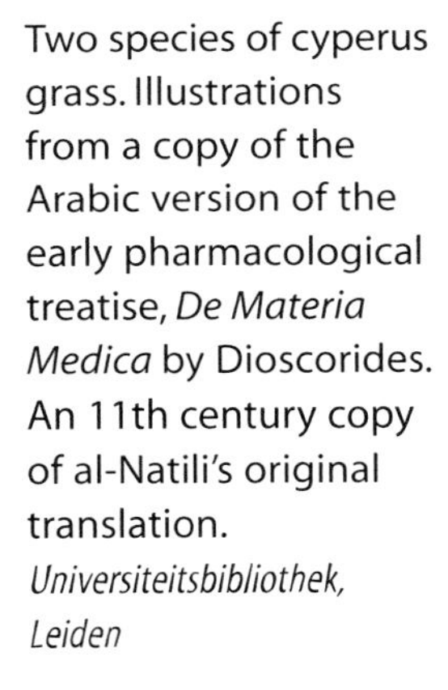

Two species of cyperus grass. Illustrations from a copy of the Arabic version of the early pharmacological treatise, *De Materia Medica* by Dioscorides. An 11th century copy of al-Natili's original translation. *Universiteitsbibliothek, Leiden*

Greek kypeiros and possibly other plants as well, rather than a generic name for the plant in question or its substitute. The word *shebin*, on the other hand, appears to be the equivalent of 'kypeiros'. Today the rhizomes of *Cyperus longus* are employed in perfumery.

A commentary to an Arabic translation of Dioscorides's kypeiros suggests *sa'ad* which is now the name used for *Cyperus rotundus* L., found in Egypt since Late Paleolithic times. This variety, too, has fragrant roots, which are employed in Eastern perfumes. When Prospero Alpini travelled in Egypt (c. AD 1583) the plant was called *hodveg*. It grew in the Nile and around lakes. Alpini provides a drawing and says that the black roots resemble a string of olives. They have a penetrating scent.[24] Both are now common in Egypt.[25]

In his paragraphs on '*cyperos*' Pliny too[26] compares the roots of 'cyperos' to dark olives and the leaves to those of leeks. His best 'cyperos' comes from 'the region round the temple of Hammon', i.e. the temple of Amun in the Siwa Oasis in the Libyan desert, the second best from Rhodes, the third from Thera (Santorin), and the least desirable from Egypt itself. The species of true cyperos, he says, smell very much like nard.

Theophrastus mentions 'kypeiros' in his list of plants used in perfumery. Elsewhere he refers to 'The Eritrean' perfume which (belying its geographical name) is made from the same ingredient, at that time obtained from the Cyclades and from Euboea.[27]

DILL

Anethum graveolens L.

Theophrastus included dill in his list of herbs used in perfumery. In ancient Egypt it was known as *imset*, though Dioscorides quotes the Egyptian name in his day as as *arakhou*.[28] Whatever the ancient name of the herb, there is no doubt about its existence, for actual dill stems and flowers were found on the mummy

Above: Bearded lily (iris) and *Right:* Henna. Illustrations from the Arabic translation of *De Materia Medica* by Dioscorides, 11th century. *Universiteitsbibliothek, Leiden*

of Amenhotep II. Imset was an ingredient in aromatherapy c. 1550 BC (see p.118).

HENNA
Lawsonia inermis L.

Pliny claims that *cypros* (henna) grows in Egypt ('a tree found in Egypt is the cypros, which has the leaves of the ziziphus and the white scented seed of coriander'). The seeds boiled in olive oil and crushed were sold as a commodity called cypros at 5 denarii a pound. The best, he says in this passage, is made from the tree grown at Canopus on the banks of the Nile, the second best at Ascalon in Judaea, and the third quality on the island of Cyprus 'which has a sort of sweet scent'. Further on in his work Pliny mentions a scent called *cyprinum* of which the best was made in Cyprus, to be later superseded by that from Egypt. He gives details of this cyprinum, which was apparently the designation of a finished product that contained cypros, among other things. Here the best is said to be made in Sidon, the second best in Egypt.[29] Dioscorides prefers Egyptian henna from Canopus.[30]

Leaves of henna have been found in Late Period tombs and the herb was obviously in use at this date, if not before. In a medical text from ca. 1500 BC *henu* is mentioned as a means to invigorate the growth of hair, and it is tempting to relate the ancient word henu to modern henna. A second ancient word, *ankh-imy*, has also been suggested for henna. The odour of this herb was thought to be potent enough to resurrect a dead person!

Nowadays a fragrant essential oil is distilled from henna flowers (called *mehendi*). This is used as a perfume.

IRIS
Iris spp.

Varieties of iris grow wild in Egypt today; Dioscorides gave *nar* as its Egyptian name.[31]

Petals of *Iris albicans* Lange or *I. florentina* have been identified in an Egyptian burial of Graeco-Roman date, and the dried root could well have reached the country, this being the part of the plant that is used in perfumery ('orris root'). It was on Theophrastus's list of aromatic plants.[32]

Juniper trees. From the Arabic translation of *De Materia Medica* by Dioscorides, 11th century. *Universiteitsbibliothek, Leiden*

Women gathering lilies. Limestone relief, 26th Dynasty, c. 600 BC.
Musée du Louvre, Paris

⋆ JUNIPER
Juniperus spp.

Two of the Greek kyphi recipes characteristically include two words, each of which has been translated as juniper: *arkeuthos* and *brathy*, referring, apparently, to large and small berries of the plant respectively. Dioscorides quotes arkeuthos (Arabic *arar*) in his kyphi recipe. This plant is called *libium* in Egyptian, he says. He also knows of brathy (Arabic *abhal*). Apart from being used medicinally it is mixed with hot ointments.[33]

The hieroglyphic versions of kyphi mention *wan*-seeds, with the synonym *peresh* for one (for the other, called *shena*-berries, synonym *mereh nar*, see under pine kernels below).[34] A Demotic medical papyrus mentions *wan*, as well as a word *arw*, determined by a tree. It is the sole ingredient in a remedy. Wan-seeds occur frequently in pharaonic pharmacology. Actual berries have been found in excavation, for example in the tomb of Tutankhamun. They included *Juniperus oxycedrus* L. with the smallest berries. This tree now occurs sporadically in the Isthmus area. The berries, however, are frequently found on Egyptian sites. The other juniper berries of Tutankhamun were from *Juniperus excelsa*, only known from here. The berries may have been included in the burial because of their rarity.

The red berries of *Juniperus phoenicea* have been found on sites of all dates. This species grows in Sinai and around the Mediterranean. Pliny mentions it as 'the Lycian', growing in Phoenicia.[35] Old Kingdom reliefs show harvesting of what the inscription calls *an*-seeds. In Egyptian folk medicine the berries of *J. phoenicea* are used in fumigation to stimulate the skin. *Sef wan,* an oil extracted from the wood of the Syrian juniper, *J. oxycedrus,* was referred to by Herodotus as *kedros* in connection with mummification.[36]

LILY
Lilium candidum L.

Egyptian reliefs from about 500 BC depict the collection of a plant reminiscent of lily in its

Marjoram. Illustration from a manuscript of the Arabic translation of *De Materia Medica* by Dioscorides. 11th century. *Universiteitsbibliotheek, Leiden*

appearance (p. 21) and the preparation of an extract of the flower (p. 69).

Recipes for lily perfume (*susinum*) provided by Theophrastus, Dioscordies and Pliny give a good idea of how the Egyptians, too, may have prepared a fragrance from such a plant of which a number of examples have been identified in finds from Egypt from Late Palaeolithic times to the Second Intermediary Period.

LOTUS
Nymphaea lotus L. and *Nymphaea caerulea* Savigny

No recipes for pure lotus perfume have survived in the Egyptian records, and the flower would not have been available *au naturel* to the inhabitants of the classical world. It was by far the most important scented plant in Egypt, often represented and also identified in plant material from the Twelfth Dynasty and on.

Its presence in perfume can be surmised from numerous sources. The word *seshen*, lotus, does occur in a recipe from the Edfu temple for an unguent for use during the ceremonies for the Opening of the Mouth.

MARJORAM
Origanum sp.

Pliny quotes Diocles, a physician, and the people of Sicily using the name *sampsucum* for the Egyptian variety of *amaracum*, i.e. sweet marjoram.[37] Elsewhere[38] he rates Egyptian 'origanum' as superior to Roman savory. The Egyptian name, according to Dioscorides also abbreviated to *sopho*[39], means 'herb of [the crocodile god] Sobek'. The Copts knew it under its Greek name ορικανον. *Origanum majorana* L. is known from Graeco-Roman plant material in Egypt.

The herb is cultivated on a large scale in Egypt and no doubt grew there in antiquity as well. Sprigs have been found in mummy garlands from the 1st century AD.

According to Theophrastus it was used in perfumery,[40] while Dioscorides reports specifically that a perfume, *sampsuchinon*, was named after it.[41]

MINT
Mentha spp.

It has been suggested that Egyptian *nkepet* means mint because of its synonym, *akay*, undoubtedly the hieroglyphic version of Coptic ⲁϣⲓ ⲛⲥⲧⲟⲓ, 'odoriferous plant', *hedeosmos* in Greek (a designation for mint).[42]

Dioscorides provides no less than four Egyptian names for mint, one of them, *this*, being used in Latin as a designation for wild mint. Varieties of mint are known from Predynastic to Graeco-Roman times.

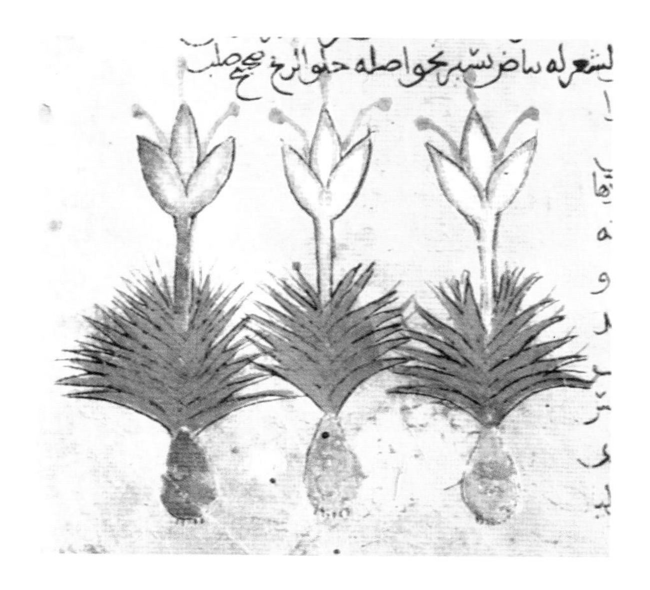

Saffron.
Illustration from an Arabic translation of *De Materia Medica* by Dioscorides.
11th century.
Universiteitsbibliöthek, Leiden

PINE KERNELS
Pinus pinea L.

The Ebers version of kyphi as well as those from the temples of Edfu and Philae include an ingredient known as *peru shenu*. Although in the Greek this is replaced by brathy, a kind of juniper, the Egyptian original appears to refer to *Pinus pinea*, a tree also known as '*ash* of the western countries'. Wood, cones and seeds of pine are well documented in finds from Egypt from late Paleolithic times onwards. A synonym is given as *mereh nar*.[43] Pine kernel oil is only faintly aromatic.

SAFFRON
Crocus sativus L.

The well-known flower pistils of *Crocus sativus* relate to Egypt only as far as saffron is an ingredient in the kyphi recipe provided by Galen. This presumably occurred because saffron was much loved in the classical world for its scent as well as its colour. It was known in the Bible as *karcom*. It has long been grown in Europe, and grew in Persia where it was cultivated in the 10th century AD.

Pliny praises saffron from Soli in Cilicia, later superseded by saffron from Rhodes. He quotes a recipe for saffron perfume, crocinum, which also included cinnabar (a naturally occurring mineral), wine and alkanet (a dyeing plant).[44] Theophrastus claims that in his day the best saffron for perfume came from the island of Aegina and from Cilicia.[45]

SPIKENARD

The Galen recipe for kyphi includes *nardostachys*, spikenard (a member of the Valerian family). The fragrant oil present in all its parts is a well known ingredient in ointment and is still used in oriental perfume manufacture. A hundred years ago the root was imported from Nepal for use in Egyptian folk medicine. Its scent was said to be reminiscent of valerian and patchouly.

The plant is known from the Bible.[46] According to Theophrastus it was imported to the Mediterranean from India, the root being the part of the plant used.[47] When speaking of Indian nard Pliny, on the other hand, refers to the leaf of the nard as being fragrant, the root having a musty smell and an acrid taste. Similar plants are used to adulterate nard, he says, but pure nard can be detected by its light weight.[48] According to Theophrastus, nard perfume, *nardinon*, lasts a long time, and is thus particularly suited for women.[49] Pliny reckoned it to be the ultimate perfume.

The root could well have reached Egypt along with other spices from India, and it is possible that the name of this ancient plant is yet to be identified in the Egyptian texts.

*SWEET FLAG
possibly *Acorus calamus* L.

An 'aromatic rush' (*calamus aromaticus*) of classical antiquity, in late antiquity known as 'true rush' (*acorus verus* or *calamus verus*), it was called in the medieval Arabic translation of Dioscorides *qasab al-zoreira,* now known as *Acorus calamus* L. The identity of this calamus has yet to be confirmed, and the calamus known in antiquity may have been another, similar plant. *Acorus calamus* has been identified once in an Eleventh Dynasty context.

This plant is found in the Greek kyphi recipes. In the ancient Egyptian sources for kyphi, the space given to the ingredient in question refers to a plant named *kenen,* giving as a synonym *shebi nedjem,* literally 'sweet rush'.[50] A Demotic medical papyrus contributes both an Egyptian form (*kennet*) and a Greek (*iker* - from 'acorus'), but the two need not be synonyms. However, on tracing the word *knn* back to pharaonic times, we find a word *gnn,* in a similar context, namely a recipe for kyphi, where *genen* is something which is part of a 'tree' called *niuben.* This has led other scholars to identify the substance not as 'sweet flag', but 'styrax', a resin exuding from *Styrax officinalis.*[51]

Pliny describes *calamus odoratus* as growing in Arabia, India and Syria, the latter country producing the best. It has 'a specially fine scent which attracts people even from a long way off. . . The better variety is the one that is less brittle. . . Inside the tube there is a sort of cobweb which is called the flower; the plant containing most of this is the best. The remaining tests of its goodness are that it should be black - white varieties are thought inferior - and that it is better the shorter and thicker it is and if it is pliant in its breaking. The price of the reed is one denarius.'[52] Pliny agrees with Theophrastus concerning the habitat of sweet flag. Theophrastus adds that the plants (sweet flag and *schoinos*) cover an extent of over 30 furlongs. 'They have no fragrance when they are green, but only when they are dried, and in appearance they do not differ from ordinary reeds and rushes; but as you approach the spot, immediately a sweet smell strikes you. However, it is not true, as some say, that the fragrance is wafted to ships approaching the country; for indeed this district is more than 150 furlongs from the sea.'[53] Dioscorides, on the other hand, quotes the herb as growing in India.[54]

There is no evidence of the reed having ever grown in Egypt, nor does it grow there at the present time. About a hundred years ago the root of qasab al-zoreira was in use in Egyptian folk medicine. It was sold in one piece, deprived of its outer skin, or carved into pieces lengthwise. It was of a rosy yellow colour, the inside being white, with spongy texture. At that time the drug was imported from India and the Far East. The root would have travelled equally well in antiquity, especially if it was imported the shorter distance from Syria.

If sweet flag was in ancient times a commodity that was imported and not readily available in the Egyptian countryside it would be much treasured for the mere reason that it was exotic. After its long voyage it would be carefully kept and guarded until required. We would have to look for it in the treasury of the palace or of the temple, which is exactly where we find it. Rekhmire, vizier under Tuthmosis III (c. 1475 BC) was in charge of the storehouses of the king, and so proud was he of his position that he chose to have scenes of his official life depicted on the walls of his tomb at Thebes. He is represented supervising workshops and storehouses. The merchandise is piled up everywhere, each item labelled with a hieroglyphic inscription. Twice we are presented with a square stack of reeds, bound

'Sweet flag', according to an illustration from the Arabic translation of *De Materia Medica* by Dioscorides. This is actually a reed, probably *Arundo donax,* not *Acorus calamus.* 11th century. *Universiteitsbibliothek, Leiden*

Conical houses on stilts among doum palm and incense trees on the coast of Punt. Painted relief in the temple of Hatshepsut, Deir el-Bahari, 18th Dynasty, 1473-1458 BC

with two pieces of string, with the inscription *kenen*. The joints of the reeds are clearly marked, and there can thus be no doubt of the type of plant in question. It is in one case shown stored between jars of incense and a stack of tisheps, another perfume ingredient, which suggests its purpose.

The scent of the whole of *Acorus calamus* is said to be sweet and aromatic with a sharp tang. In Europe it has been used as a strewing herb, and taken to treat acidity, dyspepsia, flatulence and indigestion. Chopped root is usually available in herb shops. It is prescribed for a number of treatments; it has a slight sedative action on the central nervous system. In addition, in powder form, it is nowadays used as a perfume additive to fix other scents (in the manner of orris root).

Gums and Resins

Scent in its most basic form is provided by the raw material itself: herbs and flowers, sniffed or crushed between the fingers. As we shall see in Chapter 5, the former was a custom the Egyptians indulged in and appreciated beyond this life. The flora of Egypt already provided a good choice of flowers to enjoy, but, as it is often the case with luxury items, the more exotic and expensive the ingredients, the greater was the demand for them. As already indicated above, Egypt imported very large quantities of fragrant raw material from abroad. The distances covered were often considerable, and the goods had to have either a sufficiently pungent scent to last as long as required, or the fragrance should be of a kind to be revived on arrival. Such characteristics are shared by resins and gum resins, wood, bark and roots. These were the items brought from faraway places.

One way of capturing and bringing out natural fragrance is to subject the material to heat. The resulting smoke emanating from the substance can be very powerful. In the daily temple ritual and funerary cult large amounts of scent went up in smoke, and combined with the commodities used for private consumption, so to speak, no basic substances were more in demand than myrrh and frankincense. Records of the use of these

Frankincense. Illustration from an Arabic translation of *De Materia Medica* by Dioscorides. 11th century. *Universiteitsbibliothek, Leiden*

two essential ingredients go back to the Fifth and Sixth Dynasties. Neither frankincense nor myrrh was available inside the borders of Egypt, and the imports were on a large scale.

We are, however, once more faced with serious philological difficulties when it comes to identifying the substances which can be said with reasonable confidence to have been available to the Egyptians with the terms used to designate these substances.

FRANKINCENSE AND MYRRH

Boswellia spp. and *Commiphora* spp.

Frankincense can be collected from small trees native to Somalia and southern Arabia. They belong to the genus *Boswellia*, some of which may be found in eastern Sudan and neighbouring Ethiopia. It is a gum-resin, exuding from the trees in the form of large translucent tears.

Having been collected and undergone the drying process, the material gradually acquires a coating of its own fine dust, turning a milky white colour. In many languages the name given to the material refers to this milky appearance (e.g. Arabic *libân*). The white colour makes it easy to distinguish from other resins and gum resins, and when 'white incense' is mentioned in Egyptian records, this is probably an exact reference to frankincense. Pliny emphasises that the white colour was a mark of quality.[55] With time, the milky white colour may become yellowish-brown.

When in the 1920s the tomb of Tutankhamun in the Valley of the Kings was cleared, a modest bowl of incense was found in it. The report of the chemist suggests that this was indeed frankincense. When burnt, the material still gave off a 'pleasant aromatic odour', after 3,500 years underground.

Myrrh, too, is a gum-resin, originating in Somalia and southern Arabia. The source is various species of *Commiphora*. But unlike frankincense, its colour is yellowish red. Samples of myrrh which can be assigned a date appear to stem from the New Kingdom.[56]

There can thus be no doubt that frankincense and myrrh found their way to Ancient Egypt. But what was it called, and how may we recognise it in the numerous texts that deal with this subject? Investigation of the Egyptian literary sources for references to frankincense and myrrh yields a number of designations, which at times appear to confuse the issue.

The word *antiu* has long been taken to mean myrrh.[57] But according to the results of the French philologist Chassinat, who some fifty years ago made an extensive investigation of the texts of the Ptolemaic period, the ancient word antiu has a wider meaning and includes gum resins from several *Boswellia* and probably also other resins from the Red Sea region.

There were two main sorts: fresh antiu from evergreen (or perhaps previously un-

Myrrh. Illustration from an Arabic translation of *De Materia Medica* by Dioscorides. 11th century.
Universiteitsbibliothek, Leiden

tapped) trees and dry antiu from deciduous (or possibly older) trees.[58]

A list of resins carved into the walls of the Ptolemaic temple at Edfu is an abridged version of a more comprehensive one in an older Ptolemaic temple at Athribis which, however, is only partly preserved.

The original work, which was no doubt contained in a papyrus scroll whence it was copied onto the walls of the buildings, concerned both the tree itself and its resin. The list gives an interesting idea of the many facets of one of the resins used in Ptolemaic Egypt.

'First class dry antiu. It comes forth from the divine limbs. A preparation is made from them in the temples of the south and the north. . . .

1. First class dry antiu. It springs from the eye of Re, the gods live on its fragrance, *aui-sha* is its name. Its colour is like gold. It has many grains, its egg-shaped grains are shaped like the egg of the swallow, no bigger than this.[59]
2. An antiu whose name is *gar-pekher* and which springs from the eye of Osiris, truly antiu which springs from the left eye. Its colour is red.[60]
3. An antiu whose name is *gar-nu*, it is a summer antiu which comes forth from the eye of Re. Its colour is of gold like the *aui-sha*. Its 'egg' is no bigger than that.
4. An antiu whose name is *gar-ta,* its colour is white. . . . it comes out of the bones of the divine limbs, its 'egg'. . .
5. An antiu . . . white is its shape . . . colour . . . sun disc it comes out of the white of the eye of Thoth and is brought . . .
6. An antiu whose name is *maa-maa... astiu* is its name . . . It is an antiu which absorbs its liquid when it is dry.
7. An antiu whose name is *ki-res.* It is white, it is a white antiu whose colour is like gold . . . it comes out from the eye of Re.
8. An antiu whose name is *mesh-ib,* an antiu from Asia which comes out from the the spittle . . . Its colour is red like that, it is soft in its liquid, its scent is sweet. When it is pressed in a bag, a fourth of what is in it dribbles out.[61]
9. An antiu whose name is *ki-risawi.* This is the *meshib* which springs from the great . . . It is soft in its liquid and the colour is black . . .
10. An antiu whose name is *inhasaasenen.* Its colour is like gold. It is soft in its liquid, it is very good. It comes forth from the back of Horus.
11. An antiu whose name is *ahm.* It comes forth from . . . It is red, what is in it is white and soft. It produces its liquid and dries it on its tree.

Total 'dry' antiu trees: 11.

Five additional sorts of antiu are listed, but they are all said to be bad, and no preparations are made from them in the temples. Apart from the references to strange synonyms and mythological contexts the mentions of different colours such as black and red are confusing when we attempt to identify antiu with the milky white frankincense.

That antiu is here said to come in a red variety is interesting when we consider the best attested shipment of the commodity to have reached Egypt, namely the load of antiu brought back from Punt by Queen Hatshepsut of the Eighteenth Dynasty. The heap of the substance, piled up in front of the god Amun, is red in colour. This has led scholars in the past to identify antiu with myrrh.

Another word is significant in this context, for throughout ancient Egyptian history it is of all the most frequently used designation for burning resin. In texts dating from the Sixth dynasty we are informed that a substance called *senetjer* was taken to Egypt from the land of Wawat.[62] The latest research suggests that senetjer was a designation for frankincense deriving primarily from *Boswellia*. It is in any case significant that the material came from a direction where such frankincense trees would be native. Wawat, placed in a region of the Sudan, is already halfway to Somalia. In the Eighteenth dynasty the country that negotiated the goods was Punt, of which more shall be said later. In either case the port of embarkation was not necessarily in the country of origin.

In Ptolemaic texts wee meet a word *khery*, which survived in Coptic as σηαλ or ηελ (the letters *l* and *r* being commonly interchangeable). It designates a resinous substance from a tree called *nuhi-heri*. Chassinat argued that this should be the word for myrrh, at least at the time during which these texts were written down.[63]

In the Eighteenth Dynasty incense was also shipped to Egypt from Levantine and Mesopotamian centres such as Retenu, Djahi, and Naharina. Clearly, it is again a case of re-export of commodities.

BDELLIUM

from, among others, *Commiphora erythraea* and *C. africana* Engl.

This tree grows in Somalia and Ethiopia, well within reach of the Egyptians. Related species grow in Arabia, India and elsewhere. Bdellium is very similar to myrrh, which is also produced from *Commiphora*. The two were probably confused in ancient times.[64]

The bdellium known to Dioscorides came from a 'Saracenian' tree, transparent, fat and sweet-smelling when burning. But there was another kind, 'filthy and black' which came from India, but its smell was less sweet.[65]

According to Groom, bdellium has a much stronger smell than true myrrh, with a hint of turpentine. It is more oily than true myrrh. When old it turns black. In Pliny's days the retail price of a pound of bdellium was 3 denarii,[66] and it was thus among the least expensive scents ('scented myrrh' cost 12 denarii and frankincense 3-6 denarii).

FIR RESIN

from *Abies cilicica* (Ant. & Cot.) Carr.

The word *sefet* occurs in many Egyptian texts, and it is also the name for one of the seven traditional scented oils used in funerary offerings. It is probably to be identified with oil made from the resin of pine trees which grew in Lebanon. The trees were known as *ash*.

In the tomb of Tutankhamun a small alabaster vase was found, labelled 'ash resin'. An analysis of the material adhering to the inside walls confirmed that this was a true resin, probably collected from a coniferous tree.

Dioscorides refers to the sweet smell of fir resin and its resemblance to frankincense.[67]

GALBANUM

from *Ferula* spp.

Galbanum is a gum-resin with fragrant properties in the form of brownish-yellow tears,

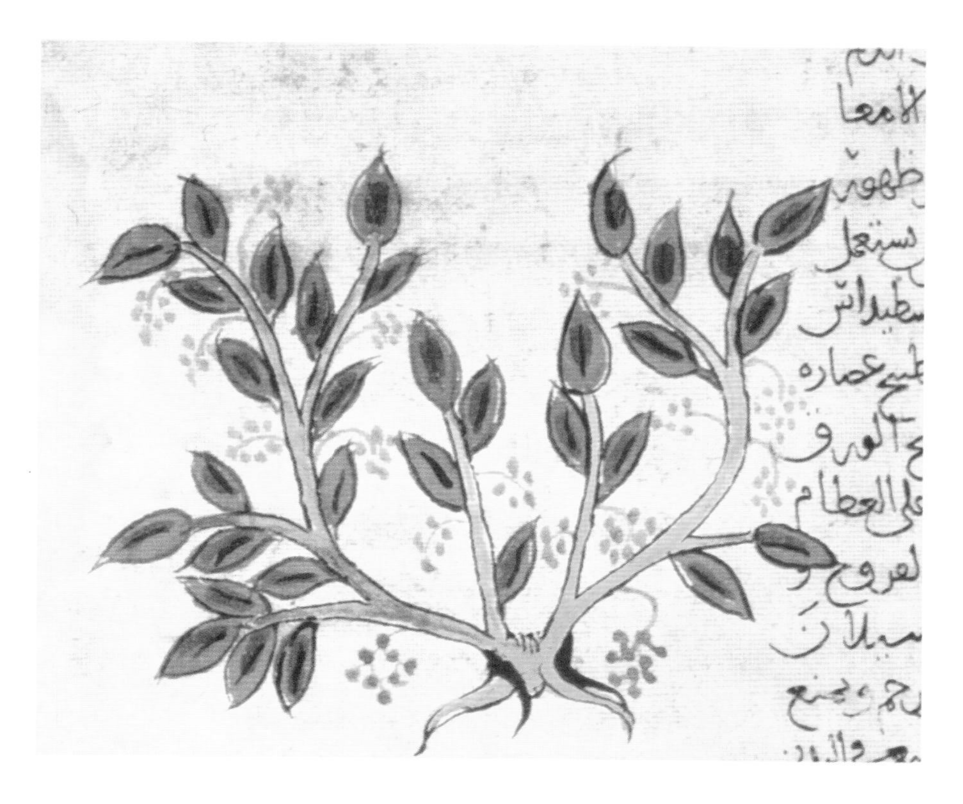

Mastic (*Pistacia lentiscus*). Illustration from an Arabic translation of *De Materia Medica* by Dioscorides. 11th century. *Universiteitsbibliothek, Leiden*

often with a greenish tint. The umbelliferous plant was a native of Persia, and its resin may well have been available to Egyptian perfumers of the New Kingdom and later. Dioscorides says that the Egyptians of his time called it *metopium* and that they used it in the preparation of the ointment of that name.[68]

MASTIC
from *Pistacia terebinthus* L. and *P. lentiscus* L.

Mastic is a resin from the shrub still common on the island of Chios or, alternatively, from a shrub that grows in the eastern Mediterranean. Chios mastic was sweet-smelling when white and clear, Dioscorides reports, and was chewed for a sweet breath, as it is to this day. Terebinth resin, surpassing all other resins in odour, was supplied from Arabia although the tree grew elsewhere, for example in Syria, Cyprus and in Africa.[69] *P. terebinthus* was apparently used in mummification and has thus been found in an Egyptian context. In Ptolemaic texts it is perhaps to be identified with the item *fetet*.

PINE RESIN
from *Pinus* spp.

The identity of the wood known as *qed* with Aleppo pine (*Pinus halepensis*) has been convincingly demonstrated by Chassinat.[70] The ingredient occurs in the Edfu kyphi recipe, where it has previously been interpreted as cassia after comparison with the ingredients supplied by the versions in Greek (see further below). In the Egyptian recipes it is specified as *khet en qed* or *djed en qed*, which refers to its tree-like resinous nature. Hence no doubt the fragrant resin of the trunk is meant. It appears to have been used in mummification; Dioscorides recommended it for medicinal uses.[71]

UNIDENTIFIED RESINS

The 'laboratory' in the temple of Edfu contains an inventory of different resins. Among these a substance called *ab* is frequently used. Three kinds are listed: dark, red and white. These are qualified as 'the ab resins which come forth from the two divine eyes, from the eye of Re and from the eye of Horus and which unite in the eye of Osiris. The splendid *medjat* unguent is made [from it].'

Ab resin is said to derive from a tree called *nenib*. In the Edfu laboratory there is a representation of the 'people from Nenib who bring Nenib wood and extract the resin'. In recent times an identification as styrax (a solid resin deriving from *Styrax officinalis* L.) has been suggested.[72] Styrax featured in Theophrastus's list of scented matter.[73]

STAKTE

is the name of an oil produced from myrrh, either by bruising or by the addition of balanos, according to Theophrastus, 'the only simple uncompounded perfume'. [74] Egyptian sources also appear to refer to extracting an oil from resinous material. In his monograph on the subject, Steuer, who advocates a translation 'myrrh' for antiu,[75] proposes that the resulting liquid, *madjet*, is stakte. It remains a possibility that there was a change of terminology from the Eighteenth Dynasty (where Steuer obtained his evidence) to Ptolemaic times (the source on which Chassinat based his translation of 'frankincense' for antiu).

Oils

Egypt produced a number of oils which were of use in the preparation of perfumes. Ideally, such an oil should not be greasy; it should have a bland smell which would not interfere with the scent added to it; and it should keep well without turning rancid. Two of the oils produced in Egypt were well suited for the purpose: balanos and moringa.[76]

BALANOS

The thorny *Balanites aegyptiaca* L. (ancient Egyptian *ished* ?) was once a frequent tree in the Nile Valley. It is the kernel of the date-like fruit that produces the oil, though Theophrastus says that the perfumers use the husks of the fruit, though the oil in itself is sweet-smelling.[77]

Balanites wood was known from the days of the pyramid builders, and the kernels have been found in tombs. The ancient name for the tree and its oil has not yet been identified with certainty, but Greek writers refer to balanos oil in connection with the Mendesian perfume.

MORINGA

Moringa oil, also known as *behen*-oil, is derived from the seeds of the pods of *Moringa oleifera* (*M. pterygosperma*), known as *bak* in ancient Egyptian; it grew in the desert around Thebes, and it still grows in the country.

The oil, which as early as the Old Kingdom was imported from Syria and Cyprus, is odourless with a sweet taste and a yellowish hue. It was used as a cooking oil as well as in cosmetics and medicine (notably rubbed into the abdomen of pregnant women).

Prescriptions of New Kingdom date combine moringa oil with fragrant material such as frankincense and cyperus grass to make a refreshing ointment, and it must have been widely used in perfume making. Pliny knew it under the name *myrobalanum*, grown in Egypt for its scent. The Theban variety has a black nut (as opposed to the so-called Syrian kind growing in Arabia which is white), and it produces a large yield. Ethiopian *behen*-oil has a stronger scent than the others. Perfumers extract the juice from the shells only.[78]

A number of other oils would have been available in Egypt, though to what extent they were scented remains an open question.

ALMOND OIL

The earliest find of almonds was in the tomb of Tutankhamun. Centuries later Pliny mentions the oil of bitter almonds in connection with the complex preparation of the unguent called *metopium*.[79] Theophrastus thought that this was the very best. There was an abundance of such almonds in Cilicia, where an unguent was made from them.[80]

Nowadays almond oil is widely used as a vehicle for essential oils in aromatherapy.

CASTOR OIL

The raw seeds of *Ricinus communis* L. are toxic and need roasting before extracting the oil if this is to be consumed. Seeds have been found in predynastic graves and the plant thus has a long history in Egypt.

Herodotus tells that the Egyptians who live about the marshes use an oil drawn from the castor-berry, which they call *kiki*. They sow this plant on the banks of the rivers and lakes; it grows wild in Hellas; in Egypt it produces abundant but ill-smelling fruit, which is gathered, and either bruised and pressed, or

Olive branch held by King Akhenaten, offering to the god Aten, whose sun rays the artist provided with hands to pick the proffered fruit. Fragment of a relief. Height 22 cm. Amarna period, 18th Dynasty, c. 1350-1334 BC. *Norbert Schimmel Collection, New York*

boiled after roasting. The thick liquid that comes from it is collected and used as oil for lamps; it gives off a strong smell.[81]

Pliny, too, had heard of *cici* oil, produced in quantity in Egypt by boiling the seeds in water and skimming off the oil, or, alternatively, by sprinkling them with salt and cold pressing.[82]

OLIVE OIL

Olives were known in Egypt around 1350 BC, and a branch was first depicted in the city of Akhenaten at el-Amarna. Indeed, if we are to believe the representations of the royal garden, olive-bearing trees actually grew there. A branch was found in one of the garlands from the tomb of Tutankhamun.

Ramesses III attempted to plant an olive grove near the temple of Re at Heliopolis for the express purpose of producing olive oil. Theophrastus says that the tree grew in Upper Egypt in the 4th century BC.[83] Strabo saw them in the Fayum some 500 years later.[84] It is still to be found in the western desert oases.

On the other hand, the oil could easily have been imported. It appears that it was brought first from Syria and later from Greece. A distinction was made between oil of unripe olives, in the classical world known as *omphacium*, particularly suited for the preparation of ointments, and ordinary olive oil.[85] Oil from 'coarse olives' should be used when freshly pressed when it is the least greasy, advises Theophrastus.[86]

SESAME OIL

The ancient Egyptian word *neheh* is now taken to designate the oil of the sesame plant, *Sesamum indicum* L., which was known as *iku*. The plant grows in abundance in Egypt today, and seeds found in the tomb of Tutankhamun indicate that the plant was cultivated in ancient times as well, a fact further confirmed by Dioscorides.[87]

The yellowish oil is odourless, with a bland taste. According to the texts, the commodity *neheh* was used as food, as lamp oil, as well as for anointing, in which latter case it may well have been enhanced with fragrant material.

Fats

The fats used as a vehicle for perfumed preparations were especially the solid ox fat as well as goose fat, which in a climate like that of Egypt would no doubt be in a liquid state. The preparation of ox fat is described in detail in one of the prescriptions carved on the temple walls at Edfu.

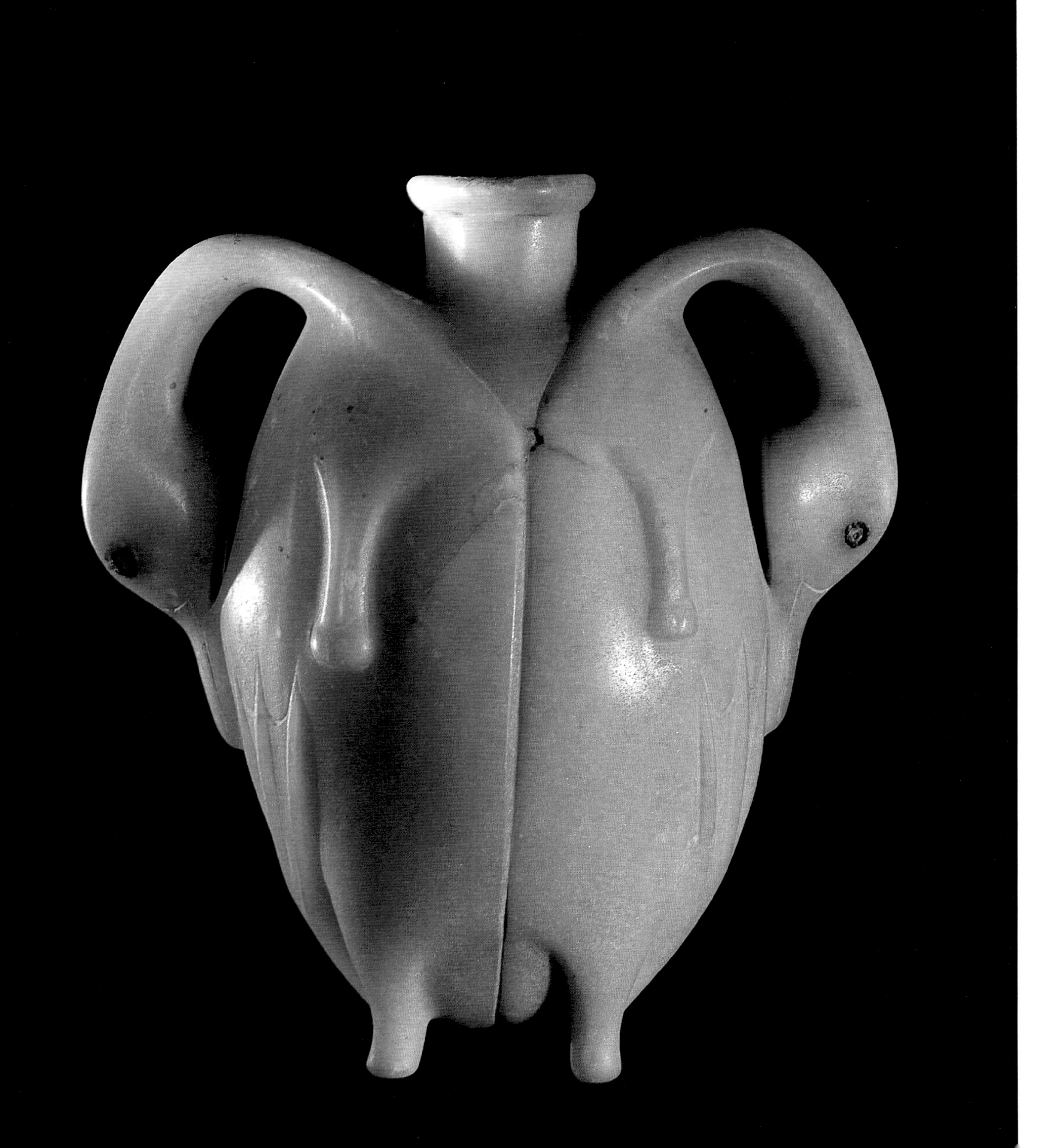

2 Scent in the Temple

Left: Unguent jar in the form of a pair of ducks trussed for sacrifice. Anhydrite (blue marble) with copper inlays. Height 17 cm. 12th or 13th Dynasty, c. 1985-1650 BC. *Metropolitan Museum of Art, New York (27.9.1 – Gift of Edward S. Harkness, 1927)*

Right: The hand of King Akhenaten dropping unguent on the offerings to Aten, presumably in a temple. Relief fragment, limestone. Height 22 cm. 18th Dynasty, Amarna period (c. 1352-1336 BC). *Norbert Schimmel Collection, New York*

An Egyptian temple was a three-dimensional representation of the world. Built in stone on a scale which made an overall view possible for the human eye, it affirmed beyond any doubt the resident god as the ruler of the created world and the king in his role of chief intermediary between the divine sphere and the people on earth. The deity took physical shape in his or her statue, placed in a shrouded shrine in the innermost room of the temple, the sanctuary, which lay in darkness. But three times a day it was lit by candles when the king, or the priests in his stead, entered to perform the daily ritual.

At a time when the soul of the ancient Egyptian civilisation was still intact Plutarch, the Greek traveller and writer (ca. AD 50-125) visited the country. He left a perceptive account of the reasons behind the daily tasks performed in the sanctuary. The seal of the shrine was broken, and the statue underwent a series of rites of cleaning, anointing, dressing and adorning just like a human being, albeit in symbolic form. The burning of incense had a specific purpose:

'Now since the air which we constantly use and live in does not always have the same composition and temper, but by night grows dense and oppresses the body and induces the soul to a state of gloom and anxiety as though it becomes clouded over and heavy, when they get up they instantly worship by burning incense of resin. Thus they purify the air with the secretion and revive the spirit which is inbred with the body and which has become enervated, the smell of resin having something violent and disturbing about it. Again at noon, when they perceive that

the sun draws up by force from the earth a very large and heavy exhalation and mingles it with the air, they burn incense of myrrh; for its heat loosens and disintegrates the turbid and muddy mass which gathers in the atmosphere. In fact doctors believe that it is helpful, in treating pestilential conditions, to make a big fire in order to rarefy the air; this is done more effectively if fragrant wood is burnt, such as that of the cypress, juniper and pine ... Aristotle says that the fragrant breaths of perfumes, flowers and meadows are no less conducive to health than to pleasure, in that they spread softly with warmth and mildness through the brain which is by nature cold and congealed.'[1]

At sunset, however, kyphi was burnt.[2] An offering meal was served before the doors of the shrine were once more sealed. The statue itself was never exposed to the public.

Incense and unguent feature prominently in the incantations and spells above the entrance to the King's burial chamber. Pyramid of Unas, Saqqara, 5th Dynasty, c. 2350 BC

The rites were accompanied by incantations, and this act was a most dramatic way for the priests of communicating with the deity. The part played by fragrant incense was significant in that by means of odour the officiants could reach parts of the divine power which they could not even see. By anointing the statue with fragrant oils they had an opportunity of a very direct form of contact with the deity: the priest would dip his little finger into the oil and extend it towards the statue, touching it very gently.

Scents were believed to originate from the gods in the first place, to have sprung from their eyes or their bones, in particular the eye of the sun-god Re. Many plant ingredients were known as 'fruits of the eye of Re'. The eye of Horus in particular played a crucial part, as he had lost his eye during the battle for revenge for his father Osiris.[3] Scent became identified with the eye of the god which was restored to its owner: when the burning incense drifted towards the statue it re-enacted the occasion when Thoth, god of magic, presented Horus with his eye, healed and sound. The act was considered significant for all gods, not only Horus. The incantation performed over the burning incense glorifies the part played by it, confirming the identity of the scented substance with the eye:

> The incense comes, the incense comes.
> The scent is over thee,
> the scent of the eye of Horus is over thee.
> The perfume of the goddess Nekhbet
> which comes forth from the town of Nekheb
> it cleanses thee, it adorns thee,
> it makes its place upon thy two hands.
> Hail to thee, oh incense!
> Take to thyself the eye of Horus.
> Its perfume is over thee.[4]

This text is written on an offering table on which the bowl of incense was probably placed. It is interesting that it was found at el-Amarna, but bearing the cartouche of Amenhotep III; thus it predates the religious revolution of his son. The recipient of the

Right: Precious incense and unguents were elaborated and stored deep inside the temple such as the splendid temple of Horus at Edfu. Built during the Ptolemaic period, it was completed as recently as 57 BC

offering is not mentioned, but if the slab was actually used at el-Amarna it could have been Aten, the sun disc. In any case it must have been an heirloom taken to Akhenaten's city from elsewhere.

Burning and offering incense was a means of communication between the earthly and the divine spheres. Thus it would also serve as a link between a deceased king and the deities in whose company he was believed to travel across the sky every night in eternity, when he himself became part of cosmos.

This was an idea established at the very beginning of Egyptian civilisation nearly 5000 years ago. We first encounter it in the so-called Pyramid Texts, a corpus of writings of miscellaneous origin put together in the Old Kingdom. These texts were inscribed in the burial chambers of kings of the Old Kingdom from the reign of King Unas by the end of the Fifth Dynasty. They consisted of hymns, incantations, dramatic and magical texts and so-called transfigurations, devised to enable the king to achieve his goal of eternal life in cosmos.

Again we find incense, offered by priests in the mortuary temple, playing a vital part as an intermediary between the dead king and the gods in the sky:

> The fire is laid,
> The fire is lit.
> The incense is placed on the fire.
> The incense glows.
> Your scent comes to the dead King Unas,
> oh incense.
> The scent of King Unas comes to you,
> oh incense.
> Your scent comes to King Unas, you gods.
> King Unas is with you, oh gods.
> You are with King Unas, oh God.
> You live with King Unas, oh gods.
> You love him, oh gods.[5]

Scent was similarly efficient when brought forward in the form of an unguent. By having his body anointed the deceased king would absorb the very body fragrance of the

Record of a delivery of unguents imported from abroad was carved on a door jamb of a temple store at Karnak.
Middle Kingdom, 2055-1650 BC.
Photograph by Lise Manniche

sun god Re, so far removed from the foul odour of death and decay. The unguent had healing properties, for it would restore his body just as the eye of Horus had been healed and restored and made to see again.

> I come to you king so-and-so
> To anoint you with the unguent
> which sprang from the eye of Horus.
> Anoint yourself with it.
> It will unite your bones,
> It will bind your flesh to you,
> It will rid you of the bad sweat
> so that it falls to the ground.
> Take its scent that your scent
> May become sweet like the scent of Re
> when he rises to the horizon
> And the gods of the horizon
> rejoice with him.[6]

The nature of scents presented to the dead kings in the pyramid temples of the Old Kingdom remains unknown. But in Egypt, tradition was long-lived, and in view of the fact that this was a civilisation which had developed a system of writing by the beginning of the 2nd millennium BC, religious practices were kept unaltered for extensive periods of time by being written down on scrolls of papyrus or carved in stone. Thus when during the entire course of Egyptian history we meet a list of seven 'sacred oils' which remained virtually unaltered, there is firm reason to believe that the tradition of these oils goes back further than the specific written record of their names. Funerary cult and temple rites go hand in hand; the subject is dealt with in Chapter 5 (p. 108).

When deliveries of incense arrived in the temples they were taken to be stored in a depot specially designed for the purpose. At Karnak, where Amun-Re, king of the gods, was in residence, architectural elements of such a room have survived from the Middle Kingdom, in spite of the fact that the greater part of this early temple has vanished under later buildings.[7] The door jambs bear inscriptions recording the delivery of precious unguents from distant localities in the eastern Mediterranean. In the Eighteenth Dynasty Queen Hatshepsut achieved fame not only by bringing incense from Punt, for others had done so before, but by attempting to transplant the very incense trees to the gardens of Amun-Re at Deir el-Bahari, directly opposite the temple at Karnak on the other bank of the river. Part of the incense shipment was no doubt delivered at the gates of the Karnak temple, for facilities were at hand to store it there; yet another jamb has been recovered there, telling that 'Her Majesty had built a store room for antiu resin to produce pellets [of incense] every day so that the temple could be always enveloped in the scent of god's land.'[8] The jamb was re-used in a later monument, and the exact location of this incense room remains conjectural, but it was probably in the heart of the temple, extensively rebuilt by her successor Tuthmosis III. In one of the rooms near the sanctuary he left an inscription very similar to that of Hatshepsut, but with the interesting addition that in the same room a precious substance called *nudj* was prepared, a term that occurred in the so-called 'Magic book of unguent mak-

Men of the trading expedition to Punt carrying a basket with an incense tree to their ship. Painted relief in the temple of Hatshepsut, Deir el-Bahari, 18th Dynasty, c. 1473-1458 BC.

ing'.[9] On the inside walls of the room the King is represented offering the sacred oils (for which see Chapter 5) and presenting heaps of incense as well as incense trees, the act (or the motif) being inspired by the wall decoration at Deir el-Bahari.

Such store rooms, or 'laboratories' as they are often called, can be identified in Ptolemaic temples as well. Here they are better preserved, and their wall decoration is even more specific.[10]

By the time we reach the Ptolemaic period, the recipes for unguents and other sacred preparations were deemed important enough to be inscribed in stone on the walls of the temples, not in a public place where they could be read by all those who were able to do so, but in a tiny chamber inside the temple, where only the priests and other staff had access. The recipes may well have been copied from a work called 'The Book of Unguent' which is quoted on the walls of the temple of Hathor at Dendera.[11] Although the identity of some of the ingredients is still open to discussion, we can gain a fairly good impression of the nature of these preparations at the time they were written down. Their composition may well have changed over the centuries due to the availability of raw materials and other factors. The number of ingredients mentioned for the various preparations is surprisingly restricted and contrasts with the fact that the same rooms in the temples contain lengthy lists of for example the many different varieties of resins and gum resins available. It is largely the quantities of the items and the base material which is to carry the fragrance that differ. Some unguents are based on plain ox fat, others on the pulp of starchy seeds, rather different from the scented oils used by ordinary people.

It is in these inscriptions that we read in detail about the methods of preparation of a namesake of one of the 'seven sacred oils' (which may not all have been of oily consistency). Ideally these oils were used in rituals or presented as offerings in compartmented vessels where each cavity was inscribed with the appropriate name of substance. Their use is attested in connection with the funerary cult of private individuals as well as in a temple context. The inclusion of a recipe on the walls of the temple and the complexity of its preparation suggests either that the name of the oil and its use had been transferred to a commodity used in the temple cult, or that in one form or another it originated in the temple and had been used in the cult of the gods during a period so remote that no written records survive.

It is *hekenu* that is singled out in the temple inscriptions. But when the list of seven oils was augmented to ten, it included an item called *madjet* which is also among those recorded in the Edfu temple.[12]

HEKENU UNGUENT[13]

The lengthy recipe for this fragrant preparation is written down on the east wall of the 'laboratory' at Edfu, adjoining the hypostyle hall where the statue of the god was carried in procession on festive occasions during the course of the year. It is unlikely that the

Ramesses II burning incense to honour Amun's boat shrine carried by priests in procession. Relief on the wall of the Great Temple of Amun, Karnak, 19th Dynasty, c. 1279-1213 BC

unguents were actually prepared in the room, for most of the unguents required cooking. The room is unsuitable for this purpose, for it is not open to the sky. It is too small to carry out lengthy preparations in quantity, and no soot remains on the walls and ceiling to show that fire had been lit here on a major scale. But some unguents may well have been stored here, and the mere fact that the recipes were recorded on the walls would have ensured the correctness of the concoctions and perpetuated their supply at the same time as establishing their sacredness and affiliation to the temple and the resident deity.

The total quantity of finished hekenu was estimated at 1 *hin*, or 0.5 l. As in other recipes recorded by the Edfu priests, the extent to which individual ingredients reduced their weight and volume during the course of preparation had been meticulously observed and worked out. The total period of preparation amounted to 365 days. It is specified as being 'hekenu of first class antiu resin and ab resin' intended for 'anointing the divine limbs'. This suggests that it was not so much a specific 'brand' as a certain type of fragrant unguent for which ingredients could be substituted if required.

It is based on the extracted pulp of the seeds of a tree called *nedjem*, 'sweet', a designation to be taken as a description of the product rather than a generic name of the tree. It is clear from the texts that the tree was not native to Egypt, but that it grew in Ethiopia (rendering implausible the tentative identification, sometimes found in literature, of nedjem as 'carob', for this tree existed there). In the hieroglyphic texts it is described as

Right Ramesses III offering incense to the god Ptah. Detail of a wall painting in the tomb of the king's son Amenherkhopeshef, Valley of the Queens, 20th Dynasty, 1184-1153 BC.
Photograph by Lise Manniche

having 'black' wood, and its seeds were set in pods. When subjected to pressure, these seeds yielded a liquid substance known as *reben*. It has been compared with the 'akakia' extracted from acacia seeds (the acacia was native to Egypt and it and its produce was known under a different name, hence it cannot be the same as this nedjem).[14] Although nedjem was by definition 'sweet' (the exact translation of the word), the substance was not necessarily chosen for its smell, but rather for its lack of smell and for its ability to absorb other scents.

The nature and consistency of hekenu as given in this recipe rather depends on the interpretation of the word nedjem and on the identity of the tree in question, whether it had oil-producing seeds, and whether these seeds were reduced to a fruity paste. The existence of such paste as a base for perfume will become evident below.

The preparation took place in five stages:

a) Preparing the vehicle (in this case the paste or liquid of nedjem pods);
b) Making the vehicle astringent;
c) Preparing 'liquid';
d) Preparing 'dry';
e) Adding resins and final boiling.

The quantities in all recipes have been converted to modern units:

1 Egyptian hin = 0.5 l;
1 deben = 91 g;
1 kite = 9.1 g.

a) *Preparing the vehicle*

1. Take 4.5 l of the seeds required to make 0.647 l of liquid.
2. Reduce to 2.699 l by removing the shells [?].
3. Reduce to a fourth by pressing [*aref*],[15] making 0.647 l of liquid.
4. Place the liquid in a cooking vessel on a fire of acacia wood and add 31 g water. On the morning of day 2 the liquid measures 0.65 l. Boil for 3 days more, adding 123 g water drop by drop.
5. Sieve the boiled hekenu liquid which will now measure 0.6 l [slightly less than foreseen in 1].

b) *Making the base material astringent*

6. Take the following: 13 g *tit en qet* [pine resin?], 23 g tisheps [cinnamon?], 9 g aspalathos, 9 g tubers of cyperus grass. Grind it in a mortar and mix with 28 g tisheps [cinnamon?], 9 g aspalathos, 9 g tubers of cyperus grass. Grind it in a mortar and mix with 15 g of best oasis wine.
   'Seal the container with the seal of the priest.' Place 9 g of second sort antiu resin in another vessel with 120 g water.
7. On the morning of day 5 place a pot on the fire, take the herbs in the mortar and mix with them the hekenu liquid and the antiu resin. Let boil three times on a fire of acacia wood, then extinguish the fire at once.

c) *Preparing 'liquid'*

During the next 121 days, 11 portions of 'liquid' are to be prepared, each taking 11 days to make and consisting of a total of 1.001 kg second sort antiu resin and 1.001 kg water. The quantity is not the same for every portion.

8. Prepare the first portion from 136 g of first class second sort antiu by grinding in a mortar with 136 g purest water.
9. Stir the contents with your hand and pour in drop by drop the 546 g of the hekenu liquid prepared earlier, mixing it well. Place the pot on the fire. Heat it while stirring with a silver implement. Remove the hekenu liquid from the fire and leave to cool for 11 days.
10. For portions 2 - 11 the quantities are 86 g antiu resin per portion [and an equal amount

Good wine was required for several sacred unguents. This illustration of the plant is in a Persian translation of *De Materia Medica* by Dioscorides. 15th century .
Persian Manuscript No. 2127, Topkapi Palace Library, Istanbul

of water?]. Add to the hekenu liquid in the same manner as the first portion. In the end, the quantity amounts to 0.5 l.

d) *Preparing 'dry'*
Now three portions of 'dry' are to be prepared. For each one 182 g first sort antiu resin and 32 g water is required, and each takes 20 days to complete.

11. For the first portion of 'dry' place 182 g first sort antiu resin in a mortar [with the water?] and grind finely.
12. Add to this the prepared 0.5 l hekenu liquid drop by drop. Mix carefully 'with two helpers who have the bag of antiu with them.' When it is done, leave in a khebeb vessel for 20 days.
13. Proceed in the same way with the second and third portions of 'dry'. When the procedure is completed, the 'dry' measures 0.6 l.

e) *Adding ab resin and more antiu resin*
Then the three portions of ab resin from the nenib tree are to be prepared, each taking 60 days to complete, the total amount of ingredients required being 546 g first sort ab resin and 91 g water.

14. Grind in a mortar 182 g first sort dark ab resin and sift three times until three-fourths [136 g] are left. Boil over a slow fire with 30 g water.
15. Add to this 136 g first sort antiu resin mixed with 34 g especially good oasis wine. Add hekenu mixture which had been left in the khebeb vessel for a total of 60 days. Place in a cooking pot on the fire and pour in 45 g wine drop by drop. In the end 0.563 l of hekenu will remain.
16. Prepare the second portion from 182 g ab resin. After grinding and sifting as before 121 g remains. Add 121 g first sort antiu, mixed with 31 g wine. Add the hekenu liquid drop by drop, mix carefully as before. Leave in the khebeb vessel for 60 days. Place in a pot on the stove. Add 31 g wine drop by drop. In the end 0.529 l will remain.
17. Prepare the third portion from 182 g ab resin. After grinding and sifting as before 106 g will remain.
18. Add to the third portion of ab resin 106 g first sort antiu resin mixed with 25 g especially good wine from the Dakhla oasis. Add the hekenu liquid to the third portion of ab resin and leave in the khebeb vessel for 60 days.
19. Place in a pot on the stove and keep the fire going. Add 40 g wine.

Final quantity remaining: 0.5 l of hekenu.

If we look at the nature and quantity of the ingredients we will find that initially we have about $2^1/_2$ kg dry ingredients, whereas the liquid ingredients (nedjem seeds pulp, wine

One of the exquisite reliefs in the Luxor temple representing Tutankhamun, in this case censing, with cartouches of the name of Horemheb, his ambitious former deputy who became king four years after Tutankhamun's death. 18th Dynasty, 1336–27 BC

and water) amount to $2\frac{1}{5}$ litres (ca. $2\frac{1}{4}$ kg). Yet the final amount is just 1 hin, or 0.5 l. The preparation is constantly reduced during cooking, and the mass in the pot never amounts to more than just over 1 hin in volume or about $\frac{1}{2}$ litre (the weight is not indicated.) Although during the course of the preparation a total of 56 g, or 2 fl oz, of wine was added, it is hardly comparable with 'medicated wine' as has been suggested.[16]

In one of the Edfu recipes for kyphi (cf. below Chapter 3) the wood, or wooden substance, of the nedjem tree is given as a synonym for tisheps. The recipe for a tisheps unguent resembles in many details that for hekenu.

TISHEPS UNGUENT[17]

The Edfu laboratory includes a recipe for preparing 1 hin, or 0.5 l, of 'tisheps made of ab resin', an unguent 'for anointing the golden goddess Hathor, the great mistress of Dendera and all the goddesses of the South and the North with its fragrant liquid'. The Edfu temple was dedicated to Horus, but it had close relations with the temple of Hathor at Dendera, 177 km distant. The statue of Hathor travelled south to visit Horus at Edfu, and it may have been on such an occasion that the unguent was used.

Like hekenu, this is probably a certain type of unguent rather than a specific one. The numbers of the individual stages of preparation have been adapted to those of hekenu for easier reference, although some are not included. For this preparation, too, the quantity continually hovers just over 1 hin. The tisheps mentioned would appear to have nothing in common with the word tisheps which was rendered as 'cinnamon' in Chapter 1. No substance (spice or other) called tisheps is actually added to this preparation. Perhaps we are to understand the name of the unguent as 'substitute cinnamon unguent' or 'cinnamon flavoured'.

a) *Preparing the vehicle*

1 - 2. This is based on the same seeds as hekenu, 3.833 l of nedjem seeds. Deprived of the pods 2.3 l of seeds remain.

3. After 'pressing out' the pulp, a fourth of the volume, or 0.575 l of tisheps liquid remains [proportionally the same quantity as for hekenu].
4. On day 1, when the preparation begins, a minute quantity [0.025 l] of water is added to make up for a loss in quantity of 0.025 l. A further loss during boiling of 0.025 l will bring the total tisheps liquid to 0.55 l.

Unguent vessel for offerings in the form of an ibis. Marble breccia, height 13 cm, Predynastic period, 4th millennium BC.
Ägyptisches Museum, Berlin

The tisheps liquid is then carefully boiled while 0.5 l of water is added. [This is about 3 1/2 times as much water as was required for a similar amount of seeds for hekenu, and the cooking does not go on for three days. The liquid must thus be substantially thinner. Only 0.045 l of the tisheps liquid is said to evaporate, 0.5 l of tisheps liquid being left. Either there is a serious error in the calculations, or the scribe forgot to say that the 0.5 l of water evaporated to make the end result remain at 0.5 l.]

b) *Making it astringent*

6. To this tisheps liquid are added 22 g sweet flag and 9 g first-class 'dry antiu' previously moistened with 22 g wine.
7. Boil together.
   [For tisheps stages 8-10 - the preparation of 'liquid' - are omitted. The liquid added in hekenu at this stage was also made to evaporate.]

d) *Preparing 'dry'*

Prepare three portions of 'dry', each consisting of 182 g 'dry antiu' and a little water, 0.033 l.

11. For the first portion prepare 9 g each of aspalathos and cyperus grass and 13 g *tekhu* seeds[18] moistened with 15 g wine. Leave overnight [these herbs were omitted at this stage of preparing hekenu; instead, similar herbs were added at stage 6]. Place 2 deben 'dry antiu' in a mortar, adding the herbs.
12. Add drop by drop the 0.5 l tisheps liquid. Mix thoroughly and leave it in a khebeb vessel for 20 days.
13. Prepare the second and third portions of 'dry' as the first, but without the three herbs. This takes 60 days altogether. [Add tisheps liquid to each portion at 20 days' interval]. At this stage it measures 0.6 l [as did hekenu].

e) *Adding ab resin*

Now add three portions of ab resin, 182 g each, and each taking 60 days [i.e. added at 60 days' interval], a total of 180 days.

14. Grind 182 g ab resin in a mortar with 30 g water.
15. Proceed as with the antiu resin. [Place the ab resin in a mortar and add the already prepared tisheps liquid drop by drop, as in stages 11-12.]
16. Repeat with second portion.
17. Repeat with the third portion.

f) *Adding antiu and more ab resin*

18. Add to the tisheps liquid another 364 g first class 'dry antiu' resin, grind it with 364 g ab resin and moisten with 206 g wine.
   [It is difficult to understand how the c. 0.6 l unguent from stage 13 can be reduced to 1 hin (0.5 l) by the end of stage 18, when unlike hekenu no cooking takes place and 548 g ab resin moistened with water, 364 g antiu and a further 364 g ab resin moistened with wine are added.]

Final quantity remaining: 1 hin [0.5 l].

The dry ingredients (resins and herbs) here amount to 20 deben 5 kite (1.865 kg) while the liquid ones (tisheps liquid, water and wine) add up to 1.227 kg. Whereas it took one year to prepare a batch of hekenu, Hathor's tisheps could be made in 241 days, or 8 months and 1 day. The preparation was left to mature undisturbed for 361 days (121+60+180) in the case of hekenu and 240 days (60+180) in the case of tisheps. The initial preparation of the base material requires 4 and 1 days respectively, thus bringing the total time involved to 365 and 241 days.

The final consistency of the two preparations may have been similar in spite of tisheps containing slightly less liquid, because it was less subject to evaporation during its simpler processing.

MADJET[19]

Madjet is the name of yet another sacred unguent, added to the seven when they were made into ten. Like the other sacred unguents it had originally been used in the funerary ritual. When used in the temple it is specifically stated that madjet 'binds the bones, unites the limbs, pulls together the flesh and relieves it of foul odour.' The unguent will unite the members of the body as once in a remote past the dismembered body of Osiris had been restored. It came to play a vital part in the daily cult ritual in the temples.

There was a madjet for daily use and others for feasts. But in some contexts it appears to have become a generic designation for a type of fatty unguent rather than the name of a specific one. According to the instructions in this recipe the unguent was applied to the divine image by using two fingers, the one touching the god being sheathed in a golden 'thimble'.

Regarding the composition of the unguent we are on firmer ground, for the vehicle at least is a known substance, namely ox fat. It is thus an unguent of a firm consistency. In fact, the name is composed with the word for 'fatty matter', *adj*. In the Edfu temple the caption specifies its particular purpose as being a 'recipe for preparing madjet for the room of the "First Feast" in the temple by the unguent makers in the workshop of the temple.' This room was a special kiosk used for

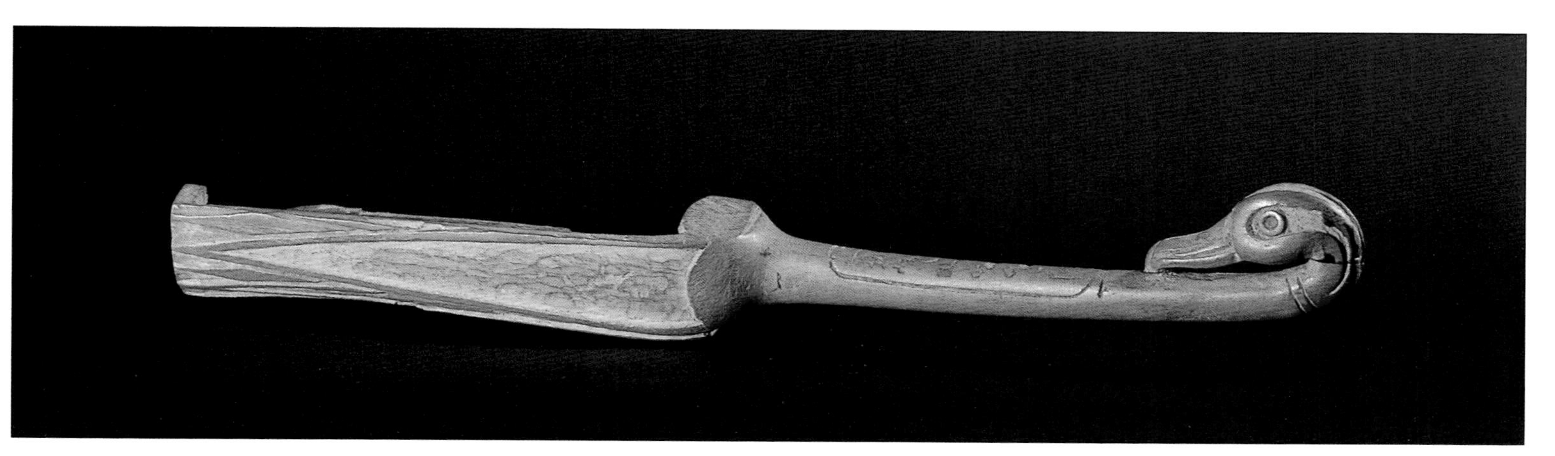

Unguent or incense spoon with a handle in the form of a duck's head and the name of Queen Mutemwiya, wife of king Tuthmosis IV and mother of Amenhotep III. Wood, length 16 cm, 1419-1386 BC. *Musée du Louvre, Paris*

the celebrations of the most important feast when the statue of the deity was carried along a precise route imitating the course of the sun, to the roof of the temple to be exposed to the sun rays. Such facilities existed in other Ptolemaic temples as for instance at Dendera and Kom Ombo.

The preparations for the vehicle had begun two years in advance. A specially chosen castrated bull whose nostrils had not been pierced with a ring had been washed in the sacred lake of the temple every morning to be physically and ritually clean and had had its feet wrapped in palm fibres.

When finally its throat had been cut and the head and limbs cut off, the body was opened and, after washing the blood off his knife, the butcher would carefully remove the fat, transfer it to a stone vessel with a stopper and leave it in the treasury for one year.

Compared with the lengthy proceedings of the previous recipes the task of perfuming the fat was quite simple. When the year had passed the fat was removed from the vessel.

a) *Preparing the base material*
1. Cook 1.092 kg of fat to reduce it by one-sixth until 10 deben [910 g] remain.

b) *Making the fat astringent and fragrant*
2. Moisten the following aromatic substances with 1 l wine from the oases and 1.5 l water: 91 g pine resin, 182 g cinnamon, 91 g aspalathos, 91 g Cyperus grass rhizomes, 91 g juniper berries, 91 g pine kernels and 182 g dry antiu (2nd class). Add to the fat. Leave overnight.
[There is no mention of removing the liquid

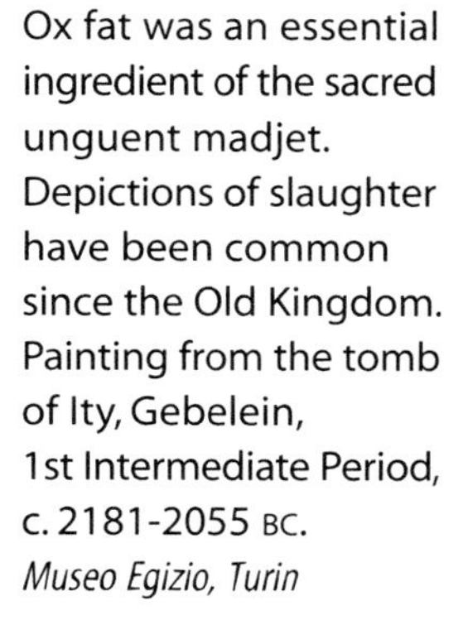

Ox fat was an essential ingredient of the sacred unguent madjet. Depictions of slaughter have been common since the Old Kingdom. Painting from the tomb of Ity, Gebelein, 1st Intermediate Period, c. 2181-2055 BC. *Museo Egizio, Turin*

the purpose of which must have been to allow maceration of the aromatics. As the finished product is intended to be greasy, the water and wine must have been discarded.]
3. The next morning boil the herbs with the fat.

c) *Dyeing*
4. Add *nesti* plant[20] to dye the unguent a beautiful red colour.
Store the unguent in a sealed stone vase.

Recently this madjet has been recreated by a German pharmacist who included a colour photograph of it in two recent publications.[21] It is of a reddish brown tint, is said to be of a greasy consistency and has a quite sharp scent that would last for hours. His fragrant ingredients, however, differed from those suggested here.

SECRET MIN UNGUENT[22]

This preparation was intended for the divine limbs of the god Min-Amun and for [anointing] 'every statue of wood and stone. It is a secret unheard and unseen by any [ordinary] people. It has been transmitted from old folk to their sons.' Only the purification priest who carried out the ritual in the temple was to be party to the secret of preparation. No human being was to come near it 'for it is a secret which one does not know.' It is an unguent of the tisheps type, based on the same seeds as the two recipes quoted above.[23]

1. Take 0.5 l of prepared tisheps pulp from the nedjem tree.
2. Mix with 910 g menen.[24] Grind together, pass through a sieve and stir during the night until dawn.
3. Place in pot on a slow fire and stir until it sets. Leave for two days.
4. Place on the fire as the first time. Add 0.5 l incense concentrate. Boil together and leave for two days.
5. Place on the fire as the first time to boil it. Add ab resin[25] and boil together. Add sweet scented aromatic substances [as indicated below?] and pass through a cloth.
6. Add to this 182 g 'dry antiu', 18 g aspalathos, [18 g] sweet geget wood; 18 g sweet flag, 18 g pine kernels, 18 g juniper berries, 1 l sefy bitumen.[26] Leave for two days.
7. Place on fire like the first time and boil. Leave for two days.
8. Place on fire like the first time. Leave for two days.
9. Place on fire like the first time. Leave to boil while stirring with a spoon made of christ-thorn wood. Leave for two days.
10. Place on fire like the first time to boil. [Afterwards] add 18 g of each of all minerals, namely gold, silver, genuine lapis lazuli, genuine red jasper, genuine green felspar, genuine turquoise, genuine faience and genuine carnelian, each of these finely ground. Leave for one day.
11. Place on fire as the first time. Test the concoction with a wooden stick. If it is too weak, bind it together with dry antiu. If you find that it is too strong, dilute it with tisheps of the nedjem tree and reduce it by placing it on a fire of sycamore wood.

Such was the secret preparation recorded in the Edfu temple. It lasted in total 21 days. According to the instructions it was to be applied while still warm with a spatula to the divine limbs of the statue. Any surplus is to be gathered and re-applied. After this treatment the statue of the deity was ready to have its mouth opened and become functional as a divine being.

The addition of precious metal and minerals may seem peculiar in an unguent. But it is not a unique combination, and it had a very specific purpose. Gods were believed to consist of a number of elements, including vegetable, mineral and resinous substances, and by means of transferring these ingredients to a statue through the process of anointing, the statue absorbed them and became divine.[27] It is appropriate that this unguent should be applied to the statue with a spatula, for one of the main ingredients was wood tar, which would have been black and sticky.

The appearance of the divine image after this treatment would be like the well known black statues from the tomb of Tutankhamun, which had no doubt been subjected to these same ministrations. The black colour, reminiscent of the fertile Nile mud, and achieved by the application of black unguent, would refer to the regenerative powers of the deity (or deceased king) in question. The preparation is similar to that used for funerary purposes, discussed in chapter 5 (p. 106).

In addition to all these highly complex preparations offered in the temples there was one single ingredient, of suitable colour and consistency and with a delicate sweet scent which was presented alongside perfumed unguent: pure honey. The golden liquid was an ingredient in kyphi and various preparations for cosmetic and medicinal use. Honey was hailed as 'the secretion of the eye of Re.' It had the same effect as unguent in restoring the limbs of the deity as he sniffed its scent.

However, the most famous sacred scented preparation from Ancient Egypt was unquestionably kyphi itself, the subject of the following chapter.

3 Kyphi and Tiryac

Part of a kyphi recipe. Inscription on a door jamb at Philae, 2nd - 1st century BC.
Photograph by Lise Manniche

Of all the scents manufactured in Ancient Egypt, kyphi is the one whose name was remembered by posterity.[1] However, it was not a sacred unguent like those described in the previous chapter. It had two main purposes: as an incense and as a remedy in the treatment of various ailments. Prescriptions for kyphi were quoted by writers in Greece and Rome and repeated by medieval unguent makers. It has even been revived in modern times. A product of similar nature known as tiryac was developed in classical antiquity, and it remains in use by herbalists in the sûq in Cairo to this day. To study the two together is a very interesting exercise in fragrant archaeology.

Kyphi is the Latin version of the Greek transcription of the ancient Egyptian *kapet*, a word which originally meant any substance used in fumigation, just as the word 'perfume' defines a scent released 'through smoke'. By the end of pharaonic civilisation it had come to designate one particular brand of scent.

Two of the four existing recipes for kyphi have survived in the Greek language. Galen, the Greek physician who practised around AD 200, provides a sound starting point for an investigation. He had studied at the medical school in Alexandria and wrote many learned works. He would have been familiar with the corpus of writing of his predecessors as well as of his contemporaries. He is the most recent in the chain of transmission of kyphi prescriptions from classical antiquity. The work of his that concerns us here is his essay entitled 'On Antidotes'.

During his research into the medical wisdom of the past, he had come across a scroll written by a certain Damocrates, an Athenian physician who flourished in the days of Nero a century earlier. Damocrates made reference to kyphi, saying that he himself had prepared it according to a recipe given by Rufus from Ephesus in modern Turkey. Kyphi does not come from a tree, like mastic, Damocrates explains to his readers, nor does it grow from the earth. In Egypt, they use it for censing in the temples. He could have added that, unlike frankincense and myrrh, it consisted of more than one ingredient. It is characteristic of many of the works of the classical writers that they quote Egyptian practices. Hence they remain so precious to Egyptology, even though they

Unguent spoon in the form of a young woman carrying an amphora and a bag. Wood, height 31.5 cm, late 18th or 19th Dynasty, 1338-1186 BC.
Musée du Louvre, Paris

were devised on Greek or Roman soil, and in a language that was not native to Egypt.

This Rufus, who provided the recipe, enjoyed considerable reputation in his day. Next to Galen he was the most highly regarded physician in the Roman Empire. Galen himself refers to him as 'an excellent man and skilled practician'. He lived around AD 50, some five generations before Galen, and - this is important - he had lived for a long time in Egypt. Spanning a century and a half between them, Damocrates quotes the recipe given by Rufus, and Galen repeats it.[2]

RECIPE FOR KYPHI BY RUFUS OF EPHESUS (1st century AD) via Damocrates, via Galen

base:	90 g raisins with skin and pips removed
	'a little' wine
	'sufficient' honey
gum resins:	90 g 'burnt resin'
	45 g 'nails' of bdellium[3]
herbs:	45 g camel grass
	33 g sweet flag
	11 g pure cyperus grass
	4 g saffron
	11 g spikenard
	2 'semis' aspalathos
spices:	15 g or cardamom
	11 g good cassia

Mash raisins with honey. Grind together bdellium, myrrh and wine until it has the consistency of runny honey. Add the raisin and honey mixture. Grind the remaining ingredients and add to the mixture. Shape into pellets for censing the gods.

Rufus indicates that cardamom may be substituted for cinnamon, and he adds that a measure of 1 drachme (3.75 g) of the substance is used to treat lung and liver complaints. This is important. Not only does kyphi provide an agreeable scent, but it is also used as a medicinal, healing substance to be taken (not inhaled). This explains why we find it quoted in Galen's work 'On Antidotes' in the first place, for according to him

Right Unguent spoon in the form of a female dancer playing a tambourine among lotus flowers. Wood, height 34.5 cm,18th Dynasty, c. 1350 BC. *Ägyptisches Museum, Berlin*

it is used in the treatment of serpent bites. It is significant that in Egyptian tradition, fumigation (*kapt*) was often employed in connection with herbal drugs to treat snake bite.[4]

The idea of using fragrant kyphi as an antidote is reflected in the works of one of Rufus's contemporaries, Dioscorides, one of the greatest names in the field of herbal medicine.[5] His works came to have an enormous influence, and in many respects he provides the key to Egyptian pharmacology. In his writings he often quotes Egyptian sources, even Egyptian plant names. In their present form they appear somewhat distorted, but they provide a true challenge to philologists interested in botany and vice versa. The identification of several ancient Egyptian plant names has been facilitated through comparison with names provided by Dioscorides.

Concerning kyphi Dioscorides says that it was chiefly used as incense in the temples, but also as an antidote, and, he says, mixed in beverages to treat asthma. There are many recipes for kyphi, he adds, and he quotes one of them. It contains ten ingredients:

Recipe for kyphi by Dioscorides
(1st century AD)

base:	5.448 kg 'sun' raisins
	4.828 l old wine
	1.136 l honey
gum resin:	42 g myrrh
	2.270 kg pure resin
herbs:	0.284 l plump juniper berries
	0.454 l sweet flag
	0.454 l camel grass
	0.454 l aspalathos
	0.284 l cyperus grass

Stone and chop the raisins and grind with wine and myrrh. Grind the other ingredients, except the honey [and resin], and add to the raisin mixture. Leave to steep for one day. Heat the honey until it thickens. Melt the resin and mix carefully with the honey. Mix everything together, grind it carefully. Store in an earthenware pot.

This recipe contains no exotic spices. We may infer from this, then, that these were perhaps not considered to have any essential medicinal properties in the present context, that is to say, as an antidote. When used as incense, on the other hand, the kyphi of Dioscorides would differ noticeably from that prepared by Galen in that the exotic spices were absent. It should be noted that the two prescriptions quoted so far involve hardly any cooking. The only use of fire is for heating the honey and melting the resin in the version quoted by Dioscorides. The rest is prepared in a mortar.

There is more to discover about kyphi in the 2nd century AD, when Galen tried out the prescription which to him must already have been ancient; but in order to do so we have to travel around the Mediterranean. At about the same time that Galen copied Rufus's recipe, a scholar in the Eastern Mediterranean was working on a comprehensive book on medicine. His language was the ancient Semitic language, Syriac (Aramaic), but in his work he incorporated pharmaceutical remedies from other parts of the ancient world, including of course Egypt.[6] On looking through the index of a modern edition of this book, an item transcribed as 'kupar' will catch the eye. There is no doubt that the name is but a distorted version of our kyphi, for the ingredients are very similar. The recipe is for once delightfully simple:

SYRIAC RECIPE FOR 'KUPAR'
(2nd century AD)

base: 168 g stoned raisins 'cleaned inside and out'
strong smelling wine
'sufficient' honey
resin: 15 g frankincense
15 g myrrh
herbs: 4 g spikenard
4 g crocus/saffron
8 g mastic tree flowers (*Pistacia lentiscus*)
8 g aspalathos
spices: 4 g cinnamon
8 g cassia

Unguent vessel for offerings in the form of a fish.
Marble breccia, height 10 cm, Predynastic Period, 4th millennium BC.
Ägyptisches Museum, Berlin

Dissolve the raisins and soluble ingredients in the wine. Pound the dry ingredients in a mortar and 'clean' them. Heat frankincense and honey. Mix it all together and store in a jar.

'Kupar' may be burnt as incense, 'for its smell is very pleasant', or alternatively administered in a beverage 'suitable for the particular ailment' to treat diseases of the liver and chest, as well as coughs. Remember that about the same time Galen also prescribed kyphi for the treatment of liver and lung diseases.

Travelling further back in time, we find ourselves in Egypt. The primary purpose of kyphi was for it to be used for fumigation in the temples. The recipe was included among the preparations listed in the 'laboratories' at Edfu and Philae, built in the 1st century BC. In Edfu it occurs twice,[7] one version being provided with explanatory terms and synonyms of ingredients. 'Recipe for the preparation of excellent kyphi for divine use' it says. If we encountered problems in translating and identifying Greek plant names, they will not decrease when we are faced with ingredients written in hieroglyphs. In addition, as in the recipes quoted above, great attention is paid to quantities and measures, and the method of preparation is described in some detail. For the first time the heating involves more than just melting honey and raisins. The unguent makers were aiming for the equivalent 910 grammes (or 100 deben) of finished kyphi, and it was a source of some amazement how the weight reduced during cooking, for the kyphi makers started out with ingredients that weighed rather more. On the one hand, it was the process of evaporation that confused the calculations. On the other hand, rather more of some ingredients was used than was required, and the excess amount had to be taken out again during the course of preparation.

That kyphi at this time was a category of scent, rather than a specific brand, is suggested by the existence of the two versions in the Edfu temple and the one at Philae. The ingredients are the same, but there are variations in the quantities of the second Edfu recipe (Edfu 2).

THE EDFU AND PHILAE RECIPES FOR KYPHI (2nd century BC)

	Edfu 1	Philae	Edfu 2
base:	3.3 l raisins from the oases	3.3 l	2 l
	2.5 l wine	2.5 l	2.5 l
	2.5 l 'fresh Horus eye' i.e. oasis wine	2.5 l	2.5 l
	3.3 l 'sweet Horus eye' i.e. honey	3.3 l	2.5 l
gum resins:			
	1,213 g frankincense (*senetjer*)	1,213 g	910 g
	1,155 g myrrh (*khar*)	1,155 g	910 g
	★273 g mastic	273 g	182 g
	★273 g pine resin	273 g	203 g
herbs:	★273 g sweet flag	227 g	227 g
	★273 g aspalathos	273 g	91 g
	★273 g camel grass	273 g	227 g
	★273 g mint	273 g	227 g
	+1.5 l cyperus	1.5 l	1 l
	+1.5 l juniper	1.5 l	1 l
	+1.5 l pine kernels	1.5 l	1 l
	+1.5 l *peker*[8]	1.5 l	1 l
spices:	★273 g cinnamon	364 g	203 g

Place the items marked ★ in a mortar and grind them. Two-fifths of this will be in the form of liquid to be discarded. There remain three-fifths in the form of ground powder. Reduce the ingredients marked + to powder. Moisten all these dry ingredients with wine in a copper vessel. Half of this wine will be absorbed by the powder [the rest is to be discarded].

Leave overnight. Moisten the raisins with oasis wine. Mix everything in a vessel and leave for five days. Boil to reduce by one-fifth. Place honey and frankincense in a cauldron and reduce volume by one-fifth. Add to the honey and frankincense the kyphi macerated in wine. Leave overnight. Grind the myrrh and add to the kyphi.

The method of preparation, and the resulting calculations of the volume of the substance, are far more complex than in any of the later recipes quoted above. In particular, more cooking is involved. The main difference in the three recipes, philological points apart, is the fact that Edfu B apparently used far less raisins. Yet curiously the final quantity was only marginally smaller than that resulting from the other two recipes (928 g as opposed to 940 g). Perhaps the instructions concerning the quantities are not to be taken too literally, but as general guidelines.

At about the time that the hieroglyphs in the temple of Edfu were being carved, Egypt had a visitor who through his writings was to have a considerable impact on posterity: Plutarch, the Greek traveller, who died around AD 125. He is generally quite a reliable source as far as Egyptian matters are concerned. Plutarch gained access to a treatise called 'On the preparation of kyphi materials' written by the Greek historian, Manetho, who lived in the 3rd century BC. Manetho is best known for having grouped the Egyptian kings in dynasties. He wrote on a variety of topics, but unfortunately most of his works have perished, including the one which would have been of interest in this place. The ingredients later given by Galen do not entirely correspond to those given by Plutarch, who in turn had gathered his information from Manetho. But they both list 16 items. Manetho's work on kyphi is otherwise lost, but there is no reason to suspect that Plutarch did not quote his source correctly.[9]

MANETHO'S RECIPE FOR KYPHI
(3rd century BC) via Plutarch

base:	raisins
	honey
	wine
gum resins:	myrrh
	resin
	mastic
	bitumen of Judaea
herbs:	cyperus grass
	aspalathos
	seseli[10]
	rush
	lanathos[11]
	large and small juniper berries (arkeuthos)
	sweet flag
spices:	cardamom

Thus in this recipe which predates Galen, mastic, sorrel and seseli appears instead of the bdellium, saffron, and spikenard given by Galen. The Edfu recipes, however, did include a word that may mean mastic.

Plutarch gives more hints on the method of preparation: The ingredients are not to be poured into the mortar together, but are added one after the other whilst someone recites religious texts. The key to success in any scent manufacture was the order of the ingredients and careful timing. The later an ingredient was added, the more it affected the final result. This would apply even in a preparation that was not directly subjected to heating.

According to Plutarch, incense was burnt in the temples three times a day. This we know from various Egyptian sources on the daily ritual in the temple. But Plutarch is specific: frankincense is burnt in the morning; myrrh at noon;. and kyphi in the evening. This particularly applied to the temples of the sun god Re. Other classical authors[12] make special mention of a 'sun kyphi', containing 36 ingredients. A 'moon kyphi' was also known.[13]

Plutarch is a mine of information on all sorts of matters, and he is the only one to provide perceptive knowledge on the spiritual effects of kyphi. He had been told that the Egyptians took kyphi in a beverage to cleanse their bodies, and he thought it worth recording that the scent of kyphi was soothing and induced sleep. 'The [ingredients] emit a sweet breath and a beneficent exhalation by which all is changed, while the body, being moved by the whiff softly and gently

Hatshepsut in her role of king censing the sacred bark of the god Amun behind the guardian statue of herself. Detail of a relief from the chapel demolished by her successor. Karnak, 18th Dynasty, 1473-1458 BC

acquires a temper that seductively brings on sleep, so that without intoxication it relaxes and loosens the chain-like sorrows and tensions of daily cares. The scent purifies and polishes like a mirror the faculty which is imaginative and receptive to dreams, just like the notes of the lyre which the Pythagoreans used before sleep to charm and heal the emotive and irrational part of the soul. For scent often restores the power of perception when it is failing, while they often obscure and calm it, since the exhalations penetrate the body because of their smooth softness'.[14]

Scent had a therapeutic effect. Nowadays we recognize this in the art of aromatherapy. The Egyptians in the days of Plutarch were well aware of its benefits. The concept had more ancient roots, as we shall see in a moment, though none of the surviving records are as articulate about it as Plutarch.

The juxtaposition of frankincense, myrrh and kyphi, as burnt in the temple of Re, has an interesting parallel in quite a different context. A Demotic tale, copied in the 2nd century AD, but with an earlier version dating back to the 4th century BC, tells of Petese, prophet of Re in Heliopolis, one of the three major cities in Ancient Egypt. Petese's wife gives birth to a girl at the same time as his mistress (wife of a priestly colleague) bears a boy. Ignorant of the true situation Pharaoh decrees that the two children of his favourite priests shall marry. As it was considered an act of blasphemy for half sisters and brothers to marry (unless they were divine or members of the royal family) the gods decide to punish Petese by inflicting a fatal disease on him. His wife takes myrrh, frankincense and kyphi, throws it on the flame (there is a short gap in the text here), and suddenly Re, the sun god himself, speaks with Petese's voice. This was obviously brought about by Petese's wife using a potent combination of morning, noon and evening incense to awaken the deity and give her dead husband the power of speech.[15]

One of the priests presenting offerings including a leg of meat, a duck and bread, is shown burning incense. Kyphi was frequently used in temples. Relief in the temple of Amun in Luxor. 18th Dynasty, reign of Tutankhamun, 1336-1337 BC.

Kyphi was used in great quantity in the temples, and since the recipes were recorded in stone on the walls of the buildings, we must assume that, like unguents, the product was manufactured within the temple compound, not in the little room itself, as some ventilation would be required for heating the cauldrons, but somewhere outside. In order to be able to do so, the ingredients for the kyphi must have been stored on the premises, and their entry into the temple would have been recorded. Such documents have survived, notably the so-called Papyrus Harris I in the British Museum. Written in the reign of Ramesses IV (1145-1141 BC), it records the donations given to various temples by his predecessor Ramesses III (1182-1151 BC). In one section we read of a delivery of six items which correspond to those listed in the Edfu and Philae recipes for kyphi: pine, cinnamon, sweet flag, camel grass, mint and mastic.[16] Considering the fact that at this time there is already some indication that fruit paste had been the basis of scented matter, as for instance at el-Amarna, where an unguent based on sycamore figs was in use,[17] we may safely add both fruit (such as raisins) as well as honey to the six ingredients in order to arrive at a recipe for kyphi which spans what would otherwise have been a gap between Ptolemaic Egypt and the New Kingdom.

KYPHI OF RAMESSES III
(12th century BC)

base:	[raisins]
	[honey]
resin:	mastic (jed)
	pine resin (or wood)
herbs:	camel grass
	mint
	sweet flag
spices:	cinnamon

The kyphi of Ramesses III may have contained ingredients not included in the delivery mentioned, but it is indeed very suggestive that the six items occur together, and that they are identical with those required for making kyphi at Edfu. Raisins and honey were commonly available and there was no need to donate and store them with the more precious products.

In order to trace kyphi even further back in time, we shall have to rely on its use in a secular context, as a remedy intended for human beings, thus bringing it back into the realm of medical men such as Rufus and Galen. In the medical papyri of the New Kingdom, written down around 1500 BC, kyphi, or kapet, is used to cense the home and clothes, as well as to disguise bad breath.[18]

KYPHI IN PAPYRUS EBERS
(c. 1500 BC)

base:	honey
gum resin:	frankincense (antiu)
	mastic (shebet)
	mastic (demten)
	genen of niuben-tree[19]
herbs:	pine kernels
	cyperus grass
	camel grass
	inektun-herb
spices:	cinnamon

Boil the dry ingredients in honey and shape into pellets.

The most significant difference is that this early kyphi omits the raisins which were the predominant base ingredient in the later recipes. As it stands, it is virtually a fragrant honey, boiled to the extent that it would form a solid mass when cool. It is possible, though, that the inclusion of raisins, or other fruit paste, was taken for granted and left out of the prescription.

A variant recipe takes us back into the field of the psychological effect of the drug, for kapet is here used to avert harmful influence of gods, demons and dead persons. The recipe not only calls for the herbs and resins already mentioned, but it includes ingredients from what is in German aptly known as *Dreckapotheke*, that is 'dirt pharmacy': the excrement of the following creatures: lion, crocodile, swallow, gazelle, ostrich, cat as well as scorpion poison, donkey's hair, barbel of Synodontis catfish and deer horn. The medicinal use of such ingredients deserves a chapter in itself, though it exceeds the scope of the present work. Their inclusion in kapet can be explained by the use of the drug to avert the influence of unknown and dangerous forces. By including parts of lions and scorpions, for example, the remedy was no doubt believed to work in these two cases, and it is but a small step to use it not just as prevention, but as treatment. The kyphi of Galen's 'On Antidotes' of AD 200 thus reflects the use of the kapet of the Egyptians of 1500 BC. The more peculiar ingredients it contained, the more efficient the remedy. We should not be surprised to find an apparently innocuous swallow in this company. In theory, deceased persons were believed to be able to achieve any transformation they desired. One of those specifically mentioned was the form of a swallow. Since the dead were not necessarily kindly disposed towards those left behind, swallows had to be watched.

Although no more recipes for kyphi are forthcoming in even older texts, the substance known as kapet occurs as early as in the days of the pyramid builders. The corpus of texts written inside the pyramids of the Fifth and Sixth Dynasties contains a reference to kapet as one of the items which make life in the Hereafter agreeable to the deceased king.[20]

It is of course very tempting to try out all these apparently accurate recipes for the famous kyphi. A hundred years ago the instructions given by Dioscorides, Plutarch and Galen were tested and compared by the French scholar Loret and a French perfumer. It should be remembered, though, that some of the ingredients had not been identified with absolute certainty, and with respect to some there remains uncertainty to this day. Before that, around 1850, Parthey, the translator of *De Iside and Osiride*, had also experimented with the preparation of kyphi with the assistance of a chemist friend in Berlin. The version given by Dioscorides was said to be the most pleasant when mixed with wine, rather like the Greek retsina. About one quarter of kyphi consisted of resin or mastic

The ancient remedy tiryac has always been on sale in the Cairo bazaar. Flanked by a butcher and a baker on one side and a jeweller on the other, the apothecary's stall in the *sûq* is depicted in an illustration of the medieval Arab manuscript of *Warqa and Gusah*, a heroic romance. Early 13th century. *Topkapi Palace Museum, Istanbul*

or similar, and a quarter of other scented matter, added to the main base ingredients, raisins and honey.[21]

Loret and Parthey were not the first ones to attempt to prepare kyphi according to the ancient recipes. In late antiquity it was referred to in medical works. Alexander from Tralles in Lydia, who lived under Emperor Justinian in 6th century AD, includes kyphi in composite remedies as well as on its own. Headache was treated by anointing the forehead with *kyphonion*.[22] When treating patients suffering from epilepsy he had satisfactory results by making them drink sun kyphi.[23] For ear diseases and stomach and liver complaints he prescribed remedies containing a so-called priest kyphi mixed with other ingredients.[24] In 6th century AD kyphi was still known in Egypt, for it appears in a Coptic prescription to treat skin disease, ground with marjoram and wine.[25]

In the Middle Ages kyphi was prepared by Nicolaus, the unguent-maker from Alexandria (again Egypt is firmly on the map of fragrance).[26] After listing his 50 ingredients he provides an interesting piece of information: while the solid ingredients are ground with the liquid the Greek vowels α, ε, υι, ου, ω are to be recited. In Hellenistic times Egyptian priests used to sing the vowels α, ο, η, ι, ο, υ, ω while they adored the god.[27] Another Hellenistic tradition aims at achieving perfect harmony by the assignment of a vowel to each of the seven spheres of the universe. Plutarch, too, had mentioned the recitation of religious texts during kyphi making. Are we to infer that the kyphi is supposed to absorb the qualities and spirit of the words and perhaps produce similar harmony?

It would seem that after this Nicolaus (around AD 1300) kyphi was forgotten in European tradition. But when in 1850 the book by Plutarch on Isis and Osiris was translated by Parthey into German with a commentary, someone in Vienna had the idea of marketing kyphi as an aphrodisiac.[28] In the 1960's a lady in England claimed to have studied 'the sacred instructions of the ancient papyri' to reproduce kyphi: 'Sprinkle a few grains of precious kyphi incense on glowing charcoal or a hot metal surface' the ad runs, 'and experience yourself the subtle

mystery of this fragrant link with an ancient civilisation'.[29] This is an intriguing thought, but as long as the identity of several ingredients remains uncertain, the authenticity of the kyphi 'made in England' remains questionable.[30]

On Egyptian soil, kyphi continued to enchant. The works of Dioscorides were translated into Arabic, and thus, although the hieroglyphic texts were not understood by the Egyptians of that time, they were able to acquaint themselves with the fragrant practices of their past. It is in one such Arabic Dioscorides manuscript that we have the only picture (reproduced overleaf) of a bowl of burning kyphi; hence one may perhaps assume that the recipe had actually been tried out at that time.[31] In view of the importance of scent in the world of Islam, this is indeed quite plausible. But it looks as if the medicinal use of kyphi had been overshadowed by another famous substance also known from the classical writers: tiryac.

Islamic tradition has it that tiryac was a remedy used in the 7th century AD. This is recorded among other places in a work by Ibn Qayyim al-Jawziyya in the 14th century, dealing with the medicine of the Prophet.[32] In view of the fact that the Prophet himself was said to have used it, it gained the seal of approval for Muslims of posterity. Gathering his information from the works of Galen,[33] Ibn Sina (Avicenna), writing in the 11th century AD, quotes tiryac as an antidote,[34] and this is taken up by European Medieval herbalists. In both *Regimen sanitatis* as well as in *Taquinum sanitatis*, two books in Latin on healthy living, written in the 12th - 13th centuries, tiryac treats poisonous bites.[35] In the French commentary to the latter, made in the 15th century, tiryac appears as 'triacle'. The source of all these prescriptions, transmitted in Arabic by such scholars as Ibn Botlan, was Galen quoting Andromachus, a physician at the court of Nero.[36]

As a matter of fact, tiryac is a Greek word (Θηριακα). In his essay 'On Antidotes' Galen mentions it next to kyphi. He not only repeats some of the ingredients included in kyphi (cinnamon and cassia, frankincense and myrrh, seseli and sweet flag among others), but he includes kyphi itself. The 'tiryac of Andromachus' quoted by Galen contains 46 ingredients plus 'sufficient honey'. Both the nature of the two products and the purpose for which they were employed are strongly related. Although tiryac is not reported to have been used specifically for the sake of its fragrance, it was taken as an antidote, and, like kyphi, it was used to dispel anxiety.

Towards the end of the 16th century Prospero Alpini, a Venetian scholar, visited Egypt. He wrote a detailed account of Egyptian botany and medicine based on his studies in the field. Among many other things he includes a recipe for tiryac.[37] At this time, tiryac was shrouded in mystery, and it was only with great difficulty that Prospero Alpini succeeded in getting hold of a list of ingredients. And they were many - 57 plants plus serpent skin and clay, all to be mixed with old wine, or pomegranate wine, and honey. This was the recipe of 1574, especially

In this illumination a physician is apparently describing to a colleague the treatment he has devised for the patient. From *Kitab al Hash'ish*, the Arabic translation of *De Materia Medica* by Dioscorides, copied in Baghdad in 1224 AD by Abd Allah ibn al-Fadl. *4/1997, The David Collection, Copenhagen*

composed for the 'king of Turkey' and hence known as 'tiryac of Farouq'. There are others with up to 96 different ingredients. Some contained bitumen of Judaea, or 'mumia' as it was known then, an ingredient which occurs in kyphi prescriptions as 'asphalt'.[38] Theban opium was another significant ingredient (among the four second-largest amounts mentioned after squill paste) to be mixed with honey, the main ingredient. But in his version of tiryac kyphi was not included.

The combination of herbs and spices, wine and honey, resin and myrrh is altogether reminiscent of some of the recipes for kyphi. Serpent skin, or sometimes snake spittle, was no doubt included because tiryac was here used as an antidote for serpent bite. This was already the case with one of the New Kingdom recipes for kyphi. Most significantly, it was also taken by some people regularly over several years in the belief that it would keep them young and actually prolong their life.[39]

Even in the work of Alpini, who relies firmly on Arabic tradition, the remedy is known as 'tiryac of Andromachus', and this in spite of the variations caused by the omission of some ingredients and the inclusion of others. A recent French edition of Alpini quotes an interesting reference to an 1822 edition of *Description de l'Égypte* which also deals with tiryac. The remedy in use in the late 18th century was not much different from 'tiryac of Andromachus' quoted by Alpini. The editor ventures the idea that the Egyptian tiryac in use in his day is very ancient and has not changed, that in fact Andromachus worked out his prescription on the basis of an Egyptian version, introducing a few new ingredients and omitting those that might be harmful in a climate different from Egypt. This hypothesis thus takes the tradition of tiryac back to Egypt, to a date prior to the first century AD.

The contemporary Syriac manuscript mentioned earlier also includes a recipe for tiryac.[40] The author says that it consists of four ingredients, suitable for treating pains of the liver and spleen, stomach ailments, heart problems, as well as dementia and delirium! In spite of the fact that it does not contain any parts or secretions of a serpent, it is still used to treat poisonous bites. But one of the herbs used may have been chosen as a substitute. The Syriac version contains equal quantities of entian, aristolochia, myrrh and laurel mixed in honey. The former three ingredients also occur in the tiryac of Prospero Alpini. It is administered in hot water. It is a much simpler version than the one given by Prospero Alpini. Costus may be substituted for myrrh and saffron added. Incidentally, in modern herbal medicine both laurel, entian and myrrh are used to treat stomach ailments; and one of the varieties of aristolochia has been used to treat serpent bite.

It is interesting that tiryac is used to treat mental disorders, not just delirium, but anxiety and worry. Elsewhere in his work[41] Alpini also implies that tiryac had an effect on the mind. The remedy is mentioned among others which are said to provoke 'abnormal states', leaving the person excited for an hour, then causing him to experience severe delirium.

One of the preparations mentioned in this context is 'the philosophers' remedy', used to fortify the vital forces and improve memory, which consists of a selection of herbs and spices (among others cinnamon, pine kernels, myrobalanos, fumitory) in a base of raisins and honey. Another called *bers* consists of honey into which are mixed not only fragrant ingredients such as Indian nard and crocus, but also henbane, euphorbia and opium. These drugs, their ingredients and their use have very ancient roots indeed. Evidence of their use in the Eighteenth Dynasty is discussed in Chapter 5 (pp. 99, 101).

The effect is strongly reminiscent of Plutarch's description of kyphi. In fact, tiryac is used to treat any kind of imbalance to the system, for it has the property of being able to make a patient revert to normal.

This useful 'rescue remedy' is still on sale as tiryac in the bazaars in Cairo. The sheikh

Right Kyphi burning in a bowl. An illustration from the Arabic translation of *De Materia Medica* by Dioscorides, copied in 11th century from the original completed in 990 AD by Abu Abd Allah el-Natili in Samarkand. *Universiteitsbibliothek, Leiden*

of the herbalists sees patients in his clinic opposite al-Azhar. After assessing the complaint and the needs of the patient he composes an individual prescription for tiryac which the patient then takes to one of the herb vendors in the neighbouring bazar where the mixture will be prepared.[42] After two thousand years this is an unbroken tradition of herbal medicine.

Many composite remedies were in use in ancient times. As already mentioned kyphi was indeed one of the many ingredients in Galen's tiryac, and it is for this reason that he deemed it useful to include a recipe for it in his essay 'On Antidotes'.

The two preparations are closely linked, and if Galen's instructions were heeded by posterity, the tradition of making kyphi would have persisted for far longer than the written sources suggest.

4 Recipes for Luxury

The queen is lovingly anointing her husband the king. Both are exposed to the life-giving rays emanating from the divine sun disc Aten in the tradition of Amarna art. Inlaid back panel of the Golden Throne found in the tomb of Tutankhamun, made with sheets of silver and gold, inlaid alabaster, faience and coloured glass paste. 18th Dynasty, 1336-1327 BC.
Egyptian Museum, Cairo

Towards the close of the pharaonic period the classical writers describe how scents travelled all over the Mediterranean. This had been the case for centuries, but evidence about it must be gathered from sources of a different nature. For instance, when around the year 1350 BC a cargo ship sank on the southern coast of Turkey, coming to rest on the sea bed 60 m below the surface of the sea, it had been doing the round of the Mediterranean, collecting en route a shipment of resin amongst many other items.[1] It appears to have been travelling around the Mediterranean, and an approximate date for the voyage is suggested by the presence of a golden signet ring with the cartouche of Queen Nefertiti. This is tangible evidence of how fragrant material travelled, either to please the gods or to delight human beings.

The wreck found at Ulu Burun carried close to one hundred jars of resin identified either as *Pistacia terebinthus,* a tree that grows on Cyprus and Chios among other places, or *P. atlantica* which is native to Palestine. It is possible that it was being taken to Egypt for further processing.

In this particular context it is interesting to remember a fragment of a pot, found at el-Amarna, city of Akhenaten and Nefertiti (and thus roughly contemporary with the Ulu Burun wreck) carrying the following inscription: 'Fresh resin belonging to captain Ini, purified for the unguent maker Khaemwast'. Ini could have been the master of a similar merchant ship that made a more fortunate voyage 3,500 years ago, returning safely to the port at Memphis in the north and including in its cargo jars of resin for Ini's personal use, perhaps as part of his remuneration in kind.

Around the time of the Nineteenth Dynasty in Egypt, that is largely throughout the long reign of Ramesses II, the perfume industry on mainland Greece and Crete is well documented. The decipherment of the linear B script has given access to numerous clay tablets which, like those found at el-Amarna, had been preserved for posterity through disaster. At Pylos in particular information is rich, not only in written documents, but also in jars and other equipment.[2] As Mycenean objects have been found in Egypt, and Egyptian items in Greece, trading was obviously carried on in those days, and there is evidence of one of the traded goods having been perfumed oils.

Contemporary with this information are the tablets written in Assyrian giving details of the method of preparing a variety of scents. It does not differ substantially from the methods known from later sources in Egypt which are quite specific. The ingredients in that part of the world were oil, water, honey and the herbs and spices. Only the use of wine to 'lighten' the scents is omitted.[3]

In view of this possibility of interchange of scented goods it is of interest to examine the writings from the trade partners of Egypt as well as those found in Egypt itself to assess both the nature of perfumery and the availability of ingredients in the land of the pharaohs. Concerning the taste for foreign fragrance in distant Arabia an observation by Pliny may well hold true for other countries as well, that 'in Arabia there is a surprising demand for foreign scents, which are imported from abroad: so tired do mortals get of things

Unguent jar in the form of a dwarf carrying a jar engraved with lotus leaves. Alabaster, height c. 20 cm, 18th Dynasty, c. 1375 BC. Probably found in Akhenaten's capital el-Amarna.
Metropolitan Museum of Art, New York (17.190.1963 – Gift of J. Pierpoint Morgan, 1917)

that are their own, and so covetous are they of what belongs to other people.'[4] He goes on to say that they traded one scented material for another. To his mind, things that grow far away from home are not suited for medicinal use, but they should be used for luxury items, perfumes and unguents, even scents to delight the gods in the temples.[5]

Cleopatra, the mistress of luxury and extravagance, on one occasion used 400 denarii's worth of unguents just to soften and perfume her hands. As this sum of money in Pliny's days would buy one pound of unguent (see below), the report seems plausible. About a certain Antiphanes it was said that he bathed in a large gilded tub and steeped his feet and legs in rich Egyptian unguent. Egyptian perfumes were available to customers in perfumers' shops in Athens in the 4th century BC. And a perfume, known simply as The Egyptian, was famous in that city, so much so that Theophrastus refers to it repeatedly in his work 'On Odours'. It is here that we find the most sensitive remarks on scent as perceived by a Greek towards the end of the pharaonic period.

Pliny pondered on the supreme luxury of scents: 'Perfumes serve the purpose of the most superfluous of all forms of luxury; for pearls and jewels do nevertheless pass to the wearer's heir, and clothes last for some time, but unguents lose their scent quickly, and die in the very hour when they are used. Their highest recommendation is that when a woman passes by, her scent may attract the attention even of persons busy doing something - and they cost more than 400 denarii per pound! All that money is paid for somebody else's pleasure, for the person wearing the scent does not smell it herself [or himself].'[6]

If properly stored, perfume would keep its fragrance inside the jar for a while, depending on its ingredients. A long lasting perfume is what a woman wants, says Theophrastus, and this was a priority of the shopkeeper as well. Hence those made in Egypt for export would not be the delicate flower fragrances, but those having as their main components resins, roots and barks. Stored in phials of calcite ('alabaster') or glass away from sun and heat, such scents were perfect for travelling. Ten years or more would be the life of myrrh unguent, with cinnamon and cassia a close second. An exception among the ephemeral floral scents, iris perfume would last for six years and, properly stored, even as long as twenty years.[7]

Perfumes in antiquity were named either after their main ingredient or after their place of origin. The popularity of a scent changed with time, just as it does today. In the 'old days', seen from Pliny's point of view, scent from the island of Delos was unrivalled, but it was superseded by that made in the Egyptian Delta town of Mendes. The main ingredients may have stayed the same, but local differences in the habitat of the plants, the circumstances of the preparation and storage, not to mention the quantities and methods employed, caused variations in the end product. Thus for example the iris perfume made in Corinth, popular for a while, had to yield pride of place to the iris perfume made in Cyzicus. Saffron oil from Rhodes was better than that from Cilicia, and Egyptian 'cypros' scent (henna flower perfume) ousted that from Cyprus.[8]

Right The golden eyepaint or unguent container in the form of a shell could have been worn as a pendant. Gold leaf, height 5.3 cm 3rd Dynasty, c. 2660-2655 BC. *Egyptian Museum, Cairo*

In late antiquity composite scents were the ideal. Even when the rose found its way to the Mediterranean, rose perfume contained other scented ingredients to enhance the rose scent.

According to Theophrastus, there was no fixed rule for the combination of spices.[9] The result will always be satisfactory, he claims, and this is of interest when we consider the variations in certain specific prescriptions, such as the famous kyphi.

In any case the quality of the end product would vary according to the qualities and maturity of the batch of spices, herbs or fruits, even though the prescriptions might have been identical, not to mention the time and technique of the preparation. Hence the fact that for most of the perfumes we possess only a summary list of the ingredients should not worry us unduly.

Perfumed Oils

These fragrances correspond most closely to modern perfume in that they were concentrated and liquid, used in small quantities and stored in little bottles or phials such as have been found in great numbers all over the Mediterranean. The luxurious contents inspired elegant design, above all in polychrome glass, a material which itself was wont to travelling. The Ulu Burun wreck, mentioned above, also contained blue glass 'bars', shipped to be processed elsewhere, possibly in Egypt, for this is where these attractive bottles were invented. This is where they were needed, too, for Egypt was the centre of the production of a great many scents.

THE EGYPTIAN

Our source of information for this particular scent is Theophrastus. The Egyptian was made from 'several ingredients, including cinnamon and myrrh'. This would produce a rather heavy scent, but to make it lighter and sweeter, the ingredients were first steeped in fragrant (*euodos*) wine. Myrrh in particular becomes more fragrant if first steeped in sweet (*glykos*) wine. Unlike most other expensive scents, it was left colourless. It was said to be particularly suited to women because of its strength and character and the fact that it was long-lasting on the skin as well as in the bottle. Egyptian matured for up to 8 years was considered better than that freshly made.[10]

Whether this Egyptian was always *made* in Egypt is another question. In view of the fact that Theophrastus was so well informed one suspects that the scent could have been

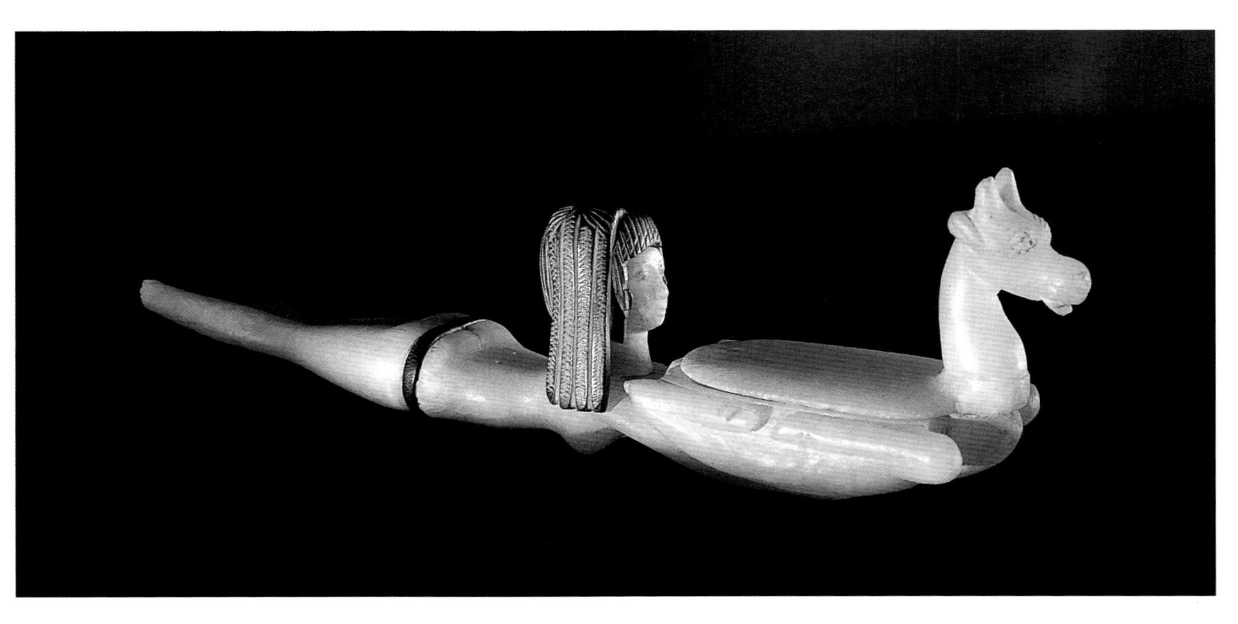

Cosmetic 'spoon' in the form of a swimming girl propelling a box in the form of a Dorcas gazelle or a similar animal. Egyptian alabaster, length 22.5 cm. Late 18th Dynasty, reign of Amenhotep III, c. 1390-1352 BC. *Metropolitan Museum of Art, New York (26.2.47 – Rogers Fund, 1926)*

manufactured, on licence perhaps, in Greece itself. Although cinnamon occurs abundantly in Greek and Latin as well as Syriac prescriptions there is often an option for alternative ingredients, such as cardamom, although this might not necessarily be more easily available. But in 4th century Athens at least The Egyptian consisted of a colourless base oil with the addition of, among other things, cinnamon and myrrh steeped in wine.

MENDESIUM
(The Mendesian)

Dioscorides and Pliny knew of this scent, which in the first century AD was considered the most excellent and already then of ancient date.[11] The base oil was derived from the kernel of *Balanites aegyptiaca* L., a tree that still grows sporadically in Egypt. To this slightly yellowish oil was added myrrh and resin.[12] But the prescription by Dioscorides[13] is more specific: 'Mendesium . . . is made of balanos oil and myrrh and cassia and resin. Some after they have cast in all other things by weight, do moreover put in a little cinnamon unprofitably. For the things which are not beaten together, do not yield forth their strength.' As Theophrastus had already laid out in detail, the mode of preparation was important, especially in composite scents. Pliny, too, expresses an opinion on the matter: 'Some people hold it enough to add a sprinkle of the most expensive ingredients to the others after boiling them down, as an economy, but the mixture has not the same strength unless they are all boiled down together.' He adds that Mendesium produces black colour (when mixed with other oils?).[14]

It is a question to what extent the presence of resin affected the final result, this depending of course on the nature of the resin chosen. Pliny mentions that resins or gums are added to perfume in order to fix the perfume added from another source, as this would otherwise evaporate very quickly.[15]

Although Theophrastus makes no reference to The Mendesian, comparison between this and The Egyptian reveals certain similarities. They share the heavy scent of myrrh, and where one has cinnamon, the other has cassia or both. There can be little doubt that the impression of the two scents would have been somewhat similar.

It was especially in the Twenty-ninth and Thirtieth Dynasties that Mendes had been prominent, i.e. in the same century that Theophrastus wrote about The Egyptian. The rulers of the Twenty-ninth Dynasty were said to have originated from that town, and with its status as once 'royal city' it is easy to understand why authorities writing four cen-

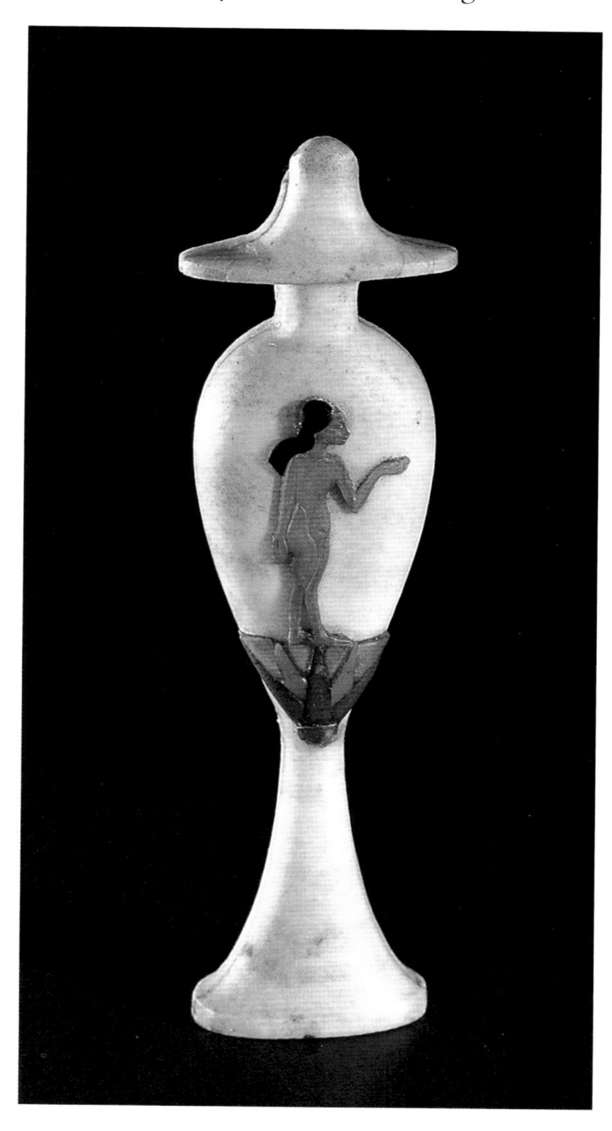

Perfume bottle with carnelian, obsidian and coloured glass inlay apparently representing an Amarna princess offering to the sun god Aten.
Height 10.8 cm.
18th Dynasty, reign of Akhenaten, c.1352-1336 BC.
Metropolitan Museum of Art, New York (40.2.4) – Rogers Fund, 1940)

turies later should mention that an unguent was made in it and was named after it. But it is puzzling that Theophrastus does not pick it up, assuming that the scent went back that far. In contrast, when Pliny and Dioscorides wrote about The Mendesian, the role of the city as nome capital had been transferred to the neighbouring town of Thmuis. In fact, there is no trace of any activity on the site of Mendes after the end of the Ptolemaic period. This strongly suggests that The Mendesian of Pliny and Dioscorides, if available at all, did not come from Mendes itself. The scent was manufactured in Mendes 'in early times',[16] no doubt when the city flourished, and the recipe survived long after the city had perished. It was said to have replaced in popularity that manufactured on the island of Delos. If the perfume was basically the same as that known by Theophrastus as 'The Egyptian', a source now lost, but known by the later writers, may have linked the latter with Mendes. It is interesting that Pliny implies that at some stage, when The Mendesian had been in vogue for a while, the Phoenicians 'appropriated' it (took over the manufacture?).[17] It looks as if The Mendesian could be produced anywhere.

METOPION
(Galbanum perfume)

It is once more Pliny and Dioscorides who are the detailed sources for a scent specifically said to be made in Egypt, but the scent was known some 300 years earlier, when it was mentioned by a certain Apollonios Mys, author of a now lost treatise of perfumes, quoted, for Metopion, by Athenaeus.[18] According to Dioscorides, Metopion is the (Egyptian) name of the plant that yields galbanum: 'There is also prepared in Egypt an ointment which is called in their country by them Metopion, because of the mixing of galbanum with it, for the wood out of which galbanum is made is (by them) called Metopion'. Yet elsewhere he says that Metopion is the designation for bitter almond oil.[19] Pliny, on the other hand, says that Metopion is the name of a scent based on the oil of bitter

An unguent container in the form of a duck pushed by a swimming girl. The upper part of the duck (the lid) has not been found. Wood, length 26.8 cm, 19th Dynasty, c. 1295-1186 BC. *British Museum, London*

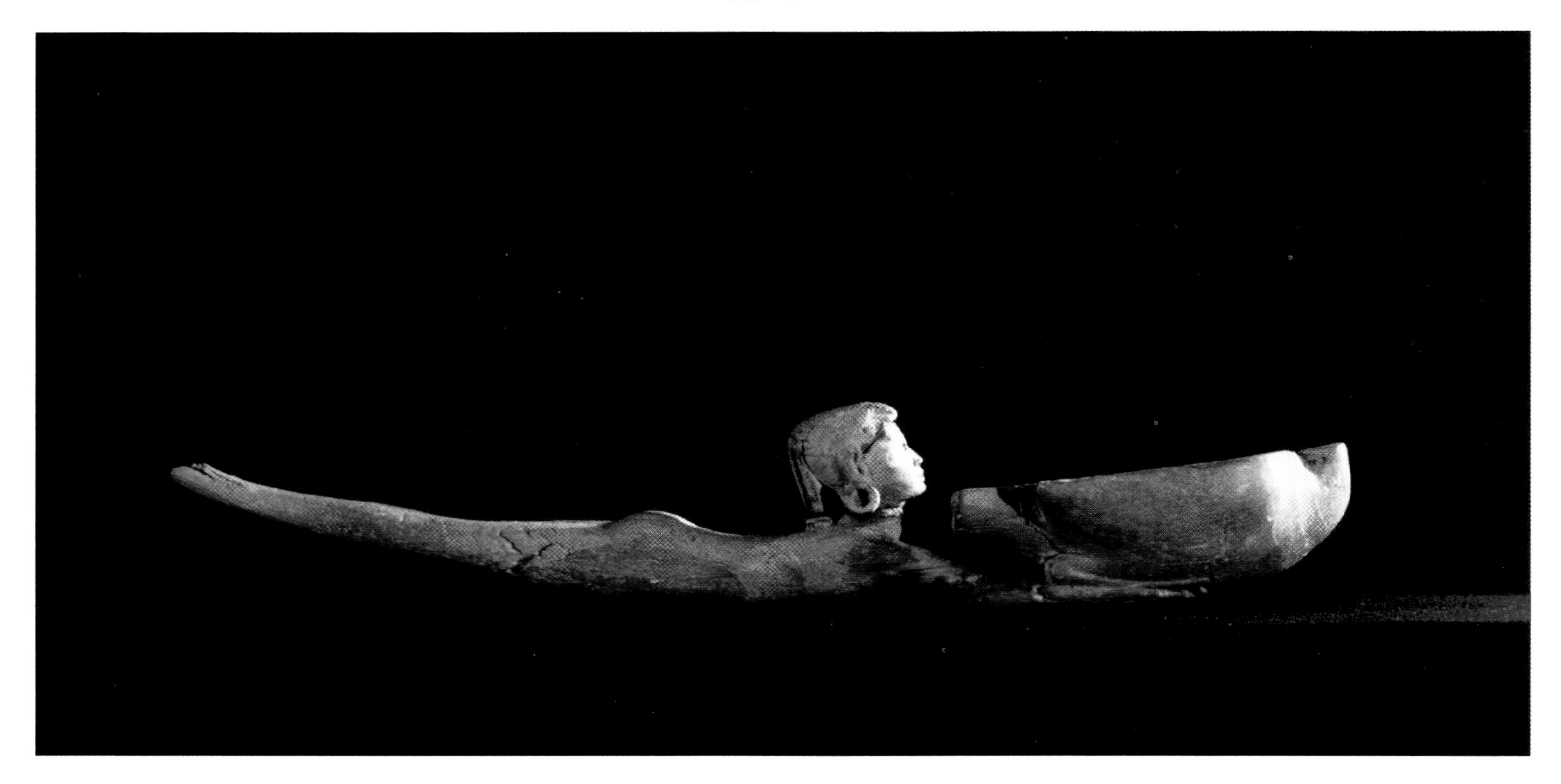

almonds with the addition of certain spices.[20]

The recipes are as follows:

Dioscorides	Pliny
bitter almonds	oil of bitter almonds
omphacium (green olive oil)	omphacium
cardamom	cardamom
camel grass	camel grass
sweet flag	sweet flag
honey	honey
wine	wine
myrrh	myrrh
balsamum seed	balsamum seed
galbanum	galbanum
resin	turpentine resin

Dioscorides adds that it is made into a mixture, and that 'that is the best which smells strongly, and is greasy, resembling cardamom and myrrh rather than galbanum'.

As mentioned above in Chapter 1, galbanum is a fragrant gum-resin of *Ferula,* a plant that was not native to Egypt, but which could have been imported from Persia. With the exception of wine and honey, all the other ingredients in Metopion would probably have had to be imported if the substance was to have been made in Egypt. It is a question as to whether the almond and the olive ever grew in large numbers in Egypt, although there is evidence of the fruits having reached the country from the New Kingdom and on. Camel grass which smelled sweet like a rose when rubbed between the hands[21] grew in Libya and Arabia, sweet flag, which made perfumes smell sweeter,[22] in India (according to Dioscorides); cardamom came from India and Arabia.

Balsamum grew in a certain valley in Judaea whence, according to tradition, it had been taken by the Queen of Sheba as a gift to Solomon. Usually it is the balm of the tree identified with *Commiphora gileadensis* (formerly c. *opobalsamum*) that is in demand, even for mixing into ointments for thickening, but in this prescription the seeds are specified.

Balsam container, 'balsamarium', in the form of a squatting man. Bronze, height 12.5 cm, Ptolemaic Period, 332-32 BC.
Christie's, London

The fruit of the tree is about the size of a small pea, of a reddish grey colour, and with an agreeable taste. Dioscorides advises to choose a fruit that is 'yellow, full, great, heavy, biting in taste and hot in the mouth, somewhat scenting of the savour of opobalsamum (the juice)'.[23]

In the 16th century AD it had found its way to certain gardens in Egypt. Already Dioscorides mentioned its presence in Egypt, but this in turn has been doubted by modern scholars.[24]

The presence of wine is explained by the lightening effect it had on some of the other ingredients, notably myrrh.[25]

Like The Mendesian, Metopion was another scent that was adopted by the Phoenicians. In the days of Pliny it was even more popular than The Mendesian.[26]

SUSINUM
(Lily perfume)

This is the name given by Dioscorides to a perfume whose main ingredient is lilies and for which he provides a most detailed prescription.[28] He specifically says that Egypt is one of the countries that produce scent of lilies, and it is of particular interest that the evidence for this can be brought back another 500 years or so.

Two reliefs of Twenty-sixth Dynasty date depict the collection of flowers that strongly resemble *Lilium candidum* L. (p. 21) and the process of squeezing out the oil (opposite).

The ingredients are as follows, also quoted briefly by Pliny[29] who gives neither quantities nor method of preparation:

Dioscorides	Pliny
1,000 lilies (x2)	lilies
4.226 kg balanos oil	balanos oil
2.354 kg sweet flag	sweet flag
140g myrrh	
fragrant wine	
1.530 kg cardamom	
(37 g cardamom) (x3)	
270 g best myrrh (x3)	myrrh
37 g crocus (x3)	crocus
281 g cinnamon (x3)	cinnamon
honey	honey
salt	

Bruise cardamom and macerate in rain water. Mix together oil, sweet flag and myrrh in fragrant wine and boil. Pour the oil through a strainer and add cardamom. Strain the oil again after thorough maceration, leaving the spices aside. Take 1.589 kg of the oil, which has by now thickened, and the lilies, stripped of their leaves, and place them in a shallow vessel. Anoint your hands with honey and mix the lilies and the oil well. Leave it for 24 hours and strain it again, discarding carefully the water that has been drawn out of the flowers (or else the oil will putrefy). Smear the inside of another vessel with honey, sprinkle with a little salt and pour in the oil. Skim off impurities if necessary. Place the strained flowers in a broad vessel, pour in another 1.589 kg of the aromatic oil and add 37 g crushed cardamom. Stir it well with your hands, leave it for a while, then strain and skim off impurities. Pour oil on once more with [the same 37 g?] cardamom and salt, pressing it out, your hands besmeared with honey. That which is strained out the first time will be the best.

Take again 1,000 lilies, stripped of their leaves, and pour on them the first batch of oil. Work methodically, doing the same things as before, mixing in 37 g cardamom and straining. The more times you mix in fresh lilies, the stronger the scent. Finally, when the required strength has been obtained, mix with every batch 270 g myrrh, 37 g crocus, 281 g cinnamon, crushed and sifted, and place it in a pot with some water. Leave it alone for a while [skim off the scented oil], then pour it into small dry vessels besmeared with gum, or myrrh, and with crocus diluted in water.

Dioscorides provides some variations to this recipe. The amount of crocus may be increased to 281 g. The oil may vary, and some use no spices at all, but only balanos oil and lilies. Since this is said to be superior to that made in Egypt and Phoenicia one may conclude that the Egyptian version contained the spices. The amount of cardamom used is truly extraordinary. In places other than Egypt an oil was made from lilies, which is left in the open air to steep in the sunlight and moonlight and frost. Pliny says that susinum is the most fluid of all scented oils, but on the other hand that when mixed with others it gives a greasy consistency. Theophrastus, too, knew of susinum. Like other light perfumes, lily scent, this time referred to by the name of the plant itself, *krinon*, is deemed suitable for men.[30]

IRINUM
(Iris perfume)

This was well known in the classical world, from Theophrastus to Pliny. So far, evidence of its use in Egypt is slender, but not entirely

Women squeezing freshly gathered lily blossoms to obtain oil for susinum, the lily perfume. Limestone relief fragment, 26th Dynasty, 664-525 BC.
Musée du Louvre, Paris

irrelevant, for in his section on iris, Dioscorides quotes an Egyptian name for the plant, *nar*. Further on he includes a whole section on *irinon,* iris oil.[31] Varieties of iris grow wild in Egypt today, and the rhizome has been known in Islamic and popular medicine for centuries. There are thus reasons to assume that ancient Egyptians were familiar with the plant and that the obvious fragrant characteristic of the root would have been acknowledged in perfume manufacture ('the iris is valued only for its root, being grown for unguents and for medicine').[32] The scent and power of iris was deemed so strong that by merely touching the roots of another tree it would impart its fragrance to it.

The main ingredients were the base oil and iris root. Theophrastus quotes a saying that iris perfume is made from the smallest number of ingredients of all.[33] A superior kind of iris perfume is made, he says, by using the root dry and not subjecting it to fire 'for then its virtue asserts itself more completely than when it is steeped in a liquid or subjected to fire'. The perfume is thus produced by simple maceration of bruised iris root, or orris powder, as it is now known.

Dioscorides provides two versions, one a fairly simple one, the other a spiced iris perfume. 'But that is by far the best that smells of nothing else, but only of iris.'

'A. Take 2.948 kg of palm tops beaten as small as possible, 33.282 kg of oil and 10 *heminae* (ca. $^1/_4$ l) of water. Pour it into a brazen vessel and boil it together until the smell of palm tops has been absorbed. Strain the liquid into a basin smeared with honey. Macerate bruised iris in this thickened oil, 6.356 kg iris to 6.356 kg oil, leaving it aside for two days and two nights. Afterwards strain it out 'lustily and forcibly'. Repeat up to four times if desired.

'B. Take 2.326 kg wood balsamum, 31.92 kg

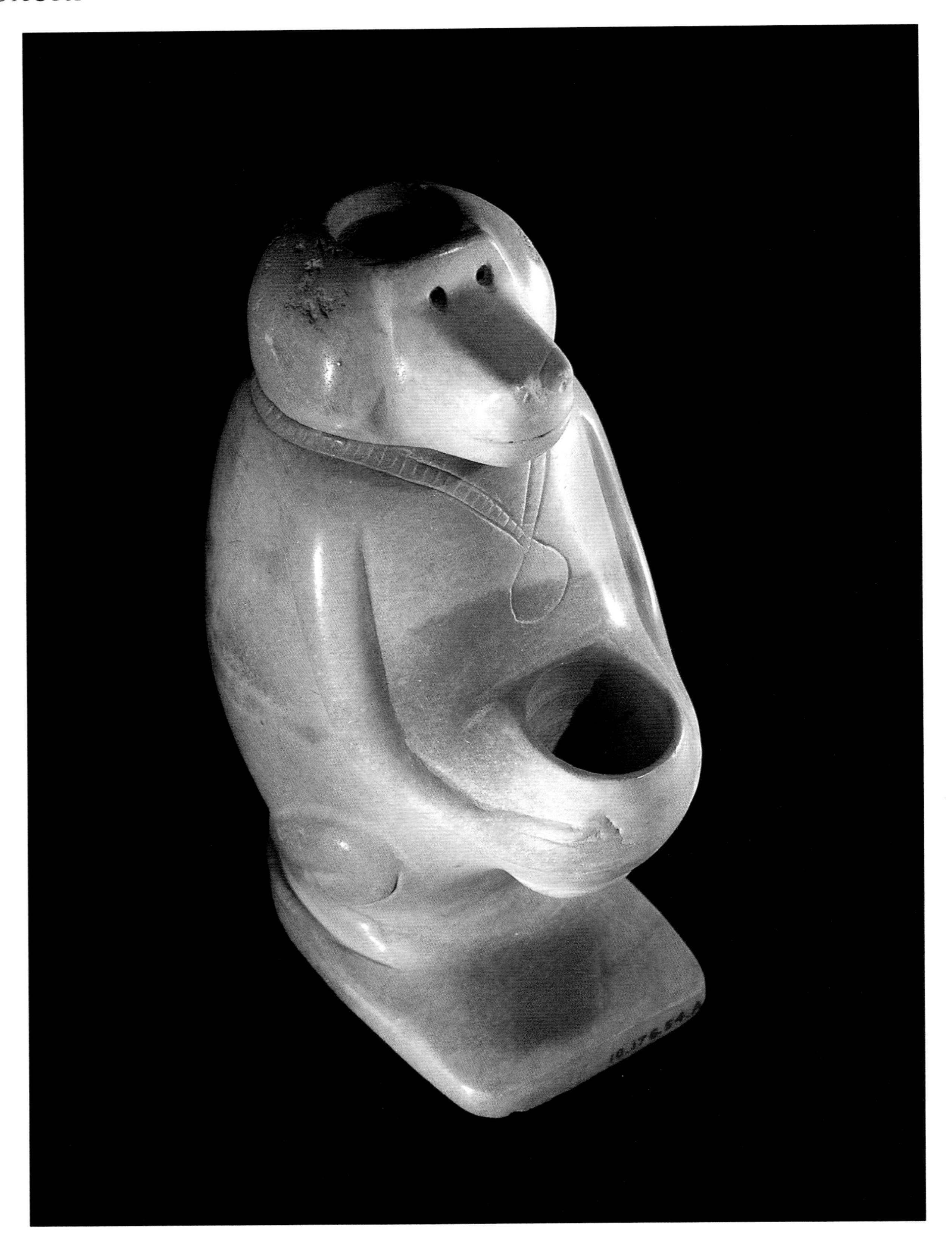

Ointment jar in the form of a baboon holding a jar, which may have contained an applicator stick. The shell pendant was a badge of office. Anhydrite (blue marble), height 13 cm, 12th-13th Dynasty, c. 1900-1640 BC.
Metropolitan Museum of Art, New York (10.176.54 – Rogers Fund, 1910)

oil, beating it together well and boil it together. Add 4.366 kg sweet flag and a little myrrh previously macerated in old fragrant wine. Proceed as above.'

This is the iris perfume made in Perga of Pamphylia and in Elis in Achaia [respectively?]. The habitat of the plant would influence the quality of the perfume. According to Pliny, the best iris was said to grow in Illyria, in the woody parts around the Drinon and around Narona. Next ranked the white Macedonian iris, followed by the African iris, the largest of all and the bitterest to the taste. Pliny, who provides these details maintains that previously the best iris oil came from Leucas and Elis, but that in his day Pamphylian and Cilician oil was superior. Elsewhere he claims that Corinthian iris perfume was popular for a long time, later to be superseded by that of Cyzicus.[34] Theophrastus, too, praises Illyrian iris.[35]

Iris perfume was dyed red with the root of alkanet. It was said to be hot and astringent, and excessively bitter when fresh, so much so that it might cause skin sores. The root itself should ideally be used three years after harvesting and never later than after six years.

The perfume itself improved with age and was known to reach its prime when twenty years old.[36]

CYPRINUM
(Henna perfume)

In classical antiquity, cyprinum was a composite scent whose main fragrant ingredient was a plant called *cypros.* This is generally, and probably rightly, taken to be henna, among other things because the Arabic translations of Dioscorides and others equate it with that plant. The flowers of *Lawsonia inermis* L. are very fragrant, and nowadays an essential oil, known as *mehendi* is distilled from them.

The tree grew in Egypt near the town of Canopus in the Delta. It still grows in cultivation both in Egypt and elsewhere in the Middle East. Dioscorides deemed this to be the best of all, along with that from Ascalon in Judaea.[37] Pliny ranked the Egyptian the highest, followed by that of Ascalon, the tree rated third growing on the island of Cypros, the latter [?] having 'a sort of sweet scent'.[38] This tree cypros that grows in Egypt has the 'leaves of Christthorn and the white scented seeds of coriander', he adds.

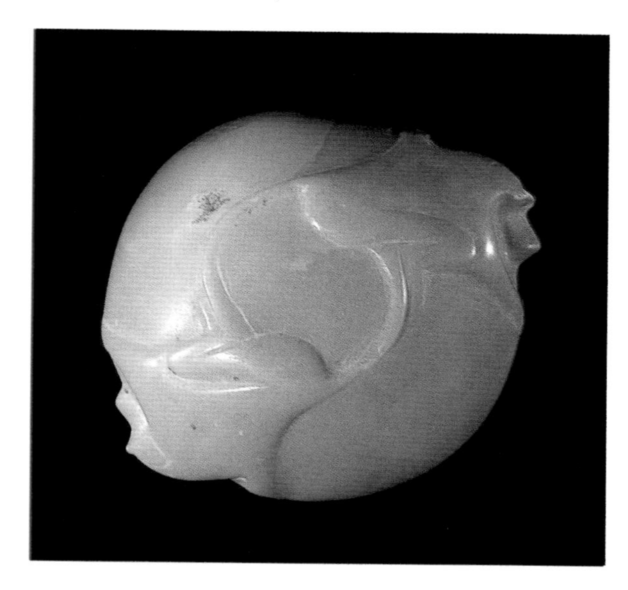

Right The underside of an ointment bowl with two baboons in relief. Anhydrite (blue marble), diameter 8.5 cm. 15th-17th Dynasties, c. 1650-1550 BC. *Metropolitan Museum of Art, New York (30.8.139 – Theodore M. Davis Collection. Bequest of Theodore M. Davis, 1915)*

Leaves of *Lawsonia* have been found in Ptolemaic tombs in Egypt, and the herb was obviously in use at this date if not before. Considering the modern use of henna in hair treatment it is suggestive that in medical texts from around 1550 BC a hair remedy includes a plant named *henu*.[39]

In order to produce what is by Pliny here called cypros (sc. cyprinum, the finished preparation) the seeds (*sic*) are boiled in olive oil and afterwards crushed. It is doubtful that Pliny was correctly informed here, since the berries of henna are not white, but blue-black. The flowers, on the other hand are white. Cypros sells at 5 denarii a pound, a modest price compared with the expensive perfumes of 400 denarii which we met above. Further on he provides more details. Cyprinum is made of henna, oil of green olives, cardamom, sweet flag, aspalathos and southernwood. Some people may add myrrh and all-heal. Oil of sesame may be added to

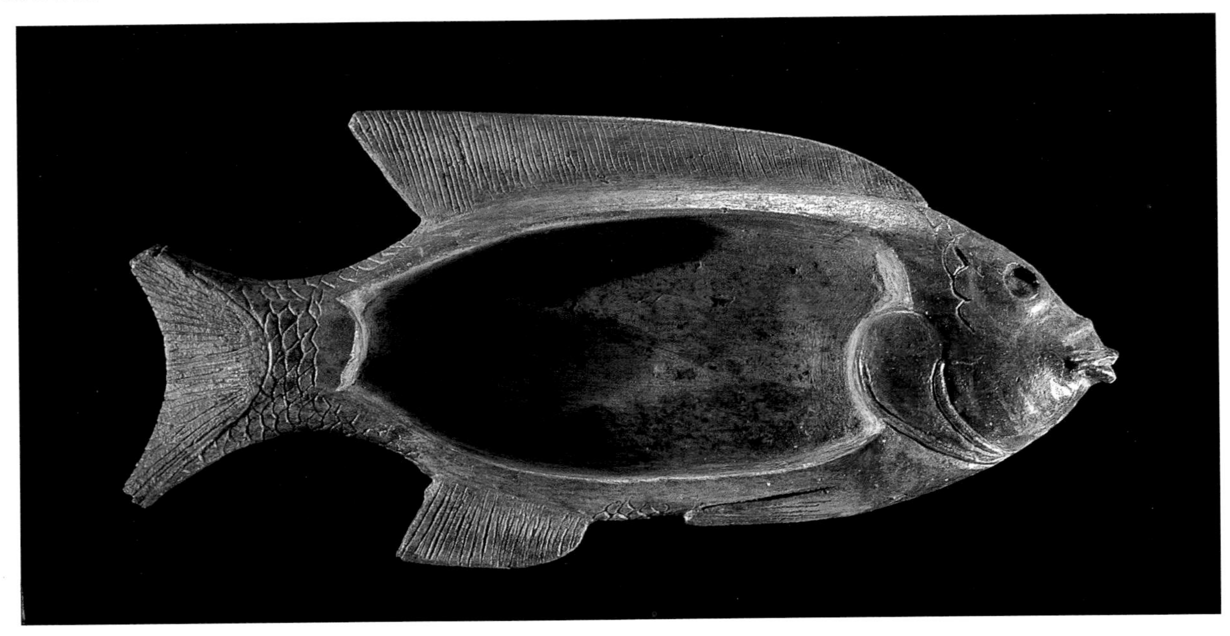

Cosmetic dish in the form of a bolti fish, probably made for use in a ritual such as anointing a statue or in connection with a funeral. Glazed steatite, length 18.1cm, 18th Dynasty, c. 1479-1425 BC.
Metropolitan Museum of Art, New York (90.6.24 – Gift of James Douglas, 1890)

enable the mixture to last for as long as four years. A further addition of cinnamon will enhance the scent. The best is that produced in Sidon, the second-best that made in Egypt, though elsewhere he claims that cyprinum from Cyprus was the best until that made in Egypt took first place.[40]

Cyprinum, which is of a greenish colour, was among perfumes invented 'in early times'.[41] It was certainly known to Theophrastus.[42] According to him it was not the seeds, but the flowers of *kypros* that were used. To make cyprinum they put in (to the cold base oil) cardamom and aspalathos, having first steeped them in fragrant (*euodos*) wine. Then one proceeds 'as when making rose perfume', i.e. adding a quantity of salt to prevent decay. The flowers must be removed soon, or the perfume will have a disagreeable smell. It is implied from the following description of quince perfume that a new batch of fresh flowers is then added, and removed before they turn black.

On turning to Dioscorides we also find a paragraph on cyprinum. The main ingredient is here referred to as *kyperos,* by a modern translator left unidentified, although elsewhere in the work *kypros* is translated 'henna'.[43] But this should not lead us to confound it with the similarly sounding *kypeiros* or *kypairos* which also occurs in Dioscorides's writings. The recipe is essentially similar to those provided by Pliny and Theophrastus, as is of course the name of the preparation, and there can be no doubt that we are dealing with henna unguent once more.

The three recipes are presented together, including the quantities provided by Dioscorides.

THEOPHRASTUS	PLINY	DIOSCORIDES
henna	henna	henna 21.108 kg
green olive oil	green olive oil	green olive oil 12.712 kg
		rainwater
aspalathos	aspalathos	aspalathos 2.497 kg
	sweet flag	sweet flag 2.951 kg
	(myrrh)	myrrh 454 g
cardamom	cardamom	cardamom 1.614 kg
		old fragrant wine
	southernwood (all-heal)	(cinnamon)

Dioscorides would proceed as follows:

The underside of the cosmetic dish shown opposite with the cartouche of Tuthmosis III below the lateral fin. Glazed steatite, length 18.1cm, 18th Dynasty, c. 1479-1425 BC. *Metropolitan Museum of Art, New York (90.6.24 – Gift of James Douglas, 1890)*

'Take one and a half parts of water to the one part of oil. Mix some of the water with the oil, using the rest for macerating the herbs. Bruise and macerate aspalathos in some of the water, and boil it with 2.270 kg oil. Macerate myrrh in wine, adding sweet flag. Remove from the oil and throw in the myrrh and sweet flag mixture. When it has boiled together strain out the oil and pour it on bruised cardamom, previously macerated in the rest of the water. Stir continuously until it has become cold. Strain the oil. Into this oil cast the henna flowers. Leave them to macerate, and strain through a wicker basket. If required, add another batch of flowers to the oil and repeat up to four times, choosing always good quality flowers. Some also add cinnamon.'

The oil is thus first seasoned, or made astringent, by boiling with the herbs and spices. The flowers are then left to macerate in the oil when it has cooled off so as not to ruin the delicate fragrance of the flowers.

The recipes of Theophrastus and Pliny differ in that Pliny would use the seeds or berries and Theophrastus the flowers. Unless the former is in error it may explain why he also indicates that the material is to be boiled - this is by no means indicated by Theophrastus. As Pliny suggests two or even four additional ingredients, he clearly had his information from a different source.

The question of whether or not the seeds/berries or the flowers were used is equally relevant when we study the material of the 13th century BC from Greece.[44] On the Mycene tablets a word *e-ti* is mentioned, apparently our henna. As the henna tree did not grow on Greek mainland it has been argued that the inclusion of the name in perfume recipes was to make use of its dyeing properties rather than its scent. In other words, as the fresh scented flowers were not available, the herb in question must be the leaves, whose scent is minimal but the dye of which is used in other contexts.

The closest source for henna in those days would probably have been the island of Cyprus, too far for the flowers to arrive fresh at Mycene. The leaves, on the other hand, as well as seeds and berries, could be used when dried. But if *e-ti* referred not to the flowers, but to the seeds or berries it may still be the scented, or at least the astringent, properties that were sought and not the dye. There is no other evidence for the use of henna to dye oil.

In the days of Theophrastus cyprinum was colourless and should look white, like other costly perfumes such as The Egyptian - a remark in contrast with Pliny's reference some 400 years later to its modest price.

This discrepancy may again be explained if Pliny used the seeds/berries and not the flowers, which would presumably be needed in greater quantity. It was a light perfume suited to men, it had a delicate scent which was agreeable to the skin, and it was useful in aromatherapy against lassitude because of its heat and lightness. The disadvantage was that it was volatile and tended to evaporate.[45]

SAMPSUCHINUM / AMARACINUM
(Marjoram perfume)

There are several varieties of sweet marjoram, or oregano, and in antiquity different names designate either the same variety or different ones. Pliny knows of 'amaracus' and 'sampsuchum', specifically declaring them to be synonyms; Theophrastus only mentions 'amarakon', whereas Dioscorides quotes recipes for oils of both,[46] and solid unguent of 'sampsuchon'. Pliny explains that 'Diocles the physician and the people of Sicily have called amaracum the plant known in Egypt as sampsuchum'.[47] Further on[48] he equates sampsuchum and amaracum, adding that the most valued, and the most fragrant, comes from Cyprus and Mitylene where it is very plentiful. The best sampsuchum, says Dioscorides, is that which is of a black greenish colour, strong of scent and pretty sharp. To his mind, the best marjoram oil, or amarakinon, is that made in Cyzicus, a place, that according to Pliny produces famous amaracus. On the other hand, he also extolls that of Cos.[49]

Pliny has something to say of the character of Egyptian marjoram and other herbs. 'In Egypt . . .flowers have very little perfume, the atmosphere being misty and full of dew owing to the wide expanse of the river. The scent of some plants is sweet but oppressive. Some, while green, have no smell because of too much moisture . . . [But] southernwood and *amaracum* have pungent scents.'[50]

Male servant carrying an ointment jar with a floral motif as tribute or an offering. Wall painting in the tomb of royal scribe Horemheb, Theban necropolis, 18th Dynasty, c. 1479-1352 BC

Marjoram perfume could be made with the herb and the oil and little else, but the preference for spiced, composite fragrances prevails here as well, where the options are many.

After all this, we must turn to Theophrastus, who, although he lists amarakon as an ingredient used in perfume, produces the surprising statement that 'the superior kind of amarakinon . . . is made of all the best spices except amarakon: In fact this is the only spice which perfumers do not use for any perfume, and the name is a misnomer'.[51]

We may compare it with Pliny's observation[52] that 'narcissus oil has also ceased to be made from the narcissus flower.' It was common in antiquity to adulterate expensive scents, such as nard, but marjoram would have been plentiful in many places. The ingredient from which the perfume took its name would thus not in itself have been exotic, and hence rare and expensive. However, Theophrastus adds that amarakinon is dyed with a substance called chroma, a root imported from Syria. As he has just mentioned that it is not worth while adding colour to the cheaper perfumes, we may conclude that amarakinon was nevertheless among the more expensive ones. If we look at the ingredients given by Dioscorides

Dioscorides	Dioscorides	Pliny	Pliny
amarakinum	*sampsuchinum*	*amarakinum*	*sampsuchinum*
oil of green olives or balanos	green olive oil	green olive oil	green olive oil
wood balsam			
camel grass★			
sweet flag★			sweet flag★
amarakon	sampsuchum	amaracus	sampsuchum
costus★			
amomum★			
nard★			
carpobalsamum			
myrrh★			
(cinnamon★)	cassia★		
	thyme		
	southernwood		
	bergamot mint flowers		
	myrtle leaves		
		(chaste tree leaves)	
		(all-heal)	
honey		honey	
wine		salt	
		('foreign substances'★)	

together with the 'foreign substances' hinted by Pliny, we may find an explanation:[53]

All of the added ingredients here marked with an asterisk★ are those which are said by Dioscorides himself to be growing in places at some distance from the Mediterranean, such as Armenia, Arabia and India. His amarakinon, too, would have contained expensive ingredients.

It is interesting that one of these 'foreign' ingredients, namely *amomon*, is said by Dioscorides to have a flower like origanum, and that it smells like origanum.[54] Here may lie the explanation of the curious remark by Theophrastus: in his day, perhaps, the common marjoram was replaced by an exotic ingredient, either because of the luxury that such a substitute would convey, or possibly because of the medicinal properties of the foreign herb. But because of the similarity in scent, the name was kept.

Dioscorides's sampsuchinum is prepared according to individual preference:

> 'Take as much . . . of each of these, by guess [as you think fit], with due respect to the strength of each of them. Beat all of these together, and pour upon them as much oil as may not be enough to sap the strength of those things which are macerated in it, and so leave it alone for four days. Strain, and repeat with fresh ingredients.'

His amarakinon is equally summary: xylobalsamum, camel grass and sweet flag are added for thickening, the remaining herbs for sweetening. Cinnamon is added by those 'who make it after a most costly way'. Honey is used for anointing the vessels, and wine for macerating the aromatic substances.

Amarakinon was a long-lasting scent. It was suited for women because of this fact, but it could also cause headache.[55]

MEGALEION

The name and origin of this scent is not entirely clear. It has been claimed to be derived from the name of the inventor, one Megalus; from the name of a location where it was allegedly prepared, Megale near Syracuse; or simply to reflect the degree of its importance, *megalos* meaning 'great'.[56] There is nothing in this to link it specifically with Egypt, though the ingredients were among those favoured in Egyptian preparations. Moreover, Dioscorides says that the ingredients are like those used for amaracinum, except that resin is also included. It was no longer made in his day, but he decided to include it anyway for the record.[57] Resin, he says, is mixed with the oils not to impart its scent, but only to colour and thicken them.

Pliny, his contemporary, claims that Megaleion had achieved some celebrity. And on turning to Theophrastus we find more information about the scent. The ingredients are as follows:[58]

Theophrastus	Pliny	Dioscorides
balanos oil	balanos oil	balanos oil
burnt resin	resin	resin
cassia	cassia	
cinnamon		cinnamon
myrrh		myrrh
	balsam	carpobalsamum
	sweet flag	sweet flag
	camel grass	camel grass
	wood balsam	wood balsam
		costus
		nard
		amomum

'A peculiarity of this unguent is that it must be constantly stirred while boiling until it ceases to have any odour, and when it becomes cold it recovers its scent,' reports Pliny.

Theophrastus gives more details on the troublesome process of preparation: 'To make Megaleion . . . the oil is boiled for ten days and nights, and not till then do they put in

Cosmetic container in the form of a red lotus flower carried by a swimmer probably representing the sky-goddess Nut. Ivory and ebony, length 23.5 cm, 18th Dynasty, reign of Amenhotep III, c. 1390-1352 BC. *Pushkin Museum of Fine Arts, Moscow*

the resin and the other things, since the oil is more receptive when it has been thoroughly boiled'.

The combination of cinnamon and myrrh is reminiscent both of The Egyptian and The Mendesian, the latter including also resin. Megaleion was an expensive perfume and one of those to which colour was added. Because of its 'strength and substantial character' it was one of the long-lasting women's perfumes.[59]

CINNAMOMINUM
(Cinnamon and cassia oils)

In this context other scented oils having as their main ingredients cinnamon and/or cassia should be considered. The scent of the two components is quite similar, and, according to Dioscorides two parts of cassia would replace one part of cinnamon.[60] In ancient perfume manufacture it was not uncommon to substitute one ingredient for another, though this should not mislead us into assuming that they were identical, or that the words were necessarily synonymous.

There are many kinds of cinnamon and cassia. The best cinnamon is that of Mosul, the quality being judged by the sweetness of the smell. The best should be a little like rue, or like cardamom, but sharp, biting to the taste, somewhat salty when heated, smooth to the touch between the knots. Cassia grows about Arabia, he adds. The best should be of a biting taste, astringent with much heat, aromatical, resembling wine in the smell. This is called *daphnitis* by the merchants of Alexandria. There is an even better one which smells of roses 'most fitting for physical uses'.

Theophrastus includes a paragraph on cinnamon and cassia, saying that both shrubs grow in the Arabian peninsula.[61]

Dioscorides quotes a recipe for Cinnamominum, or cinnamon oil.

Pliny, too, knew of a very similar preparation.[62]

Dioscorides	Pliny
balanos oil	balanos oil
cinnamon	cinnamon
carpobalsamum	balsam seeds
myrrh	myrrh
wood balsam	wood balsam
sweet flag	sweet flag
camel grass	camel grass seeds [*sic*]
honey	fragrant honey

According to Dioscorides, wood balsam, sweet flag and camel grass are used as thickeners, whereas cinnamon, carpobalsamum and myrrh are sweeteners, the quantities of myrrh being four times that of cinnamon. Honey is mixed in. The best cinnamon unguent is that which is not sharp, but mild, and bearing upon the myrrh, thick, sweet smelling and of a very bitter taste (cf. the remark by Pliny: 'It is rare for a thing that smells not to have a bitter taste; on the contrary sweet substances rarely have any smell . . .'[63]). The thickness, he says, is due to the myrrh, not resin, for resin gives neither bitterness nor sweetness. Pliny says that of all the unguents it has the thickest consistency, fetching high prices, from 35 to 300 denarii (a pound). It is used medicinally, too. It may be compared with Commagene.

The combination of cinnamon and myrrh is reflected in the Bible (Ex. 30:23): 'Take the finest spices: of liquid myrrh five hundred shekels, and of sweet-smelling cinnamon half as much.' As in the recipe quoted by Dioscorides, it contains more myrrh than cinnamon, although the proportions are 2:1 instead of 4:1. This is followed (Ex. 30:24) by 'and of cassia five hundred, according to the shekel of the sanctuary, and of olive oil a hin.' These preparations were for holy oil, but the prominence of cinnamon/cassia is significant.

MYRTINUM
(Myrtle unguent)

The best myrtle grew in Egypt. This was the unanimous verdict of Pliny and Theophras-

Ihat, priestess of the goddess Hathor, represented with a lotus flower on the false door of her tomb. Lotus was Egypt's most important aromatic flower even though it features only in one of the surviving recipes. Painted limestone, 5th Dynasty, c. 2453 BC. *Egyptian Museum, Cairo*

tus,[64] the latter claiming that 'in Egypt, where all other flowers and sweet herbs are scentless, the myrtles are marvellously fragrant.' This verdict on the flora of Egypt, echoed above, (p. 74), may seem rather dismissive, yet it serves to extol the qualities of the myrtle in that country, and although our remaining sources stem from elsewhere, it is inconceivable that the Egyptians would not have put their unique plant to some fragrant use. It probably never grew wild there but was cultivated in gardens.

Myrtle leaves from wreaths or garland have been found in excavations of Graeco-Roman date. A plant identified as myrtle occurs in the Egyptian medical texts.

Dioscorides explains how myrtle unguent was prepared; Pliny provides alternative ingredients.[65]

Dioscorides	Pliny
green olive oil	myrtle oil
(water)	
black myrtle leaves	
(pomegranate)	pomegranate rind
(cypress)	cypress
(cyperus grass)	cyprus [*sic*]
(camel grass)	sweet flag
	mastic

Dioscorides gives two methods of preparation. One is to beat the myrtle leaves and press out the juices, then mixing the same measure of oil as juice, warming it over the coals until it boils, and removing the oil that floats on top. An easier way is to boil the bruised tender leaves in water and oil and skimming off the oil 'and after a peculiar manner, having laid the [coarser?] leaves in the sun, to macerate them in oil.' Some, he adds, used to thicken the oil first with the remaining ingredients. Apart from its medicinal use, it is good for all things that need binding or thickening.

In Pliny's time, this myrtle oil was one of the commonest unguents, and it was also believed to be one of the oldest. He adds that an inexpensive oil may be mixed of myrtle and laurel with the addition of marjoram, lilies, fenugreek, myrrh, cassia, nard, camel grass and cinnamon, although one fails to see how the addition of costly spices would make the end product cheaper.[66]

RHODINON
(Rose perfume)

The most exquisite single flower from late antiquity and to the present day must be the rose. Its presence in pharaonic Egypt is attested from plant remains in tombs, and our regular sources from the classical world praise its virtues. Pliny says: 'I am inclined to believe that the scents most widely used are those made from the rose which grows in abundance everywhere'.[67]

The rose appears to have originated in Northern Persia, whence it spread across Mesopotamia to the Mediterranean and, through Palestine or Greece, to Egypt where it was cultivated as a garden rose. A limited number of varieties were known in the ancient world. *Rosa gallica* was one of them, and in Egypt petals of the fragrant *Rosa ricardii* have been found in Ptolemaic and Roman tombs, used in garlands and bouquets. This variety became extinct in Egypt by Islamic times. Roses are mentioned by Homer, and the poetess Sappho called rose 'the queen of flowers'.

Rose perfume was invented 'in early times'. The simplest compound was for a long time that of oil of roses (with no added ingredients).[68] In fact, the manufacture of rose oil goes back to more than a thousand years before Pliny, for it is recorded on tablets from Mycene. For comparison, at Pylos, where the rose is not specifically mentioned, olive oil is made astringent with cyperos and coriander, the main herb (sage in this case) is added, and the preparation is dyed red with alkanet. Honey is also mentioned as one of the ingredients.[69] This becomes interesting when we study the recipes given for rose perfume by our three classical sources.[70] Here, too, the oil is first made astringent with herbs, and only then are the rose petals added.

THEOPHRASTUS	PLINY	DIOSCORIDES
[oil]	green olive oil	oil 9.220 kg
roses	roses	1000 rose leaves
	crocus blossoms	
camel grass	camel grass	camel grass, 2.494 kg
aspalathos		(aspalathos)
sweet flag	sweet flag	(sweet flag)
	honey	honey
	wine	
salt	salt	salt
	alkanet or cinnabar	alkanet

Dioscorides:

'Bruise the camel grass, macerate it in water, boil it "stirring it up and down" and strain it into the oil. Throw in the "not wet" rose petals (i.e. free from dew), and, with your hands anointed in honey, stir them "up and down", squeezing them gently every now and then. Leave them overnight, then squeeze them out. Cast the strained roses into a *labellum* vessel, pour 3.772 kg of the thickened oil upon them. Strain again. Pour more oil unto the roses and strain again. This will be your second oil. You may repeat this a third and fourth time (to make a third and a fourth oil), but anoint the vessel with honey each time. If you want to make a second infusion (of each of these four oils) proceed with fresh dew free roses up until seven times, but no further. Always anoint your hands and the vessel with honey, stir up and down, and make sure that no juice is left with the oil, or else it will corrupt it.'

An alternative method is to leave the rose petals exposed to the sun. Infuse them 227 g to just under 1 l of oil, changing them for 8 days together and sunning them for 40 days,

With mounds of solid unguent on their wigs, the ladies enjoy the fragrance of lotus blossoms. Fragment of a tomb painting, 18th Dynasty, c. 1500 BC
Ägyptisches Museum, Berlin

even to the third infusion. Some thicken the oil first by putting in sweet flag and aspalathos. Some also add alkanet to make it have a 'fair' (meaning red) colour, and salt to prevent it from corrupting.

Concerning the addition of salt, Theophrastus says that this is peculiar to rose perfume (although, as we have seen, this is not correct, for it was used in other preparations as well), and that it involves a great deal of waste, 105 kg of salt being put to 39 l of the perfume. The effect of all this salt, he says is to 'open the passages and to warm them thoroughly'.[71]

Rose perfume is dyed with alkanet,[72] a colour that would aptly reflect the nature of the rose. Although it is lighter and less powerful than any other scent, it destroys the odour of the others. 'And this is why perfumers, if a purchaser hesitates and is not inclined to buy their perfume, scent him with it so that he is not able to smell the others. The explanation is that, being very delicate and acceptable to the sense of smell, by reason of its lightness it penetrates as no other can and fills up the passages of the sense, so that being entirely taken up and filled with it, it is unable to judge any others.' On the other hand rose perfume may be mixed with other scents or flavours like blending colours on a palette.[73] Rose perfume would 'whiten' [*sic*] the colour of any other perfume it is mixed with.[74]

Rose perfume manufactured at Phaselis was extremely popular for a long time, but its fame was later overshadowed by that prepared in Naples, Capua and Palestrina.[75]

SAGE OIL

The possibility of sage perfume reaching Egypt should also be considered. As just mentioned, sage oil was popular at Mycene and could well have been contained in some of the little Mycenean stirrup jars found in Egypt. Although many varieties of sage grow wild in Egypt at the present day including clary sage, *Salvia sclarea* L., much used in modern perfumery, there is but little evidence for it in pharaonic times. However, clary sage was recorded in small quantity in the pollen analysis of the mummy of Rameses II (contemporary with the Mycene tablets). It is possible that the plant was called by one of the names as yet unidentified in the Egyptian vocabulary. According to Dioscorides the Egyptians of his day called it *apousi*.[76]

THE ROYAL

The area that saw the birth of the rose was one that would have known how to appreciate it. If we are to believe Pliny, the kings of Parthia had a special scent prepared for them which was simply called The Royal.[77] It consisted of a great many ingredients - but not the rose - all of them exotic, when seen from the point of view of Rome. Pliny is our only source, and he provides no details except for a list of the ingredients which went into a base oil made from the shells of the nut of *Moringa,* the tree that grew in Upper Egypt, Ethiopia and Arabia, though vast imports of the oil from Phoenicia and Asia Minor are recorded during the course of the New Kingdom. Honey and wine are mentioned towards the end. We have seen how some ingredients were macerated in wine, and how honey was used for smearing pots or hands. The list of ingredients runs as follows: costus, *amomum* (spice plant similar to cardamom), cinnamon, cardamom, spikenard, cat-thyme, myrrh, cassia, styrax, ladanum, opobalsamum, sweet flag, camel grass, wild grape, cinnamon leaves, *serichatrum* (Arabian aromatic shrub), henna, *aspalathos,* all-heal, crocus, cyperus grass, marjoram, jujube (*Ziziphus lotus,* not to be confused with the Egyptian lotus flowers). It is almost as if the entire list of aromata, apart from the most delicate flowers, went into the preparation, maybe as a token of reverence to the recipients conceding that they were the rulers of the world.

MYRRH UNGUENT AND STAKTE

Pliny says that 'myrrh even when used by itself without oil makes an unguent, provided that the stakte kind is used (otherwise it produces too bitter a flavour).[78] Theophrastus claims that 'stakte is the only simple uncompounded perfume'.[79] But his stakte contains a base oil: 'Having bruised the myrrh and dissolved it in oil of balanos over a gentle fire, they pour hot water on it, and the myrrh and the oil sink to the bottom like a deposit; and as soon as this has occurred, they strain off the water and squeeze the sediment in a press.' Dioscorides says that stakte is what is pressed from the congealed tears of myrrh.[80]

It would seem that in classical antiquity myrrh unguent thus came in two basic varieties: that pressed from myrrh with no additional ingredients, and that prepared with a base oil. On applying these categories to the Egyptian texts we should thus search for three designations: the name of the raw material; the name of the liquid expressed from it; and one or several names for a base oil perfumed with myrrh or the liquid expressed from it.

These lexicographical problems have been referred to in Chapter 1. Suffice it to say here that in the pharaonic texts the liquid expressed from the myrrh, which may be a perfume in itself, is recognised under the name of madjet, corresponding to Greek stakte. The madjet known from Ptolemaic texts, on the other hand, is a composite preparation which we have presented in Chapter 2. At this time a new word, *bes* was apparently used to designate stakte.

On the subject of stakte, Theophrastus says that it has the longest life of any perfumes, and that like Megaleion, The Egyptian and marjoram perfume it is admirably suited for women because of its lasting qualities. If the effect is too heavy, it may be mixed with fragrant wine, just as any scent composed of myrrh will improve by the material being steeped in wine.[81]

OTHER EXOTIC PERFUMES IN EGYPT

In the Eighteenth Dynasty it was customary for the kings of Egypt to take foreign princesses as brides, frequently to demonstrate friendship after the conclusion of a peace treaty, or as a general expression of good will towards neighbours. In the reign of Amenhotep III daughters of the Mitannian kings of Naharina travelled to the Egyptian court, and in the Nineteenth Dynasty, Ramesses II celebrated the wedding with a daughter of the king of the Hittites. Such distinguished ladies would bring a substantial dowry which would include precious scents. As far as the Amarna period is concerned we are well informed, for parts of the diplomatic correspondence, written on clay tablets in Babylonian cuneiform letters, have survived, both in Egypt and at the other end.

The daughter of king Shuttarna of Naharina, called Gilukhepa in Babylonian or Kirgipa in Egyptian, travelled from her home beyond the Euphrates to her wedding with king Amenhotep III with a retinue of no fewer than 317 women. Such an occasion was the reason for an exchange of costly gifts

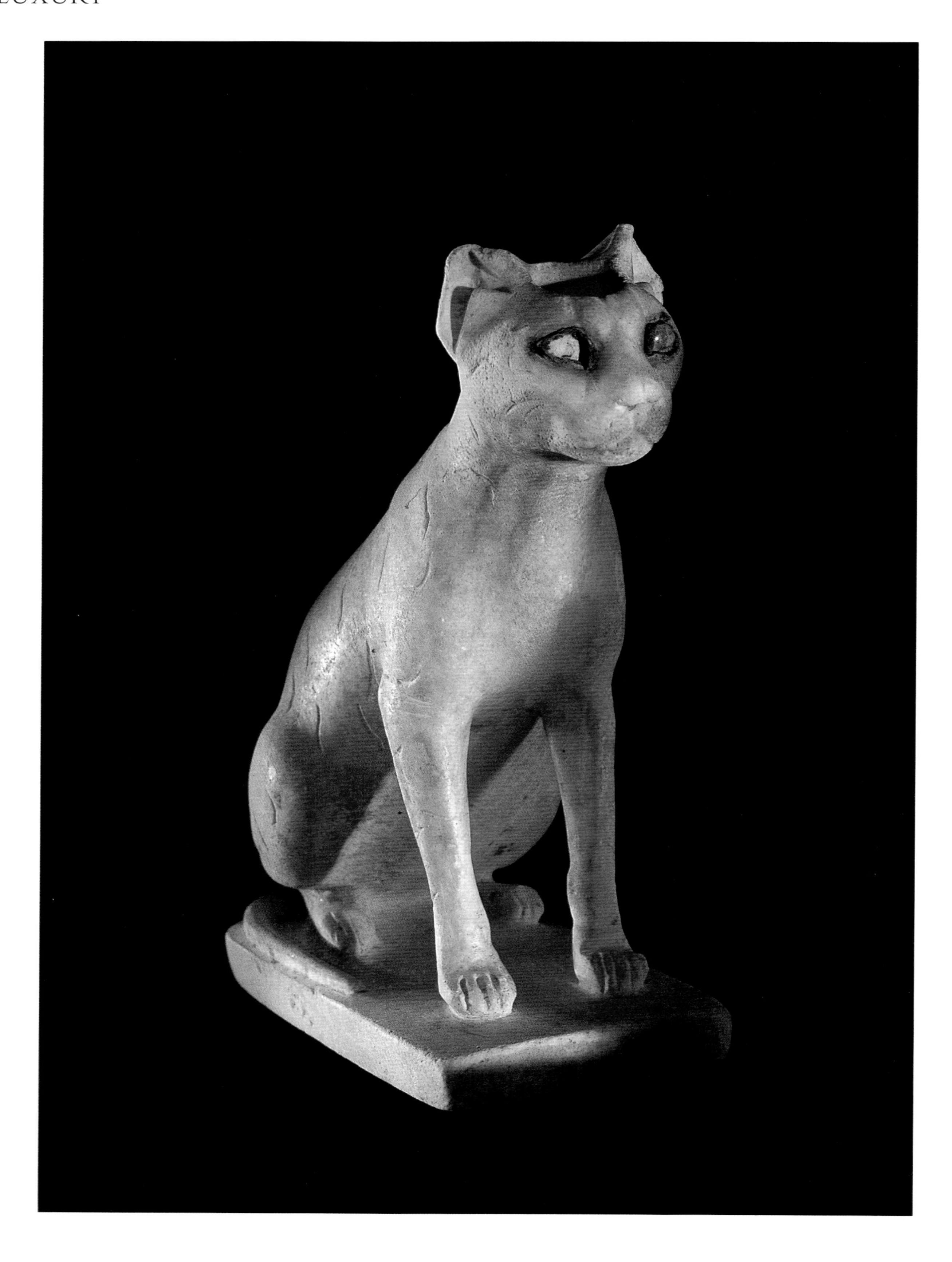

Container for perfume oil in the form of a wildcat, animal much admired for its readiness to fight poisonous snakes and regarded as an embodiment of the goddess Bastet.
The stopper, now lost, may have represented the sun disc.
Egyptian alabaster.
The eyes of rock crystal were set in copper sockets.
Height 14 cm.
Early 12th Dynasty, c. 1990-1900 BC.
Metropolitan Museum of Art, New York (1990.59.1 – Purchase, Lila Acheson Wallace Gift, 1990)

between the two courts, and perfumes found their place among gold, precious stones and splendid horses which the party brought to Egypt. Stone vessels with myrrh, liquidambar, opopanax resin, opobalsamum, cyperus grass, *Ferula communis,* myrtle(?), 'sun flower' (=heliotrope?) and an ingredient by the name *wukhizzi,* as well as composite scents, found their way to the palace at Memphis in the north or Malgatta near Thebes in the south of the country.[82]

One of these composite scents could have been the one recorded on a cuneiform tablet, consisting of sweet flag and oil with the addition of among other things cyperus grass, opopanax, 'sun flower' and myrtle. This fragrant dowry would no doubt have been for consumption in the palace, but we may compare it with the very large quantities of resin, moringa oil and wine which had been given as tribute from the princes of Retenu to king Tuthmosis III earlier in the Dynasty, though this would have been deposited in the temple of Amun for sacred use.

Later in the New Kingdom other exotic scents are brought to our notice in the so-called schoolboys' exercises. In one instance the model letter to be copied contained instructions for provisions for the king. Amongst ample items to delight the royal palate and nostrils are seven foreign scents in addition to incense and moringa oil:

Djefti from Alasia
Iinbu from Alasia
Kadjawar (best quality) from Khatti
[land of the Hittites]
Nekfitir from Sangar
Sweet flag oil from Amor
Gati from Takhsi
Moringa oil from Naharina

the latter being the same locality from which the above mentioned dowry came. These fragrant oils were meant not only for the king himself, but also for anointing his soldiery and chariotry.[83]

Solid Perfumes

In Chapter 2 we already met an unguent of a more or less solid consistency, namely madjet. Based on ox fat and with a melting point no higher than 37° C such unguent would be easily absorbed by the skin, yet it might remain solid if stored in a temperature that did not exceed this. Although recipes for perfumed oils are far more numerous, there is positive evidence for the more solid scents in Egypt.

AMARAKINON

We have already seen how a perfumed oil was made from marjoram, for which in one case an Egyptian name was given. Marjoram also entered fragrant solid unguents by the same two names as above. Both are based on ox fat and the first recipe is quite detailed. For Amarakinon Dioscorides gives the following instructions:[84]

'Remove any blood or skin from the fat. Pour over it some old fragrant wine. Boil together over a slow fire until the fat has lost its own smell and rather smells of the wine. Remove from the fire and leave to cool. Take out the fat and place in a 8.5 l pot. For 908 g fat add 1.816 kg jujube seeds. Boil over a slow fire, stirring continuously. When the greasy smell has disappeared, strain and cool.

'Take 454 g bruised aspalathos and 1.816 kg marjoram flowers. Steep them overnight in old wine. Place them in the pot with the wine with the fat and 1.5 l of wine. Boil together. When the fat has absorbed the scent, [strain, cool and skim off the fat] and store. To make the scent even sweeter 28 g of the fattest myrrh, diluted in "wine of many years' standing" may be added.'

SAMPSUCHINON

Once again Dioscorides is our source:[85]

'Take 681g marjoram carefully bruised and mixed into 454 g fat. Sprinkle with wine. Shape

Tutankhamun's alabaster ointment jars as they were found upon the discovery of his tomb by Carter in 1922. 18th Dynasty, c. 1325 BC.
Griffith Institute, Oxford

the mixture into little cakes, place in a vessel and leave overnight. The next day place the cakes in a pot, pour water over and boil gently. Strain and leave overnight to cool and set. Take the paste out and clean the pot. Mix this paste with another 681 g of marjoram, sprinkle with wine, and repeat the process as before. Store this marjoram unguent in a pot.'

GOOSE OR PORK FAT UNGUENT

Instead of ox fat, goose or pork fat is used in some of the prescriptions quoted by Dioscorides. The nature of the end product would differ in that the melting point of such fat, especially that of goose, is much lower. Dioscorides himself says that it is only successful in winter, or the mixture will separate.

It is difficult to imagine which one of the herbs included in this unguent would be the most dominant. Dioscorides left the preparation without a name.

'Place 1.1 l clean fat in an earthenware pot. Mix with 42 g each of cyperus grass, wood balsam, palm shoots, sweet flag, all finely bruised, and 1 cup of old wine from Lesbos. Bring to the boil three times, remove and cool for 24 hours. Melt again and sieve through clean linen into a clean pot. When it has set remove it with a spoon to a new pot. Seal and store.'

Dioscorides recommends adding a little wax to prevent the mixture from separating in hot weather. This is interesting since some of the material found in cosmetic pots in Egypt contained beeswax. It has hence been interpreted as a hair remedy, but this may not necessarily be so. The wax may owe its presence to the climate rather than to its use as a hair fixative.

COMMAGENUM

Goosefat is the main ingredient in an unguent invented in eastern Anatolia in a place called Commagene. Although there is no direct evidence of an Egyptian connection the recipe has been included here because of its affinity with the above. Pliny provides the details:[86]

'Mix goosefat with cinnamon in a bronze bowl. Cover with snow and steep in the icy mixture. This would keep the unguent fresh and solid.'

Pliny refers to it only as medicine, but the presence of cinnamon, favoured in perfume making, would have made it suitable as a scent as well.

UNGUENT CONES

Paintings and reliefs from the beginning of the New Kingdom and on show men and women with a lump of solid unguent perched on top of their head, either on a bald skull, on the hair or on top of a wig.[87] There is little doubt that the material is supposed to be scented matter, for in some contexts we see servants carrying bowls of the same white mass streaked with red or yellow whilst at the same time they position it on men and women seated at a banquet.

The texts, too, talk of the fragrant material: 'Place antiu resin upon your head . . .' recites the harpist. In Chapter 5 we shall discuss the significance of this further. Here it is appropriate merely to mention the existence of such unguent, which to all intents and purposes was of a solid nature, i.e. based on animal fat. Antiu on its own in its natural raw state would have little fragrance, and an oil extracted from such resin, like stakte, would be liquid. Hence the substance was scented fat, very probably with resins and herbs added. The mention of antiu could also be symbolic, because it was then widely considered to be the most exquisite fragrance imaginable, hence the ideal scent.

THE UNGUENTS OF TUTANKHAMUN

The tomb of Tutankhamun originally contained a large amount of oils and unguents, but few of the jars were left intact, and even more scarcely documented were the analyses that were undertaken of the contents in the days when chemistry was in its infancy. Today, when pollen and chromatographic analysis would be of invaluable help in identifying even the most minute samples of the contents, such samples are rarely available, if at all.

However, at the time of the discovery of the tomb, the contents of one of the jars was submitted for analysis, no less than 450g or so of material being found inside. The sample was taken from a cylindrical jar which had on its lid a figure of a recumbent lion, and on its body a hunting scene with dogs and wild animals.[88] The jar had been sealed 'by natural agency, the changes in temperature and moisture having caused certain salts . . . to crystallise round the lid and so form a hard, protective incrustation.'[89] The contents were found to consist of 87.7% fatty matter, very probably animal fat. The rest was taken to be 'some resin or balsam'. It melted, in part at least, at the heat of the hand, emitting a faint odour which has been variously described as of coconut, flowers of broom or valerian. At the laboratory it was said to have had 'a decidedly fatty smell, but certainly not that characteristic of advanced rancidity.' It contained no traces of vegetable fibre when examined under a microscope. The sample is broadly speaking consistent with the information gathered from the literature (which is, admittedly, more than a millennium later), whether or not the substance had at any time been in touch with plant material other than the resinous matter. The application of modern scientific methods would no doubt enlighten us further if only samples could be obtained.

Another sample of unguent was taken for analysis from a large bell-shaped krater.[90] The residue in this vessel, covering a fairly large area on the bottom and side of the interior, though much integrated was quite plastic when pressed between the fingers.' A panel on the front of the fluted jar gives the titulary of Tutankhamun and his queen, with the not insignificant addition 'May she live and be rejuvenated!' We shall revert to an interpretation of this wish in Chapter 5 (p. 106).

One jar still kept the fingerprints of the thief who extracted the unguent when the tomb was robbed soon after the burial. For the fingerprints to be visible, the contents would have been fairly solid, and hence prepared from a material like ox fat. According to Carter 'the slight residue adhering to the inner walls shows that the contents must have been of the nature of a stiff ointment (such as the consistency of cold-cream of today)'. The jar is shaped like a situla. It is a double container, an inner shell and an outer envelope of open work.[91]

Another jar whose contents were 'of a soft pasty substance' was of a similar shape, but with a flanking ornament. It, too, showed the fingermarks of the ancient robbers who had smashed the vase into several pieces.

On the other hand, the perfumes contained in the many jars with tall slender necks and narrow openings would have been based on liquid oils. A large amphora of calcite still contained some oil when found by Carter who says: 'At the bottom of this vessel a small quantity of its oil was left by the thieves; beneath the hardened crust the oil has remained viscid to this day.'[92] The jar has an ornamental inscription with Tutankhamun's names, but unfortunately the name of the perfume was not indicated (this is characteristic of all the ornamental vases from this tomb). Although the jar is now provided with a lid, Carter's excavation notes indicate that there were no traces of such a lid.[93] The whole of the inside of the jar was stained, showing that at the time of the burial it was full.

A little ewer on a stand had had its lid sealed with beeswax and a strip of linen and its spout 'cemented up', probably with more beeswax in order to keep the contents fresh.[94] The excavators found some traces of resinous

The famous golden mask of Tutankhamun is perhaps the most convincing evidence not only of the pharaohs' fabulous wealth but also of the skill and sophistication of Egypt's artists and craftsmen. The eye make-up on the mask is rendered with blue glass inlays, the eyes themselves with obsidian and quartz. 18th Dynasty, c. 1336-1327 BC. *Egyptian Museum, Cairo*

Unguent spoon in the form of a palm tree whose guard, armed with a stick, appears to be unaware of the mischievous youngster behind his back about to climb it to pick the ripe dates, unless his exploit is thwarted by the monkeys perching in the crown of the tree. This delightful work of art points to a keen sense of humour on the part of both craftsman and his client, who probably commissioned it as a New Year present for someone. Ivory, height 20 cm, 18th Dynasty, c.1550-1295 BC. *Calouste Gulbenkian Museum, Lisbon*

material on the jar, which had been opened by thieves by breaking off the spout but this could have been used for sealing the jar.

Three of the jars with narrow necks contained some brown substance 'fatty matter (now largely fatty acids) mixed with some other material not yet identified.'[95] The most splendid of them all apparently had some of its contents intact. It was 'dissolved with acetone and warm water applied alternately'. It is said to have consisted of aromatic gum [?], resin and fatty matter. The vase has a long, slender neck in the shape of the hieroglyph meaning 'unification' and is flanked by two Nile gods of Upper and Lower Egypt tying heraldic plants around the neck of the vase. These inscriptions confirm that this was a truly royal object which no doubt could have played a part during the king's brief rule (see further below).

A vase carved in the likeness of a heraldic lion was also found to contain 'some kind of fatty material, now dried and blackened, but probably originally of semi-liquid or liquid nature.'[96] The neck of the vase had been broken off, causing the contents to dry up, but it had apparently been left behind in the jar by the robbers. The lid was still in place, covered with a piece of white linen bound with brown linen strips.

Cartouches of previous kings on some of the jars of the less fanciful shapes indicate that they were older than the reign of Tutankhamun. The capacity of some of the jars was also indicated, such as 14 1/2 *hin* and 16 3/4 *hin*, i.e. 6.67 and 7.70 litres, but unfortunately the nature of the contents was not indicated.

These jars would have contained the solid unguents in use at that time, the finished products, rather than the raw material, since unlike vegetable oils, ox fat only reached a manageable consistency during the course of preparation.

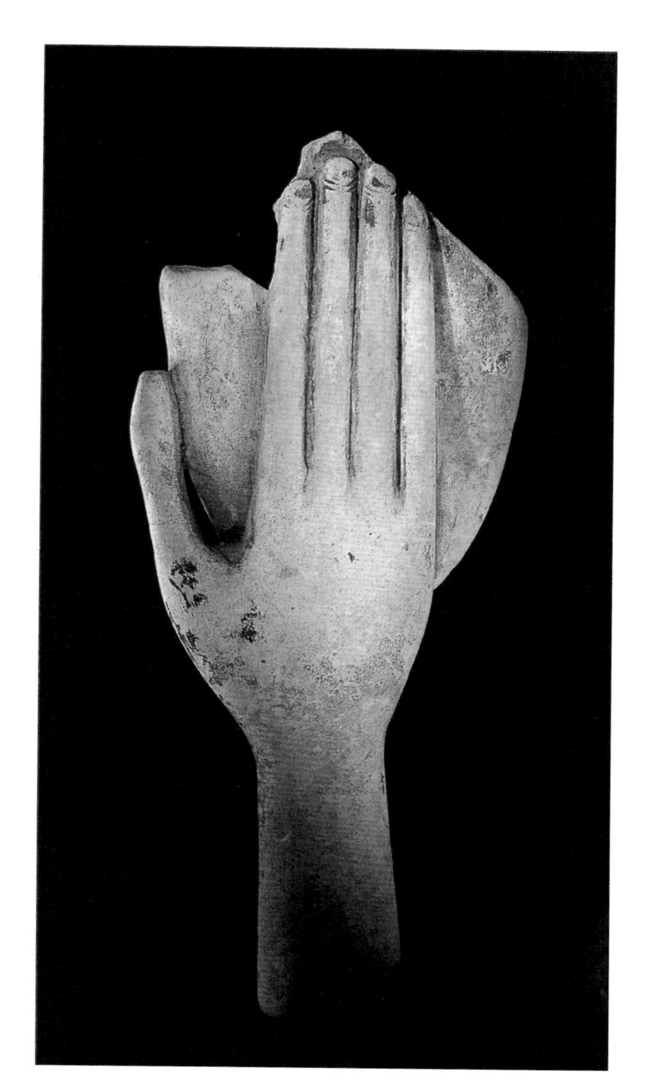

Cosmetic spoon in the form of a shell held in a hand. Glazed frit with traces of colouring. Length 15 cm. 18th Dynasty or earlier, c. 1600-1295 BC. *Christie's, London*

UNGUENT SPOONS

Just as in archaeology the existence of tent poles can be surmised by the presence of corresponding cavities in the ground, the existence of solid unguents, such as those based on animal fat can be deduced from the shape of surviving containers. In addition to the wide-necked jars just mentioned there are a great many objects generally identified as 'cometic spoons'.

Such items would contain a spoonful of solid material, heaped or not, for the immediate use of the owner of the spoon. Presumably it had been scooped from a larger container, perhaps stored in a room other than that in which the unguent was applied.

Little cosmetic receptacles with or without a lid, of materials such as alabaster or wood, may also have contained scented matter. Such containers, often of fancy shapes with wide necks would be more suitable for solid than liquid unguents. Spoons with long handles have also survived. These would have been used to transfer the unguent from the storage jar to the smaller ornamental container.

Queen Ankhesenamun brings ointments and flowers to King Tutankhamun.
A scene on the gilted shrine which once contained a statuette of the king,
judging from the impressions of its sandals on the pedestal inside.
18th Dynasty, c. 1336-1327 BC. *Egyptian Museum, Cairo*

5 Scent for Love and Rebirth

The ancient Egyptians have often been credited with having such zest for life that they wanted to prolong it endlessly after death. This may well appear to be so, but their notions of life in the Hereafter were rather more sophisticated than that.

Ordinary people may have had a vague desire to spend eternity in the realm of Osiris for which purpose a certain amount of funerary equipment was required in the manner of food, furniture, amulets, perfume and cosmetics.

Members of the elite looked for a more comprehensive programme of texts and pictures to help them along, the nature of which they may have grasped only to some extent, in spite of their exalted position. Resurrection in some form was crucial, and it would seem that by the Eighteenth Dynasty a definite coded language had been worked out in tomb decoration which answered the needs of the period. At the heart of it was a concept that relies on plays on words. This, as we shall see, will involve the question of scent as well.

First we have to examine the perception of scent as an erotic factor, then its relevance to the strategy to achieve eternal life.

Perfume is frequently mentioned in Egyptian literature,[1] and it is through stories and poems that we catch a glimpse of its significance in daily life. A tale from the New Kingdom (c. 1300 BC) relates the events triggered off by the scent of a single lock of hair. The lock was detached from its owner and eventually ended up in the bay of the river at the very spot where pharaoh's personal laundry, drenched in unguent, was taken to be washed. When the servants brought the laundered clothes clothes back to pharaoh, His Majesty was not pleased:

> '"The smell of unguent is in pharaoh's garments!" he exclaimed. And pharaoh harangued them day after day, and they did not know what to do. Pharaoh's chief laundryman was extremely annoyed because of these daily rebukes and he betook himself to the river bank. He stopped on the sand bank near the spot [where the clothes had been laundered] and he saw the lock of hair in the water. He sent someone to go down into the river and bring it up to him. The hair gave off an exceedingly sweet smell, and he took it back to pharaoh.'

The king sent messengers to find the owner of the lock of hair. Not surprisingly, she was tracked down and brought to the palace. The king 'loved her exceedingly,' but unfortunately the lady had a husband at home, and from then on the tale took a dramatic turn.

It is evident that while the scent of the lock of hair was seductive, it was not considered desirable to wear clothes heavily stained with old perfume.

One love poem describes how a frustrated lover longs to be allowed to perform the menial task of washing away the perfume from the dress of his beloved:

> I wish I were her laundryman,
> Just for a single month.
> Then I would flourish by donning her garment
> And be close to her body.
> I would wash away the unguent from her clothes
> And wipe my body in her dress.

Merit, wife of royal architect Ka, was provided for in her afterlife with a richly decorated box of flasks and jars of her favourite fragrances and cosmetics. 18th Dynasty, reign of Amenhotep III, c. 1386-1349 BC. *Museo Egizio, Turin*

Unguent was personal and intimate, something redolent of a sexual relationship between a man and a woman. Perfume was required, along with intoxicating beverages, to provide the ideal setting for an amorous encounter between two lovers.

Such situation is described in another poem, where each verse is spoken by a pomegranate tree in the garden. The tree is given the following stanza ('sister' and 'brother' being terms of affection between lovers):

> The 'sister' spends the day with the 'brother'
> under my branches,
> Drunk with grape and pomegranate wine,
> Besprinkled with the fragrance of resin . . .

Although, as we shall see, excessive drink and an abundance of perfume were acceptable, even encouraged on certain occasions, it would seem that in ordinary circumstances the Egyptians were fairly abstemious. At the scribal schools the students were taught to write by copying model writings, relating either proper demeanour or behaviour that was frowned upon. One such passage describes a failed student who tours the streets in the company of women with a garland hung round his neck, spattered with oil and reeking of beer, playing foreign musical instruments. The interpretation depends on the attitude of the beholder: a jolly night out, or a sign of declining morals . . .

The awareness of a special fragrance emanating from a body ready for lovemaking was highlighted in the official account of the divine conception of queen Hatshepsut.

The mighty god Amun had approached the queen's mother while she was asleep in the innermost rooms of the palace. She was awoken, not by hearing him enter, but by 'smelling the divine scent'. Totally overcome she smiled at him; he had an erection and allowed her to see him 'in his real god's figure'. She rejoiced at his virility and felt love for him flowing through her body. The palace became inundated by the divine scent, 'it smelled like incense land.'

The text goes on to describe their union on the royal bed. When the appropriate length of time had passed, Hatshepsut was born.

The true mark of divine virility, perhaps best expressed by the Egyptian word *nefer*, was the scent with which the god communicated his presence. The account of the divine conception of the queen was copied by one of her successors some one hundred years later, Amenhotep III, on the wall of a little room in the Luxor temple across the river. The conclusion to the story had to be adapted, though, for it was a play on words of the future ruler's name and the exclamation of the queen in the moment of climax. 'Hatshepsut - best of the exquisite!' he cries with Hatshepsut's mother. 'Amon-hotep [the god] Amon is satisfied!' the later version has it. 'This will be the name of the child I have placed in your belly, for this was what you exclaimed!', the god decrees.

In the love poems the link between fragrance and sexuality is almost as explicit as in the tale of the god and the queen. One describes a seduction scene where the release of scent coincides with the moment of the girl's climax.

> If you go to the room of the beloved,
> She being alone and without another,
> You can do what you wish with the latch.
> The door hangings flutter
> When the sky comes down in the wind,
> But it does not carry it away, her fragrance,
> When she brings you an abundance of scent,
> Intoxicating those present . . .

In spite of the inconsistency of the number of persons taking part and the slight awkwardness in the use of metaphors, the sense is abundantly clear, and it would have been greatly enjoyed by the audience for whom 'Tashere of the mayor's music room' performed this song.

A phrase of another poem is even more direct in placing the source of the fragrance emanating during lovemaking:

When I embrace her
And her arms are open,
I feel like a man in incense land,
Who is immersed in scent . . .

The word for 'embrace' (keni) was also used specifically to describe a woman's pudenda. The Egyptians were fairly discreet in their choice of words in public documents, but to deny their erotic explicitness here would deprive their poetry of an important dimension.

The same applies to art. The Egyptians knew very well how to draw erotic pictures, and they made ample use of unambiguous symbols of fertility even in official monuments. Their legal terminology leaves nothing to the imagination. But the sophisticated language of erotic poetry and images lifts the concept of lovemaking onto a different plane.

THE FEAST OF THE VALLEY

There was one situation in life in particular during which scent was of paramount importance. This brings us to the threshold of eternity. Perhaps it was with perfume as with intoxicating drink: moderation was called for, except on special occasions, these being the religious feasts of the year. This made an important difference: when beer and wine were provided on the divine offering tables, then the people were free to indulge to their hearts' content, for their inebriation had a purpose.

In the ancient city of Thebes, home of the mighty god Amun, the inhabitants of means were buried in the desert, in the plain and cliffs of the western desert. The upper rooms of the tomb, excavated in the hillside, were decorated with wall-paintings and reliefs, whereas the mummy rested below ground, in an undecorated shaft, surrounded by various tomb equipment. The decoration in the upper chambers pertains partly to the tomb owner's life and career, partly to life in the Hereafter as they imagined it to be. One of the scenes that are never absent in Eighteenth Dynasty tomb decoration is the so-called banquet scene from which we derive so much knowledge of ideal life in high society 3,500 years ago. A great many of these banquet scenes can be related to one particular occasion, namely the Feast of the Valley. On this day relatives gathered in and around the tombs of their dead ancestors in order to witness the procession of the statue of Amun, who travelled from his temple at Karnak at the other side of the river to pay a visit to the mortuary temples of dead kings on the west bank. The statue came to rest overnight in a sanctuary in the temple at Deir el-Bahari, where the god celebrated a ritual wedding with Hathor, goddess of the western mountain, before it returned to its home at Karnak.

The inhabitants of Thebes made merry on this occasion, they drank to excess, and the barriers between the human mortals and the august deity were broken down. In addition, they communed with their deceased relatives, who were thought to come out and join the festivities and watch the divine procession. At the same time they received food offerings and flowers from their relatives, and they sat amongst them bedecked in garlands and besprinkled with costly scent. This concept obliged the living to stretch their imagination somewhat, but it was greatly facilitated by the pictures on the walls, showing the dead taking part in this very occasion. The ideal situation was described in the words of a harpist:

Place antiu resin on your head
Dress in fine linen.
Anoint yourself with the true wonders
Of the divine offering.

There is no doubt that the perfume was provided by the deity, which means the temple in actual fact. Servants are depicted anointing the guests and carrying bowls heaped with solid unguent, a handful of which would apparently be placed on top of the guests' head.[2] In one such scene it is a whole jar of scented oil that is being emptied over the head and shoulders of a female guest. The

At a party to celebrate the Feast of the Valley guests and servants alike are depicted with unguent cones on their wigs. One lady is sniffing a lotus flower proffered by her neighbour while another is enjoying the aroma of a ripe yellow fruit, probably the edible sweet persea rather than the somewhat similar but poisonous mandrake. Detail of a wall painting from the tomb of Nebamun, a Theban official ('scribe and counter of grain'). 18th Dynasty, c. 1390-1352 BC. *British Museum, London*

wall-painting is now in a poor state and the upper half of the figures has disappeared. But the scene was copied in a line drawing in the 1830's. Champollion, the renowned Egyptologist, also saw it, and although he did not draw it, he provided a useful comment, namely that the liquid being poured from the jar was red. Thus it is not 'a lady having a bath', as some early travellers thought, but red perfume being poured out. Such red perfume could have been like the perfume dyed with alkanet mentioned in the previous chapter.

A similar liquid substance is frequently depicted in scenes showing the tomb owner offering to Amun as he passed by the opening of the tomb during the Feast of the Valley. Here it is labelled antiu resin.

The garments worn by the Egyptians were usually white, yet in these banquet scenes where large quantities of perfume are involved, they are often rendered with orange or yellow stains. Another song which belongs in such a context explains:

Your garments are white.
Fine oil is on your shoulders,
Garlands around your neck . . .
To give you life and health,
Antiu resin and senetjer incense of Amun,
In your house of eternity.

It is the scented oil that produces the discoloration, and it is particularly heavy where the dress lies close to the body: around the breasts and shoulders, and where the knees meet the skirt. It is possible that this effect was desired, rather than incidental. In some civilisations, on some occasions, the dress was anointed rather than the skin. Egyptian garments were chiefly made of linen, and linen does not accept dye easily. On the other hand, the fibres would absorb the fatty matter and make them supple and shiny. The yellow colour is a means for the artist to show that large amounts of scent have been applied. It is a sign of wealth and opulence.

THE UNGUENT CONES

In order to indicate that the hair or wig had been subject to a similar treatment the artist shows us the actual solid perfume rubbed into the hair as a lump on top of the head. It is generally imagined that the Egyptians did manoeuvre around with such a scented lump of fat on their heads, and it has been demonstrated that a certain tribe in Upper Egypt followed the same habit up until 100 years ago, a tribe, moreover, that shows a surprising degree of survivals of ancient Egyptian customs. It is possible, though, that the lump of fat was the simplest method available to the artist to indicate that an amount of scented fat had been rubbed into the hair. The unguent cone was not necessarily positioned on the head for any length of time - if at all.[3]

Such cones are easy to recognize. There appears to have been a fashion in unguent cones, for they change shape over the centuries.[4] When they first appear in the beginning of the Eighteenth Dynasty they are hemispherical (see p. 80), but they grow taller with time. Sometimes the outline is uneven, as if a lump had just been slapped on the head. Other cones are tall and elegant, and sometimes they even have a floral decoration which is most unusual. The basic colour is white, but towards the summit they are yellow, and this yellow colour seems to spill down the sides of the shape. Elsewhere they are occasionally red instead of yellow, perhaps to suggest the presence of antiu, as in the harper's song.

More than seventy years ago Bernard Bruyère, the eminent French archaeologist who for a long time lived in and excavated the village of the workmen, engaged in the preparation of the tombs in the Valley of the Kings, proposed that the unguent cones as we see them in representational art was 'a graphic expression of a metaphysical state, of being 'justified', blessed, deceased . . . It conveys the idea of joyous resurrection, it symbolises justification at the tribunal of Osiris.'[5] It would then perhaps be reminiscent of a halo whose significance we understand without for one moment believing that it really exists.

But to the ancient Egyptians the cone nevertheless had some substance and body. It was believed to be made of fragrant unguent. We can now return to the pretty banquet scenes and begin to understand their significance and how perfume may come to mean the very essence of life.

THE METAPHOR OF SCENT

It is possible to read more into the banquet scenes than a pictorial record of a festive event and to understand the point of the eye-catching use of perfume in this context. In order to appreciate it, we must realise that the Egyptians had a highly developed sense of puns and play on words. The creation of the world, for example, was explained in terms of plays on words. The creator god created men (remyt) from his tears (remut), and he spat out (ishesh) the first god Shu and expectorated (tef) the first goddess Tefnet. A metaphor may also work visually, that is to say that a certain subject depicted may bring to mind a certain word which in turn would recall another similar sounding word or act.

It so happens that the word for scent is written with the very same letters seti as the word for 'engender'. An identical play on words can be worked out for the word 'to shoot', an act which sometimes represents metaphorically the sexual act. In the context of the banquet scenes it has been demonstrated how yet another word seti, 'to pour' is represented visually as a pun on the sexual act. Representations of servant girls and boys, shown in the act of pouring a beverage, refer to that other essential gushing forth of liquid which is in itself the creative sexual act.[6]

Resurrection was thought of in terms of rebirth, and the elements akin to those preceding birth, namely conception, would likewise be assumed before rebirth. The presence of sexual power was essential and should be made clear by all means. The ambience preceding rebirth would be no different.

This attitude is the key to an understanding of why it is that an erotic undertone of daily life with all its charming details is reflected on the walls of the tombs, especially in the picture programme of Eighteenth Dynasty tomb decoration.

This may go some way to explain why scent has such a prominent place in these scenes. Not only did perfumed substances generally have a profound influence on the senses. In

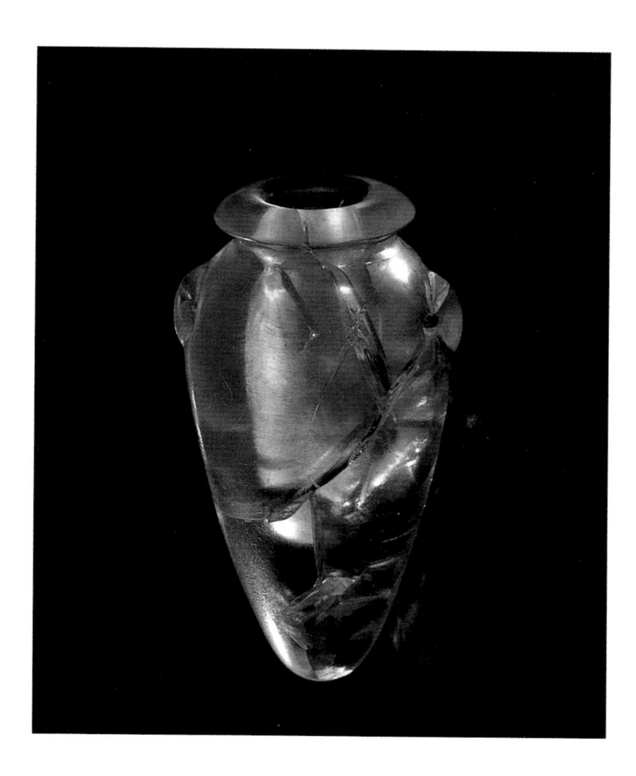

The perfume amphora would have been worn as a pendant on a string threaded through the pierced handles. Rock crystal, height 5.1 cm, New Kingdom, c. 1550-1069 BC or earlier. *Christie's, London*

this particular situation it prepared the mood for the fertile union of the sexes. But there was also a pun to back it up at a more sophisticated level.

We have already come across scented oils in the songs and phrases associated with the Feast of the Valley. Scent had a deeply religious and symbolic significance. This must in the first place have been caused by the ingredients that went into the preparations, and subsequently by the cunning play on words that was worked out as if to force the concept to fit into funerary beliefs. The motifs, involving such an obvious demonstration of the presence of scent, became a coded message conveying 'sexuality', understood by those familiar with the code. Those who were not, saw it as just an attractive, innocuous picture.

It is a golden shrine from the tomb of Tutankhamun which provides the best clue to this interpretation of sexual metaphors in funerary art. The shrine is covered with gold leaf with embossed decorations divided into panels, each one showing the king and the queen in a picturesque situation from their daily life. In one, the queen squats at the feet of her husband, absorbing a liquid which is being poured into her hand from a flask held by the king (see frontispiece, p. 2). The concepts depicted: 'pour', 'liquid', 'hand', 'mouth', 'drink' are all words which have a secondary erotic significance. The details of the representation suggest an erotic undertone: the semi-transparent garment of the queen, her heavy wig, the lotus flower.

In another panel (p. 90) the queen is shown anointing the king with one hand whereas in the other she carries a tray which supports an unguent cone decorated with a lotus flower. As the king wears his crown on his head, the cone has to be shown separately.

As just mentioned, the word for scent, written with the same three letters as the word for 'engender', also serves to write the word 'to shoot with bow and arrow', and this is just another subject in the decoration of the golden shrine. The panel representing hunting with a throwstick would 'read' the same letters as the word 'to procreate', and the subject of hunting finds its deeper meaning in the sexual context without any difficulty.

THE LOTUS FLOWER

In these representations of 'the perfect reunion' one item has pride of place: the lotus flower. Men and women carry them in their hands and bury their noses among the scented petals; they wear necklaces of lotus petals sewn together; the women wear them as a decorative hair band; and the flower or bud often adorns the unguent cone on their heads. The pale blue lotus flower, *Nymphaea caerulea* Savigny, was the most popular of all flowers depicted in Egyptian art. The open flower had a strong scent, described as being like that of the hyacinth, and it was visually attractive both as a bud, when fully blown or when separated into lancet-shaped petals (which were sometimes depicted white rather than blue, thus assimilating it with the white lotus, *Nymphaea lotus* L., whose petals are more rounded). The closed flower has no scent.

A prosperous man represented with androgynous features and a wig adorned with a stylised lotus flower, symbol of renewal of life. Mummy mask, 18th Dynasty, c.1550 - 1295 BC. *Musées Royaux d'Art et d'Histoire, Brussels*

The lotus grows in water. The blue and the white lotus have different habits. At the first rays of sun, the flower of the blue lotus bursts open to reveal its intricate shape, but come noon and it closes to a bud and sinks into the water, only to reappear the next morning. One flower repeats this pattern for three consecutive days. The white lotus, on the other hand, flowers during the night. This extraordinary continuity of forms came to symbolize the renewal of life which was so essential to the Egyptians, both in their daily existence as farmers and in the mysterious world beyond the grave.

Theologians used the life of the lotus as a setting for a creation myth, for they professed that prior to the creation of the world, the sun god Re himself had originally been born from the womb of a lotus flower, bursting with divine creative energy. This may have been beyond the understanding of ordinary Egyptians; but nevertheless they had shaped amulets and figurines showing the motif of the child in the flower for several hundred years before we meet the lotus in the banquet scenes. They knew that the lotus was special, and the belief in its creative power was transferred to an area that everyone recognized: like the red rose, the lotus came to be associated with the concept of Love. If we were to rely on pictures alone, we would perhaps suspect that this was the case, for the lotus flower is found alongside female beauty from the time of the Old Kingdom and to the close of Egyptian civilisation. But the literature of the Egyptians comes to our aid, and we have only to read through their love poems to meet the lotus flower in situations which leave little to the imagination.

The poems were part of a literary treasure which must have relied on a flourishing oral tradition. They were recited, or even sung, and it is our good fortune that someone thought of writing down some of them on scrolls of papyrus or flakes of white limestone.

Here we are in the world of ordinary people, like those depicted in the banquet scenes. They would have appreciated one of the most sensual poems of that time:

> O my divine, my lotus flower! . . .
> I love to go and bathe before you.
> I allow you to see my beauty
> In a dress of the finest linen,
> Drenched with fragrant unguent.
> I go down to the water to be with you
> And come up to you again with a red fish,
> Looking splendid on my fingers.
> I place it before you . . .
> Come! Look at me!

The lotus, the fine linen dress drenched in unguent, revealing a beautiful body underneath - these are the elements we have already seen in the banquet scene, here united in a situation which is implicitly erotic. The girl cries out 'My lotus!', an affectionate nickname for her beloved which encompasses both her desire and her hopes for its fulfilment.

To adorn oneself with lotus flowers was tantamount to declaring one's intentions and aspirations. It is invariably the blue lotus, the

Right: A bunch of lotus flowers, mandrake and poppy at a funeral. Tomb of court sculptors Nebamun and Ipuky, Sheikh Abd el-Qurna, 18th Dynasty, c. 1390-1336 BC

variety that has the strongest scent, and it may well be this scent, and its effect, that is the key not only to the frequent appearance of the flower, but also to a full understanding of the rôle of the banquet scenes and the urge to have the lotus flower depicted in the tombs.

The effect of the scent of the lotus flower, as perceived by the Egyptians themselves, can only be gauged through the rôle the flower played in offering rituals which postdate the banquet scenes by a thousand years or more, more or less contemporary with the inscriptions from the perfume 'laboratories' at Edfu and elsewhere. No doubt the rites have more ancient roots; but it is only at this late date that they are accompanied by inscriptions which are of any interest out of the ordinary. The king offering lotus to a deity is a ceremony frequently depicted on the inner walls or columns of the temple. The deity is said to be 'satisfied' by the lotus flower and his/her heart 'appeased' by its scent. The god 'enjoys the divinity' of its scent. When the god sees the brilliance of the flower, his 'eyes marvel', and when he sniffs its scent, his 'nostrils dilate'.[7] The god in turn will acknowledge the offering by saying, 'I receive your offering and sniff its scent. I cause you [the king] to be praised and loved by means of its scent.'

We can gather from this that the scent of the lotus was taken to have an effect on the deity which could be interpreted as almost sedative or hypnotic, and that the scent would cause nostrils to be quite literally dilated. If at this late stage in Egyptian history the flower was presented to the deity with the specific purpose of producing a psychic effect, it goes without saying that this same effect had been experienced by ordinary mortals for some considerable time beforehand. In view of the fact that people are represented sniffing lotus flowers as early as the time of the pyramid builders, we are faced with a practice that could well date back to the dawn of civilisation. At a time when man's senses had not yet been pampered with products obtained through distillation, not to mention modern artificial preparations, sensitivity to natural scents must

have been even more acute.[8] When an Egyptian buried his nose in a lotus flower, and perhaps kept it there for a while, the effect on him may well have been considerable, and the scent may have been sufficient to achieve an alteration of his consciousness.

The ability to cause sedation and excitement often goes hand in hand in narcotic plants.[9] It is common to a considerable number of them that the effect is a liberation of the mind. To the Egyptians, this would not be an alien concept at all, for they were accustomed to the independent life of the 'soul' in its various aspects, and the changing of forms which the deceased person would be able to achieve if he were equipped with the appropriate magical spells. One of these transformations was actually into the form of a lotus flower. During the Feast of the Valley, which was above all a celebration of communicating with the divine on the one hand and with the world of the dead on the other, a state of mind controlled by the inhaling of lightly narcotic substances would have added greatly to the experience. The fact that the lotus flower

An arrangement of garlands of grapes on a branch of vine, lotus leaves and blossoms vividly depicted on a painted relief, Amarna period, 18th Dynasty, c. 1352–1336 BC.
Private collection, New York

also had erotic connotations will be most relevant, for sexuality was clearly one of the prerequisites of the ultimate transformation.

Egyptian representation can rarely be taken at its face value alone. It is never realistic in our sense of the word. But this should not inhibit us from asking questions about puzzling iconographical details – such as: if the scent of the flower was so significant, and if its effect was a force to be reckoned with, why is it that in representations lotus buds (or closed flowers) with their lack of fragrance (as in the illustration on p. 76) are as frequent as pictures of open flowers? With the eye of faith it is possible in some cases to distinguish buds of two different shapes, an elongated, sometimes even slightly concave bud often seen next to open flowers of *Nymphaea caerulea*, and a plumper, more rounded bud which could perhaps anticipate the more spherical shape of *Nymphaea lotus*, a species whose open flower is occasionally depicted in ponds and borders but never in the banquet scenes. Maybe the artist allowed his picture to reflect the fact that one flowers during the day and the other at night, the two never coinciding in nature. With the scent restrained, or much reduced, the effect of the bud would be either visual or psychological. However, the bud/closed flower represented a stage in transformation without which the cycle of events that symbolised eternity would be incomplete.

THE MANDRAKE

Mandragora officinarum L.

In the banquet scenes the lotus is at times replaced by a yellow, slightly pointed, fruit. A girl may be shown giving it to another to sniff, or the women appear to play games with the fruits, hiding them behind their backs. The fruit could be one of two which in Egyptian art are not so easy to distinguish. One is the persea fruit (*Mimusops laurifolia* L.) which grows on a tall tree. The ripe yellow fruit contains a sweet green edible pulp with two or three stones. It has four or six short sepals, a botanical detail that becomes relevant when we compare it with the other candidate, the mandrake. This is a plant which, apart from its characteristic root, has vigorous leaves and almost stemless orange fruits. Its six sepals are longer than that of the persea. When used as an ornament on objects it is difficult to tell the two apart, for they have very similar colour and outlines, and the different lengths of the stems and petals do not always seem to have been observed. In a banquet scene one would perhaps expect to have more use for a sweet persea fruit than the less palatable mandrake which is not generally used for human consumption. But the more we penetrate into the many aspects of the banquet scene, the less we should be prepared to rely on practical considerations. It should be said, though, that in pictures of Egyptian gardens the mandrake is a frequent plant. A persea tree is more difficult to identify among the rather similar looking trees with yellow fruits. In view of the interesting properties of the mandrake, and its affinity with the lotus, this seems to be a far more likely candidate for the fruits depicted in the banquet scenes.

Lotus and mandrake are evoked to describe a girl's beauty in a love poem:

> The mouth of my beloved is like a lotus bud
> Her breasts like mandrake fruits...

In another poem they combine to form a garland which is to be placed around the neck of the loved one. The mandrake fruits alone feature in a love poem which, although fragmentary, can be reconstructed as follows:

> I wish I were her Nubian slave
> Surely, she would make me bring
> a bowl of mandrake fruits,
> And when she holds it in her hand,
> she would breathe from it,
> Thus offering me the colour
> of her entire body.

Sniffing the fruit is exactly what the women do if they are not inhaling the scent of lotus flowers, and the significance of this act is further explained in the poem by equating it with 'showing the colour of the body'. In Egyptian, the words for 'colour' and 'skin' are very similar, but the notion of the 'colour' is met elsewhere, for example when a woman offers 'the colour of her breast' to make love. When the women hold fruits to their lips and noses we must interpret these gestures in a similar fashion, and it more than suggests that we are dealing with mandrakes rather than persea fruits. These latter play no major part in erotic literature, though the foliage does: the beloved may be described as having her arms full of persea branches. Maybe the fruit was too common to be imbued with the necessary mystique. The argument hinges on the words which we translate as 'mandrake' and 'persea fruit'. Philological identifications of plants are rarely a matter of course. The frequently occurring *ished* is generally taken to mean persea fruit, and no convincing argument has yet been put forward to disprove it, whereas the word translated as 'mandrake' in the above mentioned poems is the much rarer *rermt*.

The mandrake has intrigued man for millennia, in classical antiquity and the Middle Ages largely because of the shape of its root which easily takes the form of man himself. The plant has been used as a painkiller, sedative, soporific, aphrodisiac, trance mediator and as a poison. When administered in quantity it is able to provoke a condition which resembles death. In the Bacchanalian orgies, mandrake was one of the ingredients added to wine which had effects that went beyond ordinary intoxication. The plant originated in north-eastern Mediterranean region, and it only appeared in Egypt in the New Kingdom, too late to be incorporated in the medical texts of the time, which were based on older sources. Later texts, however, make reference to the properties of the plant, notably a compilation probably made for a monastic library on the banks of the Tigris. The manuscript (already referred to in Chapter 3, p. 50) appears to have been copied by a Syrian monk in the 12th century AD. The original author of the major part of the work had studied in Alexandria and had access to the medical writings of classical antiquity. The Syrian monk also copied a corpus of 'native' prescriptions. Mandrake is here mentioned as a plant that deadens feeling, relieves pain and induces sleep. In the main part of the work, mandrake is also prescribed, but the physicians are cautioned, for the plant is said to cause injury through its coldness, quenching the natural warmth of the members (this reasoning shows influence from the school of the 'humours', apparently not known in pharaonic Egypt).

Mandrake leaves were also prescribed in a plaster of barley flour and rose oil to cool an inflamed stomach. Even more interesting in this context is the reported application of mandrake leaves soaked in vinegar to the face of a person suffering from sleeplessness. The seeds of mandrake were included in an ingredient in a composite remedy to treat 'continued fear and depression'.

So far the manuscript copied by the Syrian monk. A papyrus scroll written in Egypt in the 3rd century AD prescribes a potion including mandrake, henbane and ivy in wine to make a man sleep for two whole days.[10]

As mentioned above, the Egyptians of the New Kingdom probably knew the mandrake as *reremt*. In the days of Dioscorides it had apparently become *apemum*.[11] In Sumerian it was NAM-TAR, a word that could be the ancestor of our 'mandragora' through a transposition of the letters m and n. In that part of the world (which was where the Syriac manuscript was found) the plant was used medicinally as a painkiller, from toothache to labour pains. If administered in beer, purging of the body would result. Dioscorides, the eminent herbalist of the 1st century AD, reminds us that at his time the Egyptians called the plant *aperioum*. Nevertheless, the texts written in the Christian era all use the Greek 'mandragora', written in Egyptian (or Syriac) letters.

It is evident from the love poem quoted above that the scent of the fruit was really inhaled, and that it somehow had a stimulating effect, for the woman loses any inhibitions she may have had towards her Nubian slave. The pictures of the banquet scenes also show the fruit in direct contact with the nose.

The final proof that the presence of the mandrake had a very specific purpose comes from the lips of the Egyptians themselves. A little known love poem describes the skin (or is is colour again?) of the beloved as the skin/colour of the '*reremt* which causes love' (more evocatively translated into French as *la baie qui fait aimer*). Since it is the work of a poet who would choose his words carefully, it is possible that he was playing around with his consonants. As we have seen, the Egyptians appreciated puns and play on words, and the affinity of *reremt* with *mereret* ('the beloved') would not have escaped him. In Egypt, a small detail like this would have been enough to shape the lore of the fruit.

Mandrake has now been proven to be both hallucinogenic and soporific, containing atropine, scopolamine and hyoscyamine (a constituent well known from henbane, a herb used since antiquity as both a sedative and a love potion). With its erotic connotations, its use in Egypt thus resembles the lotus closely.

The actual scent of the mandrake fruit has been described in various ways from 'slightly unpleasant according to today's taste'[12] to 'musky and not unpleasant'[13], 'sweet smelling'[14] and 'fragrant'.[15]

SCENT ON THE MOVE

In the scheme of decoration in the Eighteenth Dynasty tombs at Thebes the banquet scene was indispensable, and in most cases it can be directly or indirectly related to one specific occasion: the Feast of the Valley. The feast was only celebrated in this part of Egypt, for this was where the deities involved belonged. Because of the large number of tombs in this area, it is statistically significant. Elsewhere in the country, as for instance in the contemporary tombs at Memphis, we find banquet scenes with similar details, but without the adjoining motifs of the tomb owner worshipping Amun.

At Thebes another motif is relevant to a study of scent and its implications regarding eternal life. On the face of it, it has nothing whatsoever to do with the Feast of the Valley celebrations. The tomb owner 'fishing and fowling in the marshes' is a scene that has been reproduced in art books almost as frequently as pretty ladies from the banquet, and it is often claimed to depict the elegant

Dioscorides, the father of pharmacology, handing over the magical mandrake to a disciple in an Arabic translation of his work *De Materia Medica,* copied in Mosul, Iraq. 13th century.
Topkapi Palace Library, Istanbul

Opposite Nebamun fowling in the marshes. In this scene which symbolises regeneration his wife is wearing party dress and an unguent cone. Both she and her daughter are holding lotus flowers. Painted plaster, 18th Dynasty, c. 1390-1352 BC.
British Museum, London

leisure activities of a member of the Egyptian upper class. The interpretation needs careful rethinking. Naturalistic it is not. First of all it would be impossible to fit in not only the tomb owner, but also his wife and child in a disproportionately small boat. Secondly, the wife is inappropriately attired for a boating trip. In fact, she looks as if she has come straight from the celebrations of the Feast of the Valley.

In the representation in the tomb of Nebamun, a scribe of the granary around 1400 BC, she wears a rippled, semi-transparent dress soaked in unguent, a wig with garland, large earrings, and a tall unguent cone decorated with flowers. In one hand she holds a bouquet of flowers and in the other a sistrum and necklace, that is, all the paraphernalia of a Feast of the Valley. What is she doing here, amidst a flutter of birds on the river?

Nebamun himself is slightly more suitably dressed for the occasion in a kilt that allows him freedom of movement. His broad chest displays a festive floral collar, three lotus flowers are draped around his neck, and he is wearing a wig. In one hand he is brandishing a throwstick, in the other he is holding three birds as decoys.

The polychrome hieroglyphs give a caption to the scene: 'Enjoying oneself, seeing something good [nefer] and the deeds of the god of the trap, the works of Sekhet, [the marsh goddess] by the one praised by the mistress of hunting, by the scribe and counter of grain. . . Nebamun and his beloved wife, Hatshepsut', a standard inscription in this kind of scene. In between the figures are hieroglyphs in a different hand, repeating part of the text: 'Enjoying oneself, seeing something good in the place of eternity for a long lifetime, without a wish in the world.' This was inserted by a later visitor to the tomb whom we meet on another wall as well. It need not concern us here, except that the phrase 'in the place of eternity' suggests what we should already have guessed: that this is no picture of daily life at all.

Counterbalancing the fowling scene we invariably find the tomb owner spearing fish with his harpoon, the motif being arranged symmetrically around the fish.

In the banquet scene, we found that the ubiquitous presence of the lotus flower was one of the main clues to the interpretation of the scene. The lotus is equally in evidence here, and in addition to the blue lotus carried or worn by the man and woman we even have the white lotus depicted in the crowded strip of riverscape below the boat. The child is engaged in pulling lotus flowers and buds directly from the river, and he/she had a lotus pendant around his/her neck in addition to the floral garland. Lotus flowers lie piled on deck. Such are the details in the now lost half of Nebamun's fishing and fowling representation, but they are similar in others.

We are obviously attempting to make sense of the imagery of regeneration once more, with all the symbols we have already discusssed. But how do the fishing and fowling belong?

The symbolic significance of fishing and fowling in the picture programme of the tombs has long been recognised as one of the stages of transformation of the deceased, immediately prior to rebirth.[16] By capturing the fish in question, the tomb owner becomes master of his own future destiny in the Hereafter. The fish in question, *Tilapia nilotica*, became a symbol of rebirth because of its habit of holding its eggs in its mouth until they hatched and later allowing the fry to seek in its mouth shelter from danger.

This to the Egyptians was a clear demonstration of the many lives of the tilapia. The fact that the fish forms the focal point of the representation, with the harpoon pointing straight at it across one half of the picture, can only be taken as an indication of the nature of the entire scene.

The presence of the child is as interesting as its absence at the banquet. So the Egyptians were perfectly capable of depicting children and adolescent boys and girls. The child and the lotus flower would be read as an unambiguous reference to the result of sexu-

Right: Upper part of an anthropomorphic coffin with a blackened face, lotus ornaments on wig and chest as well as a picture of the deceased on her knees, presenting flowers to the god Osiris. Black, the colour of the Nile mud, was a potent symbol of fertility. Late New Kingdom or Late Period.
Private collection, New York

al activities, supported by the explicit symbolism of the fish.

In a poem quoted earlier (p. 98) the girl addressed her lover 'My lotus flower' and showed off her beauty in a clinging unguent-soaked dress. We are now in a better position to appreciate the concluding lines:

> I go down into the water to be with you
> And come up to you again with a red fish,
> Looking splendid on my fingers.
> I place it before you . . .
> Come! Look at me!

The symbolism is interchangeable, and it all hangs together beautifully. Cosmetic spoons, delicately carved in dark wood or white calcite, often depict a swimming girl holding a duck. This bird has also been demonstrated to be symbolic of female sexuality, and it is present in some of the fishing and fowling scenes. The idea of the bird is thus linked with the scent that it contains. The spoons may also depict lotus flowers, or musical instruments. The figures of swimming girls would be naked, but wearing wigs. Although all the individual elements are realistic, their combinations are not, and we can only interpret the representations on a surrealistic, or metaphysical, level. The fishing and fowling scene provided the artist with yet another opportunity to express in visual terms the concept of rebirth and its preliminaries. On the threshold of eternal life scent had a crucial part to play.

It is also in the tomb of Tutankhamun and amongst its fragrant treasures that we find the final proof of a connection between scent and the life-death-rebirth cycle which is the concept behind tomb decoration and funerary equipment as a whole.

A small container of gold with inlay is shaped like two juxtaposed oval name rings. Each of the oval spaces (cartouches), four in all, shows the king in one of the four stages: child, adult, old age and child in the womb. Prior to re-birth, as an old man, the king is black. This is not a sign of mourning, but of latent fertility, just as the wet black mud from the river incorporated in it the source of regeneration. This is no doubt what this is all about. The scented oil contained in the vessels must have had a significant part to play in the transformation.

LOTUS SCENT

The scent of the lotus flower, available all over the country, was first and foremost enjoyed *au naturel*. This was not among the fragrances exported on a large scale and recorded in the works of the classical writers. The flower was too delicate to travel, and whatever preparations it was part of were obviously not accessible to our usual authorities such as Theophrastus, Galen, Dioscorides and Pliny.

A simple lotus perfume could no doubt have been prepared by macerating the flowers in oil on location, and no written recipes were required for this straightfoward operation. Lotus extract is, however, an ingredient in two preparations mentioned in the temple at Edfu. One was an ingredient in a madjet preparation, when this was included in the list of sacred oils. The other was originally prepared for the 22nd of the month of Khoiak. In view of the additional ingredients, however, this latter concoction was hardly intended for the use of the living. We are here into the traditional and magical preparations required by the dead which we shall discuss at the end of this chapter.

Lotus scent is attested in a different context, namely the ceremony of rewarding officials by the king. This event which must have been the high point of a person's career, is known in texts from the Middle Kingdom and on and in pictures of New Kingdom date. Written in year 15 of King Psammetik (c. 649 BC) a papyrus scroll records the rewarding of an official who was brought before the king to be doused in lotus oil and given his father's office of priest of Amun-Re and other gods.[17]

HESIRE'S UNGUENT CUPBOARD

From the Old Kingdom c. 2500 BC and throughout the pharaonic period unguents were an essential part of tomb equipment. Either the commodities were buried in the tomb, or a list was drawn up on the wall where, through the magic inherent in word and pictures, it would come into existence.

Representations of an abundant variety of unguents were carved on the walls of the mastaba tomb of the high official of the Third Dynasty Hesire (c. 2660 BC), although only a few have been identified so far. Depicted in colour, the unguent jars are displayed on two shelves in an open wooden cupboard. The names of the preparations are written in each compartment in large, bold hieroglyphs.

The unguents appear to be arranged according to a classification marked by headings which to some extent suggest their consistency: first quality merhet-unguents and fats of fragrance. In each case those 'of foreign origin' are grouped together and identified as such. These are followed by 'Upper' and 'Lower Egyptian' unguents respectively. Within the native categories there appears to be a further distinction between those based on trees and those derived from plants or shrubs.

Even though the precise nature of these fragrant substances remains unknown, it is nevertheless fascinating to consider that more than four thousand years ago such variety of scented materials existed and was deemed essential for survival in the Hereafter.[18]

THE SEVEN SACRED UNGUENTS

The list of these seven unguents is inscribed in tombs or on compartmented vessels intended to hold the unguents. Its history goes back to the Fifth Dynasty where the longer version from Hesire's tomb was still in use as well. The names of the seven unguents which were included on the earlier, longer list, were consistent.

By the time that we have the corpus of recipes in the Edfu temple the list of unguents, here specified as being used for the ritual of the Opening of the Mouth, comprises nine unguents. A list of ingredients used at that time is added, but with no quantities given and no further instructions.[19]

'1. Seti heb 'festival scent' (sefy bitumen, tekhu seeds, frankincense concentrate, white [frankincense], fir seeds, fresh frankincense, is flowers, him flowers)
2. Hekenu (menen wood pitch, fresh frankincense, dry white frankincense, acacia flowers)
3. Sefet 'fir oil' (wood pitch, white [frankincense], ges-fek, degem of [. . .])
4. Nesmen (menen wood pitch, pine, sefy bitumen)
5. Tua (menen wood pitch, frankincense, pine, white [frankincense])
6. Hat-en-ash 'best fir' (menen wood pitch, sefy bitumen, fir seeds, him flowers)
7. Hat-en-tjehenu 'best Libyan' (menen wood pitch, fine peresh[?] oil, him flowers)
8. Madjet (best nedjem, lotus, white [frankincense])
9. Moringa oil (menen wood pitch, white [frankincense])'

We have already come across a preparation by the name of hekenu in the 'laboratory' at Edfu, but it is an open question whether the substance described in great detail here had anything substantial to do with its namesake invented two thousand years earlier. Sefet was an oil extracted from the resin of the fir tree (*Abies cilicica*), in Egyptian called ash, the same name we meet in the penultimate item on the list. The raw material was the resin that came in the form of reddish lumps directly from the Lebanon where the trees grew. Libya, Egypt's neighbour to the west, is often mentioned in the early lists. It is possible that the country was an intermediary in the early trade in the Mediterranean.

The mother of King Cheops, Queen Hetepheres, was re-buried near the pyramid of her son. The burial was found intact, and among the exquisite funerary equipment now displayed in the Cairo museum is a wooden casket containing a set of alabaster jars, the flat, circular lids of which are inscribed with the name of the contents. Items 1, 2, 3, 6 and 7 are included in this burial along with a jar of 'black eyepaint'. The two obscure items nesmen and tua are omitted.

UNGUENTS AS FUNERARY GIFTS

The unguents are often written down as part of a list including other grave goods such as food, drink and equipment. But they are also depicted on the walls in their containers. Ideally such vases were made of stone. Hard diorite was used in the early days, or alabaster (calcite) which is much easier to work and which remained popular at all times. If not available, pottery would do, painted to imitate the harder stones. The unguents are depicted in large quantities compared to what the smaller decorative unguents vases for daily use would contain, lined up and sealed with lids, cloth and pieces of string, no doubt like those found in the tomb of Tutankhamun described above. He, too, had simple jars of 'festival scent'. 'Fir oil' and 'best Libyan' in his tomb, along with a jar of iber-scent known from other sources, and an intriguing 'fat for opening the head'.

The gifts were no doubt placed in the tomb at the burial, some expressly for use during the ceremony of the Opening of the Mouth. One such preparation was called 'That which introduces [sc. the deceased into the Hereafter] at the Opening of the Mouth'.[20] Others were depicted as being brought forward at special occasions, such as the Feast of the New Year, where the selection of fragrant matter was extended. In the tomb of User, vizier of Tuthmosis III in the Eighteenth Dynasty, a large section of a wall is dedicated to the subject of User's children bringing scents to their parents, either in jars or in linen bags. More goods, including sweet moringa oil, are stored below, all neatly labelled. The wall painting is rather damaged, but this abundance of scented material is mirrored in a contemporary tomb of Amenemhet, steward to the vizier himself, where a whole procession of relatives bring 'best Libyan', 'moringa oil', antiu unguent, madjet, fat as well as the two types of unguent called

Five ointment jars from the tomb of a princess. Obsidian, sheet gold and Egyptian alabaster. Heights with lids 8.6 - 9.7 cm. 12th Dynasty, reign of Amenemhat III, c. 1855-1808 BC. *Metropolitan Museum of Art, New York (16.1.33-38 – Purchase, Rogers Fund and Henry Walters Gift, 1916)*

werekh and merhet. The overall title of the scene runs as follows: Bringing best fir oil, best Libyan, antiu unguent, tisheps, moringa oil, werekh, nudj, from the two houses . . . For your 1000 years which your Lord Amun has decreed for you in the house of the living, while you have life, health and justification and the enjoyment of music for ever.' The 'two houses . . .' can be restored to 'the two unguent houses' mentioned in the tomb of User. They no doubt refer to depots of Upper and Lower Egypt respectively, and we are thus reminded of the classification in provenance already apparent in the tomb of Hesire.

Just prior to the New Year in the Egyptian calendar came the 'five epagomenal days', added to the year of 12 months each of 30 days to make it come closer to being astronomically correct. These five days were feast days dedicated to Osiris and his closest relatives, hence most appropriate for celebrating deceased relatives who one hoped had gained access to the kingdom of Osiris. During a special ceremony a funerary priest, or a relative taking his place, would enter the tomb at night and proceed to the niche at the innermost room. Here he would light a candle, burn incense and present a jar of madjet while he recited a short prayer asking for 'the eye of Horus' (symbolised by the unguent) to be vigilant for the deceased and illuminate his path in the Hereafter.

Archaeological finds reveal that some of these precious unguents were in actual fact left in the underground chambers of high officials. Recently the discovery of the tomb of Maya, treasurer to Tutankhamun, yielded a large number of pottery vessels, smashed by tomb robbers, but with their inscriptions and some residue intact on the inside. The analysis of the contents remains to be carried out, but the inscriptions give a pointer to what we may expect to find. Thirty jars once contained 'honey', 'sweet moringa oil' and 'fresh sesame oil', all relevant to eventual preparation of scented unguent, perhaps making use of some of the wine and water also stored in the tomb. A jar of 'fresh fat' is also relevant in this context. The unguent was intended for Maya's passage to the Hereafter, for one inscription reads, for example: 'Sweet moringa oil for the funeral procession of "Osiris", royal scribe, overseer of the treasury Maya'.

In addition to this Maya had four kinds of a preparation of the type known as merhet, one being qualified as 'southern', another intriguingly as 'for the heart'. But perhaps the most significant item was a jar containing 'four hin (2 l) best moringa oil with gum and mandrake'. In view of the part played by mandrake in representations of the preliminaries to rebirth (see above) it adds to the importance of this fruit that it was used as an ingredient in unguent, especially in a preparation that was intended to facilitate eternal life.[21]

THE PRECIOUS 22ND KHOIAK UNGUENT

This was a recipe prepared in the temple for the use on divine limbs, but possibly also for resale to private individuals.[22] Its name includes a date of completion of the process of preparing it, which always commenced on the same day of the Egyptian calendar year. Interestingly, it also contains lotus extract.

As recorded here, it was used during the mysterious rites accorded to Osiris. Like the secret Min unguent quoted in Chapter 2, with which it has much in common, its preparation was top secret knowledge, a mystery which was also 'not to be seen, not to be heard about, and which a father transmits to his son'. It concerned the ceremonies taking place during the month of Khoiak in all the temples built where parts of the dismembered body of Osiris had at one time been buried. Details of the proceedings were written down not in the 'laboratory' af Edfu, but on the enclosure wall, inside the temple where in antiquity no ordinary mortals were allowed.[23] Now, the words can be read by all those who know how.

The mystery focused on a mummiform figure, fashioned of barley, sand and incense,

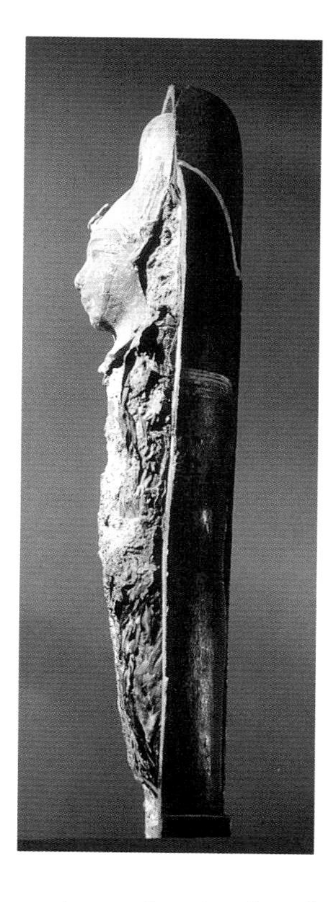
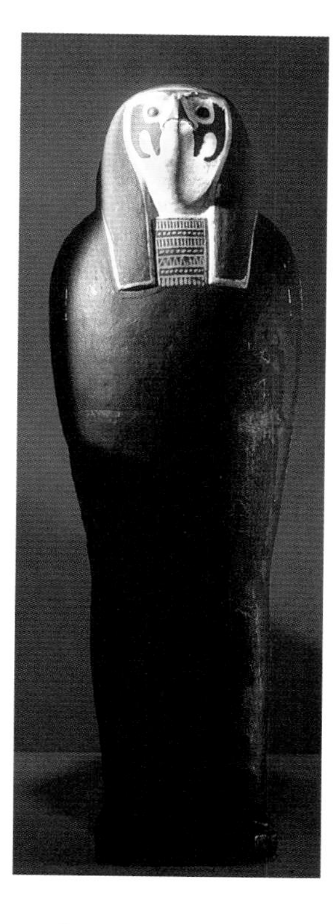

The mummiform figure fashioned from a variety of substances and placed in a mummy case representing the god Sokaris was expected to ensure a plentiful harvest. Late Period, 747-332 BC.
Private collection, New York

and another in the shape of Sokaris, made of soil, date pulp, incense, resin and aromatic substances and a small quantity of 'all minerals', mixed with water from the sacred lake. This figure was subject to certain rites, including anointing with moringa oil and incense, then concealed for a year, whereupon it was taken out and buried while a new image was fashioned. The 'sweet-scented aromatic substances' are very similar to those used for unguents: pine resin, 'sweet wood' (cinnamon?), cyperus grass (rhizomes?) from the oasis, a black wood producing a resin used for divine unguents called gaiuma, sweet flag, camel grass, juniper berries, pine kernels, mint, aspalathos and two unknown ingredients (one of which was peker, already referred to on p. 51 under kyphi). With the exception of the soil which was included in order to give a firm consistency when the figure was moulded, and the fact that the preparation was apparently not subjected to fire, it reads like a perfume recipe. The unguent, known from several sources in connection with embalming, was made as follows:[24]

1. Place in a pot for cooking 0.5 l of
   carefully ground menen and
   0.5 l of bitumen.
2. Add 0.5 l first class lotus extract,
   0.5 l first class antiu,
   0.5 l fine oil,
   0.25 l wax,[25]
   0.5 l fresh senet,
   0.5 l dry do.,
   0.5 l tisheps of nedjem,
   aromatics.
3. Mix with 0.25 l wine and 0.5 l oil.
4. Add all minerals finely ground.
5. Mix with honey.
6. Add 0.5 l dry antiu.
7. Combine and apply on the day of the
   funeral.

The mixing takes place on the 15th, cooking on 18th - 21st, and on the 22nd the unguent is removed from the fire. The recipe is a summary, and it is left to the unguent maker to judge the appropriate cooking times.

The unguent, like its Min equivalent, would be black and sticky. The essential concept of regeneration suggested by the blackness was intensified by the addition of lotus extract.

لا يشتهي الطعام او من كانت قوته تحلل وصفته على هذه الصف
يوخذ من العسل جزو فيخلطونه بالعسل ويطبخونه على الصفه الى ان يذهب

6 Fragrant Remedies

Preparation of ancient Egyptian remedies continued into the Middle Ages, as in this pharmacy depicted in an Arabic translation of *De Materia Medica* by Dioscorides. 13th century.
Metropolitan Museum of Art, New York

As in most civilisations the Egyptian pharmacopoeia was very largely based on plants. As plant material is always scented the remedy would naturally possess qualities which through its aroma alone might have been considered as having a therapeutical effect. That aspect of medicinal treatment was recognized by ancient Egyptians, as evidenced by the corpus of their medical texts, written on papyrus, dating mainly from the New Kingdom.

The earliest prescriptions of Middle Kingdom date (ca. 1820 BC) are for veterinary use, but important scrolls are dedicated to the care of human beings. Fragments of papyrus found in the mortuary temple of Ramesses II at Thebes, the Ramesseum, date from the so-called Hyksos period around 1700 BC. Papyrus Hearst and Papyrus Ebers, the former nowadays in California, the latter kept in Leipzig, were both written down around 1500 BC by the beginning of the Eighteenth Dynasty, whereas Papyrus Edwin Smith, now in the New York Academy of Medicine, is about half a century younger. The Berlin papyrus no. 3038 dates from the beginning of the Nineteenth Dynasty c. 1200 BC. Many of the remedies no doubt have more ancient roots, and in fact some are specifically reported to have been tried and tested in the past.[1]

These scrolls were for the benefit of the medical profession, that is to say the wise men of the temples, the priests who were skilled in treating the mind and body of the people, and those who were able to consult the scrolls in the temple archives where they were kept. One may imagine that people in the villages would have known their own cures, such as had been passed down through generations by word of mouth. We only have to go back a century or so to find a sophisticated tradition of herbal medicine in use in and around Cairo, preserved for posterity through the efforts of the French inspector of pharmacies in the area.[2] Even today herbalism is thriving in Egypt, as evidenced by the continued use of tiryac, referred to earlier (p. 59).

In antiquity as well as nowadays remedies were administered in a variety of ways. They were taken, or applied as bandages and poultices. They were massaged into the skin, or given by means of fumigation or inhalation. For our purposes we shall concentrate on those applications where the fragrance of the remedy was of paramount importance, the field which is today known as aromatherapy: treatment by scent. The meaning of the word itself is clear, but its ramifications are less precise. In modern terms, any treatment involving the use of essential oil would be classified as aromatherapy, from massage to breathing the scent of oil on a ring placed above an electric bulb or in a receptacle above a naked flame. But it also includes medicinal use of herbal teas or facial steam baths prepared with untreated herbs (fresh or dried).

Most plants in their natural state would be scented. Whether or not the odour was pleasant or repulsive is a matter of convention and personal preference. Yet herbs used for culinary purposes only do not strictly speaking fall into the field in question, and all herbal preparations, even with a medicinal scope, are not necessarily considered as being of use in *aroma*therapy.

In order to define the area as far as ancient

Egypt is concerned we shall here loosely classify aromatherapeutic remedies as substances applied as treatment where the scent of the remedy is emphasised by its being used in massage and other external applications, by being inhaled, or similar, and in particular such substances which are endowed with a pronounced scent. However, the qualities of the remedy and its odour may not always be appreciated by the patient's nose, but may take effect through the skin.

The Egyptian physicians were well aware of the penetrating properties of their scented remedies. For example, acacia leaves steeped in oil were applied as a poultice to stop haemorrhage in the region of the heart, and it is characteristic for both the Egyptian and the classical tradition that illnesses involving the mind were treated with *scented* herbal remedies. The invisible fragrance mysteriously permeated the shell of the body and affected the inner hidden parts.

In addition to the ancient Egyptian sources we may also turn once more to Dioscorides to examine how fragrant oils were used in treatment in his day, the 1st century AD, and we shall concentrate in particular on oils based on the ingredients which we have come across in Chapter 4. He specifically states that some ointments are also beneficial in treating diseases (i.e. in addition to being appreciated for their scent), either by being mixed with other medicines, or by being 'dropped, or poured on, or smelt unto', and he advises those who test the ointments to check whether the substance really smells of that of which it is supposed to be made.[3]

It is remarkable how many of the scented oils first discussed under the heading of luxury perfumes we find again here, used to treat ailments in the area of the vulva, that is afflictions which concern women in particular.

Theophrastus, Pliny and Galen, too, provided useful information on aromatics in treatment. Theophrastus says that 'it is to be expected that perfumes should have medicinal properties in view of the virtues of spices: for these too have such virtues. The effects of plasters and of what some call "poultices" prove what virtues they display, since they disperse tumours and abscesses and produce a distinct effect on various other parts of the body, on its surface, but also on the interior parts: for instance, if one lays a plaster on his abdomen and chest, the patient forthwith produces fragrant odours along with belching'.[4]

Aromatic Oils

Oil was the most obvious medium for capturing and administering a fragrance medicinally, but other options were available as we shall see later. The oils are here arranged alphabetically, with reference to their method of preparation if already quoted earlier.

ACACIA OIL

The acacia tree grew abundantly in Egypt, and all parts of the tree found use in medicine. According to sources from c. 1500 BC acacia oil was prepared by pounding the leaves in a mortar and mixing them with oil. The resulting scented oil, presumably relieved of the spent leaves, was used to treat a wound and help it heal. A solid version of this preparation could be made by using fat instead of oil.[5] As heat must have been used to enable the fat to absorb the fragrance, this may have been used in the case of oil as well, and the technique is that now known as maceration.

As mentioned above acacia oil was used for treating a condition described as 'blood having been taken to the heart and spread'. In this case the oil was heated to finger warmth and used as a bandage, presumably on the chest.[6] This is an excellent example which goes to show that the Egyptians understood the penetrating qualities of aromatic oils. The scent did not pass by the nose, but was diffused through the pores of the skin.

The Copts, the Christian Egyptians whose traditions and language were directly derived from the ancient Egyptians, knew of an aca-

Alabaster jar engraved with floral motifs and cartouches of King Horemheb's name. Its base has been lost. Height 38 cm, 19th Dynasty, 14th century BC. *Hermitage, St. Petersburg*

cia concentrate, known as *akakia* (see below). In the Ninth century AD akakia mixed with oil was used to treat the uterus. It was applied internally by means of a tampon.[7]

BASIL OIL

As far as our sources go, basil was not much used in ancient perfumery. But the herb was known in Egypt, for a sprig of basil was found during the excavation of a rubbish dump in the city of Memphis in a context dating it to the Late Period or the days of the Ptolemies. Essential oil of basil is produced in Egypt today, and the herb grows as an ornamental plant in gardens all over the country. The ancient Egyptian name for this useful herb has not yet been identified.

Dioscorides knew of its use in medicine, and he quotes a recipe for making basil oil:

> 'Take 9.08 kg of oil and 5.218 kg basil leaves. Leave to macerate for a night and a day, then press out the oil through a basket and keep aside. The same leaves and another 9.08 kg of oil can be used for a second maceration. Then take another quantity of basil leaves and leave to macerate in the first oil, etc. This may be repeated with fresh basil up to four times. Basil is used for the same, that is to say female, ailments as sampsuchinon [sweet marjoram], but to lesser effect.'[8]

In modern aromatherapy basil oil is employed for similar purposes, such as regulating menstruation. It is also used for treating depression and anxiety.

CELERY OIL

Wild celery is well established for ancient Egypt, for leaves of the plant (*Apium graveolens* L.) have been found in mummy garlands of Twentieth Dynasty date. The plant is endowed with a powerful scent. Dioscorides claimed that the Egyptians called the plant *mith*,[9] and this term has been traced back to the hieroglyphic *matet* which occurs in the medical texts of around 1550 BC. Celery ground in oil (or fat) was recommended for anointing swollen limbs.[10]

CAMOMILE OIL

Oil of camomile was relatively unknown for ancient Egypt until 1976 when the mummy of King Ramesses II travelled to be displayed in Paris. For that occasion permission had been granted to take four tiny samples of the skin tissue for pollen analysis. This proved a most rewarding exercise, and it added a number of new plants to the ancient flora. A great many specimens in minute quantities appeared to be linked with rather a large proportion of a member of the genus umbelliferae, probably either *Matricaria* or *Anthemis* spp. Scientific interpretation of the data suggested that the body and abdominal cavity of the king had been anointed with a substance that was probably camomile oil, and that the camomile in question had grown in a field full of weeds (which accounted for the rest of the pollen in the samples), a field which was at some distance from the water, for no pollen of riverine plants was found.[11]

Camomile oil ('melanthelaion') is mentioned by Dioscorides, who says that it has the same properties as radish oil, given that 'it is good for such which by some sickness have got the phthiriasis, and it cleanses away the scabritias about the face'.[12] He does not provide an Egyptian name for *anthemis*, and none of the species has as yet been identified in the medical papyri. Dyer's camomile (*Anthemis tinctoria* L.) has a faint aromatic scent (described as 'foetid' by some) and may in modern herbal medicine be used to treat blisters and piles. The fact that it is insect repellent may perhaps also account for its possible use in mummification.

In modern aromatherapy oil of common camomile (*Anthemis nobilis* L.) is used among several other things for treating skin ailments and by massage for relieving rheumatic pain.

CINNAMON OIL

The existence of cinnamon in ancient Egypt and the preparation of the oil has been dealt with in Chapter 1. Dioscorides says that cinnamon oil has a sharp, warming and bitter faculty. It is good for female ailments, in this case preferably mixed with twice as much oil, as well as wax and marrow to make it less sharp and more mollifying. To treat scorpion bites it is applied with bruised green figs.[13] In modern aromatherapy some of these properties are recognized: cinnamon oil raises the body temperature, stimulates the circulation of the blood and nervous system, counteracting fatigue and depression; it is effective as an antibacterial. When taken orally it is used as a laxative.

In the pharaonic medical texts the ingredient tisheps, in this context generally taken to mean cinnamon, occurs several times in external applications. In a poultice to soothe the members sweet moringa oil was mixed with equal parts of ox fat, *tisheps*, dry myrrh and *kohl*.[14]

We should mention here that during the process of mummification after the body had been rubbed with juniper oil, cinnamon was applied along with myrrh and other substances. Herodotus merely says that the abdominal cavity is filled with 'cassia and any other spices', the body having previously been rinsed with palm wine and 'bruised-spices'.[15] Diodorus, on the other hand, says that after cleaning the abdominal cavity with palm wine and spices, the embalmers spend over thirty days treating the body first with *kedria* (juniper oil) and 'certain other preparations', then with 'myrrh, cinnamon and such spices as have the faculty not only of preserving it for a long time but also of giving it a fragrant odour.'[16]

Although it is nowhere suggested that actual cinnamon oil (or cassia oil) was used, the combination of oil and spices in the same area of the body, applied more or less at the same time, would have produced a similar effect. A faint smell of cinnamon or cassia has been detected during the unwrapping of mummies in the previous century.

CUMIN OIL

The use of cumin is well attested for ancient Egypt, both in the literature (called *tepenen*) and in archaeological finds. In fact, the plant is said to be indigenous to Upper Egypt. Pliny claimed that some consider Egyptian 'country cumin', grown near Thebes, to be the best of all.[17]

An alabaster jar found in the tomb of Ramose and Hatnofer, parents of Senenmut, architect of Queen Hatshepsut. It still contains remains of the animal fat that was stored in it. Height 25.5 cm. 18th Dynasty, c.1473-1458 BC. *Metropolitan Museum of Art, New York (36.3.82 – Rogers Fund, 1936)*

At the present day it is a significant ingredient in the perfume industry, the essential oil, however, being far less agreeable than the seeds. For pharaonic Egypt it is mentioned numerous times for various remedies, mostly to be taken. But an ear lotion consisted of moringa oil, 'best unguent', a plant known as 'donkey's ear', red ochre and cumin in equal parts.[18]

Cumin was also an ingredient in an oil used to treat headache which was based on moringa oil and included *antiu* resin, lotus flowers, juniper berries and two unidentified ingredients,[19] and 'heat in the anus' was treated by a suppository of cumin in antelope fat.[20]

DILL OIL

The ancient Egyptian designation for dill has been identified as *imset*, though Dioscorides maintained that the Egyptians called the plant *arakhou*.[21] Actual leaves and flowers of dill have been found on the mummy of Amenhotep II, so there is firm evidence for its presence in the country.

In medical texts dating to ca. 1500 BC dill is an ingredient in a pain killing mixture based on wine with a small quantity of raisins and dates. The concoction is boiled and strained and taken for four days.[22] The alleged pain killing properties are reflected in an unguent of donkey fat with dill seeds and other herbs which was used to alleviate headache.[23] A pain in the vessels of the neck was treated with a poultice of dill, honey and another herb mixed with 'water from the laundryman'.[24] Today dill is used as a stimulant and to treat digestive problems in children.

Dioscorides sets out how to prepare dill oil:

> Macerate 5.218 kg dill flowers in 3.884 kg oil for one day. Squeeze it out with your hands and set aside. Repeat with fresh dill flowers in the same oil if required. Dill oil mollifies the female parts and opens them. It is useful for period pains; it is warming and dissolves lassitude and it is beneficial for pains in the joints.[25]

Dioscorides does not specify the mode of application which was perhaps external, such as massage or a poultice. It is interesting that he, too, prescribes a dill remedy as a pain killer. Modern science has not confirmed such alleged properties of the herb.

FENUGREEK OIL
Trigonella foenum-graecum L.

This plant was once used to scent inferior hay to make it attractive to animals, its odour being reminiscent of lovage or celery ('fenugreek' actually means 'Greek hay'). Ground seeds are an ingredient in various veterinary preparations. The seeds are still used in Egyptian folk medicine; they are soaked in water, sprouted and taken to treat fevers and stomach ailments; they are an excellent salad herb, also used to flavour alcohol with its distinctive scent, for ointments and plasters.

According to Dioscorides, the Egyptians called the plant *itasin*.[26] In the medical texts the word *hemayt* is taken to mean fenugreek. It was the sole ingredient in an oil prepared by boiling the ground seeds in water that allegedly transformed an old man into a young man. When the skin was rubbed with it, it was left 'beautiful without any blemishes. It is a million times efficient'.[27]

FIR OIL

Identified with *sefet* of the ancient Egyptian texts, this was a commodity that had to be imported, either as timber or resin, or as the finished product, from the lands along the eastern Mediterranean, especially northern Syria and Asia Minor where the trees, *Abies cilicica,* called *ash* in Egyptian, still grow.

Fir oil, prepared from the resin mixed with another fatty substance was recommended as a means to promote hair growth by massaging the scalp.[28]

HENNA OIL

The preparation is described on p. 72. Henna oil, according to Dioscorides, is warming and mollifying, opens the vessels and is useful in treating ailments in the female parts, for the nerves, and for fractures. It is also added to mollifying medicines, and remedies against weariness.[29] The fruit is nowadays thought to provoke menstruation.

IRIS OIL

For the preparation see p. 71. Iris oil is warming and mollifying, says Dioscorides, and he adds that it is used to open the vulva and treat inflammations in that area. It may also succesfully treat haemorrhoids. For polyps in the nose and swollen sinuses it is useful to anoint the nostrils with iris oil. Patients suffering from angina will benefit from being anointed with it.[30] Theophrastus called it astringent, recommending it as a laxative: by closing the passage to the bladder, he says, it forces the liquid to collect in the bowels.[31]

The part of the plant most frequently used today is the rhizome (orris root) the properties of which are exploited by the perfume industry. But it has medicinal value as well, being used, among other things, as a diuretic, which links it with the ancient prescription.

Dill was credited with the property to relieve pain, and Dioscorides endorsed the claim in his famous work. This illustration of dill appears in a manuscript of the Arabic translation of *De Materia Medica*. 11th century. *Universiteitsbibliothek, Leiden*

JUNIPER OIL

In modern aromatherapy, juniper oil (from *Juniperus communis* L.) is prescribed as an antiseptic, stimulant, diuretic among other things.

Juniper is frequently quoted in the ancient Egyptian medical papyri, both for internal and external application. A mixture of equal parts of juniper and 'white oil' is used to treat tapeworm. The patient is to take it just for one day.[32] For a juniper ointment based on goosefat for headache, see below.

Dioscorides includes a paragraph on juniper with reference to a juniper oil prepared from the resin (kedria), which is used in veterinary medicine for scabs and ulcers.[33]

It is, however, for anointing the dead that juniper oil was most in demand. Dioscorides says that *kedria* 'has the power of corrupting living bodies and is a preservative of the dead ones, whence some have called it "the life of him that is dead".' The general consensus is now that the substance referred to in the literature in connection with mummification was juniper oil, not cedar oil. In any case it would have been an ordinary base oil, perfumed with the conifer, rather than the essential oil, which was not available in those days (see ref. to Diodorus on p. 116).

In 16th century Egypt Prospero Alpini was told of juniper oil being used for massaging the body before an attack of fever. When the patient perspires, he is covered to maximise the effect of the scented oil.[34]

LILY OIL

The method of preparation is given on p. 68. According to Dioscorides, lily oil is warming, mollifying and opening, it is good for opening the vulva and for inflammations in that area, in brief, it is the most beneficent remedy for female ailments.[35] Oil of lilies (*Lilium candidum* L.) have in the past been used as a painkiller. Such oil was produced by maceration or similar, since no fragrant essential oil can be derived from the flowers. It is the odourless bulb only that is used in modern herbal medicine.

Pliny claimed that lily boiled with oil makes hair grow on burns.[36] It is interesting that Gerard, the English herbalist whose work was first published in 1597, recommended

Unguent chest containing alabaster jars and a mirror. The picture on the ivory front panel shows the owner, who was responsible for the king's breakfast, offering two ointment jars to the statue of the deified king. Cedarwood with ebony and ivory veneer and silver mountings. 12th Dynasty, reign of Amenemhat IV, c. 1808-1799 BC. *Metropolitan Museum of Art, New York (26.7.1438 – Purchase, Edward S. Harkness Gift, 1926)*

lily bulb ground in honey, mixed with oil or grease, for the very same condition.

LOTUS OIL

Tangible evidence for lotus oil is slim, though it must have been very common along the banks of the river Nile, so much so perhaps that its existence was taken for granted. It was used in perfumery and in funerary unguents (see p. 106). In the medical texts it occurs but once in a remedy to cause hair to fall out: 'Lotus leaves, boiled and steeped in oil or fat. To be placed on the head of a detested woman'.[37] This is a most peculiar prescription, and one wonders if it was not meant as a joke, not because of its purpose and the circumstances, but because of the erotic significance of both the lotus and hair in Egyptian civilisation. To make use of the flower of regeneration *par excellence* as a means of depriving someone of one of the manifestations of their sexual power seems contradictory, and the proximity of the very flower on or near the hair in tomb paintings and reliefs would in itself be too dangerous if the lotus had these alleged properties.

In Egypt in the 16th century AD lotus oil was used in treatment to reduce fever. The patient was left in a warm room to bring about perspiration, after which he was anointed with the oil and immersed in a lukewarm bath and towelled off. After a good rest and sleep he would be served a light meal. In those days lotus oil was generally considered cooling.[38]

MANDRAKE OIL

This particular commodity would have gone unnoticed, were it not for the recent discovery in the late 18th Dynasty tomb of Maya, treasurer of Tutankhamun (see p. 110). In spite of its 'apple-like' scent, mandrake fruit is not known to have been used in perfumery anywhere, and we must take it that the plant was chosen because of its rather different qualities and connotations. In traditional herbal medicine, the leaves of mandrake, though of a 'foetid' odour, are used externally in ointments for their cooling qualities. The root, however, infused in wine or water, was used as a painkiller and soporific, an anaesthetic and to treat diseases of the mind. Even the fruits were formerly believed to be able to induce sleep and are still claimed to have narcotic properties. The mandrake oil from the tomb of Maya may have been used for any of these purposes. Considering that it was part of funerary equipment, provided to ease the resurrection of the deceased, the latter possibility is significant.

MARJORAM OIL

For the preparation of the two kinds of marjoram oil see p. 83. Dioscorides provides ample information on the medicinal uses of both.[39]

Amarakinon. This is warming, soporiferous, mollifying, heating, and diuretical. It is good for anointing haemorrhoids and for inflammations and similar in that region. It induces menstruation by being applied to the vulva, and in the form of a woollen poultice it is beneficial for aching muscles and sinews.

Sampsuchinon. This is warming, with extenuating, sharp faculty. It is good for treating various conditions of the vulva. It soothes pains in the loins and female parts. It is best to use it when mixed with honey, since otherwise it will harden the area. It is used as a poultice for convulsions.

Modern aromatherapists use marjoram oil as a general sedative, and, in agreement with Dioscorides, marjoram is used to provoke menstruation. Until this 'herb of Sobek' is identified in Egyptian medical texts we shall remain ignorant of its use in pharaonic times.

MEGALEION

Amongst the compounded perfumes Theophrastus reports that Megaleion (made of balanos oil with burnt resin, myrrh, cassia and

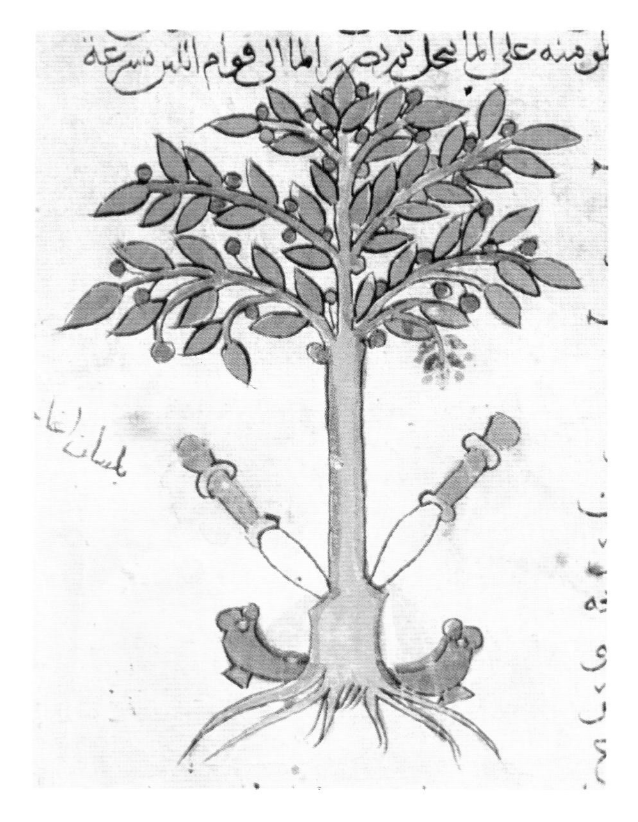

Balsam tree depicted in the Arabic translation of Dioscorides's *De materia medica.* Balsamum seed was an ingredient of Metopion, the scent with medicinal properties. *Universiteitsbibliothek, Leiden*

cinnamon, cf. p. 76) is believed to relieve inflammation caused by any wound.[40]

THE MENDESIAN

This perfume, consisting of balanos oil with myrrh, cassia and resin (see p. 65) had the same use in medicine, according to Dioscorides, as Metopion (see below), but to a lesser degree.[41]

METOPION

The only other specifically named compounded perfume to be used medicinally was Metopion (made from oil of bitter almond or green olives, camel grass, sweet flag, galbanum, balsamum seed, resin myrrh, honey and wine, cf. p. 66). It was considered heating and able to 'open' the vessels, especially those of the vulva, and drawing and purging ulcers.

It was used for treating injured sinews and muscles and stiff limbs, being generally a mollifying remedy. It also provoked perspiration.[42]

MYRTLE OIL

For the method of preparation, see p. 78. Dioscorides says that it was considered binding and hardening and good for all things that have need of binding or thickening.[43]

Myrtle leaves have been found in Egypt, and it has been suggested that the herb is identical with *khet-des* of the medical texts, which occurs abundantly, though in connection with oil or fat for external application only as a hair remedy made of a red mineral, kohl, gazelle dung and hippopotamus fat.[44]

In Coptic medicine essential oil of myrtle with fresh rue and a mineral was used to treat skin ailments.[45] The herb is nowadays used as an astringent and antiseptic, and has in the past been used internally for psoriasis and sinusitis.

PINE OIL

The Aleppo pine grows, as its name suggests, in North Syria and Asia Minor. It yields a resin from which an oil can be extracted. Resin, probably from the Aleppo pine, has been found in an ancient Egyptian (though undated) context, and the suggestion has been made to identify the word *ked*, one of the ingredients in kyphi, with this tree. If pine was a regular ingredient in Egyptian pharmacopoiea it should be sought in the older medical texts under a more ancient designation.

Pine needle oil is now used as an antiseptic, antirheumatic and revitalising remedy.

ROSE OIL

For a method of preparation, see p. 79. Apart from it being mixed into other remedies to be taken, Dioscorides recommends rose oil as a lotion for headache and a 'collution' in the beginning of toothache. It is also a good ointment for eye-lids that have grown hard.[46]

Pliny, too, quotes rose oil in ointments for headache, mixed with either heliotrope, thyme, chicory juice and vinegar, or aloe and vinegar. Prepared with alkanet or aspalathos or camel grass it is useful for complaints of the uterus and dysentery.[47] Theophrastus recommended rose oil for the ears because of the salt that it contains: salt is drying and warming. The salt will also be helpful in treating strangury while the rose scent supplies the stimulus.[48]

In modern aromatherapy rose oil is used to treat the nervous system and skin problems.

RUE OIL

The occurrence of this in Ancient Egypt is possible, but can only be inferred from a passage in Alpini's work on 16th century AD practices.[49] The Egyptians in those days used rue oil for massaging patients with a temperature 'like the ancients did'. We do not know from which source Alpini drew his information, though it was probably one of the classical authors who quote the plant repeatedly, rather than an ancient Egyptian one. Rue oil may nowadays be used in perfumery among other things.

SAGE OIL

Concrete evidence for sage in Ancient Egypt rests solely with the minute samples of the pollen found in the tissue of the mummy of Ramesses II. Yet as sage was a prominent ingredient in the perfume industry of Pylos at the very same time, it is more than likely that sage oil was contained in some of the Mycenean stirrup jars which have been found on Egyptian soil. Considering the medicinal properties of sage, and the fact that other imported compounded oils such as Metopion and Megaleion were also used medicinally, it is quite possible that sage oil was found to be a useful remedy in Egypt. But as long as its name remains unidentified in the ancient texts, we must remain ignorant. Dioscorides had been told that the herb was called *apousi* in Egyptian.[50] The plant in question was clary sage. Its oil, known as Muscatel oil, is much in demand in herbal medicine to treat vomiting and in the perfume industry.

Solid Perfume

Some of the scents suspended in fat were used in treatment as well as for pleasure. In the days of the New Kingdom the greasy substance was applied either by massaging it into the skin, or by fixing it to the area in question as a bandage or poultice, or even introducing it into an orifice of the body.

To 'cool the vessels and make firm what is weak' fresh acacia leaves, sawdust of fir and ox fat were ground together and used as a bandage for four days.[51] Acacia leaves boiled in ox fat constituted a toe remedy.[52] General stiffness was treated by bandaging the limb with a mixture of myrtle, beans, frankincense and ox fat.[53] If a patient suffered from headache, his head was to be anointed with a mixture of frankincense, cumin, juniper berries and goose fat in equal parts boiled together,[54] no doubt a refreshing and stimulating remedy. To alleviate heat in the anus a suppository was made of cumin and antelope fat.[55]

Some two thousand years later the Copts continued the tradition of using scented fat medicinally. The herb in question was purslane, which was known to their ancestors, though not at that time used in medicine. 'Anything swollen' could be treated with purslane ground in pork fat;[56] the same remedy was useful for inflamed breasts,[57] and it could even be used as an eye ointment.[58] This latter is interesting, for in modern herbal medicine purslane is used to treat inflamed eyes.

Other Herbal Remedies

It is possible to suspend herbs in other matter apart from oil and fat, just as we nowadays

Linked wooden ointment containers individually inscribed: 'Excellent kohl', 'Opens vision' (eye solution), 'Repels blood' (checks bleeding), 'Repels ... (illegible). Height 5.5 cm. 18th Dynasty, c. 1570 – 1293 BC. *Presented by J. F. Champollion to the Musée du Louvre, Paris*

may use herbal teas, either to be taken or applied to the skin. In the New Kingdom celery pounded in cold water was placed on the temples of the patient to make him get well soon.[59]

The Copts had a useful remedy known as akakia: It was made by steeping acacia leaves in water and placing the pot in the oven until it boiled. Then it was brought into the sun and stirred. This concentrate was used as an ingredient in a remedy for eye complaints.[60] In more recent times, about a hundred years ago, akakia was pressed from the seeds and pods of acacia and reduced by boiling. The resulting syrup was a common remedy in Egyptian folk medicine to treat diarrhoea among other things. Gum and water was used for bandaging broken bones, with the addition of acacia leaves or a blend of acacia, willow and sycamore leaves and emmer grains.[61] In both cases the treatment lasted for four days, the usual span of time suggested in ancient Egyptian prescriptions.

Honey mixed with acacia and ziziphus leaves and ochre was applied as a poultice to swollen legs.[62] Fermented honey with the addition of ground coriander seeds, dry antiu resin and dregs was used to treat herpes.[63] We have not previously met coriander in the scented recipes. The plant was known in ancient Egypt, for a small quantity of seeds was found in the burial of Tutankhamun. In the 12th century BC coriander was used as an oil astringent at Mycene, and it was a commodity that was among offerings to the god.

Fermented plant juice is one of the more peculiar ingredients in pharaonic remedies. It was used either for its own properties, or as a medium for other ingredients, such as myrtle, which was ground with it to treat a urinary disorder in a man, applied to the male member.[64] Mixture of fir chips with the juice was reputed to be effective in treating a swelling in any part of the body.[65] On the other hand, fir resin mixed with salt and dissolved in beer dregs was prescribed as a remedy to soften stiff limbs.[66] As far as we can tell, the Egyptians did not use vinegar in this context. But the Romans did, and Pliny quotes a few examples with basil for fainting (cf. rose and myrtle); with rose flowers and water for menstrual discharges; with rue, thyme or bay applied to the temples for phrenitis; or with lily flowers applied to wounds.[67]

Two more unusual materials for binding the herbs were in use in ancient Egypt. Fruit paste was one of them, and we have already seen how this was used in kyphi. A mixture of fresh dates, date kernels, dry myrrh and wax was beneficial for a swelling if used as a bandage for four days.[68] Porridge was equally useful. Barley flour, emmer flour, honey and myrtle was applied as a bandage to treat pain especially in the abdomen.[69] A remedy 'to remove mucus when you suffer from it on the right or left side of the chest' was similarly composed of myrtle and porridge.[70]

Among the remedies to be taken was a palatable mixture of sweet beer, honey and acacia leaves for cough,[71] and beer mixed with coriander, peas and an unidentified ingredient to treat suffering inflicted by a demon. This was to be taken before sleep.[72]

Fumigation and Inhalation

When used in fumigation the herbs truly came into their own, and it was the scent above all that was important.

The fumes could be administered over an open fire in the manner of incense, or, if intended for inhaling, could also be given through a straw stuck into a pot placed on the fire. One of the most ancient medical texts, dating from the Middle Kingdom, recommends fumigation with incense and fresh oil and with the shanks of a bird in the area of the vagina. The symptoms of the disease thus treated were disturbed vision and neck pain, but the section of the papyrus deals with gynaecology. The fumigation was followed by the consumption of fresh ass liver, a treatment with vitamin A which would not be out of order for disturbed vision. The fumigation with scented matter was here probably of therapeutical significance. A prolapsed uterus might be treated with fumigation of dry excrement and frankincense, or with the fumigation of a figure of an ibis made of wax.

Evidently the primitive use of scented matter dispensed by means of heat and smoke ('profumo') was essential when concerned with the mental state of the individual, both in treatment as a patient and in a magico-religious situation a as a means of communication betwen the various spheres, such as the earthly and the divine on the one hand, and earthly and the Hereafter on the other. The best example of this is the extensive use of kyphi (cf. Chapter 3) in a domestic context and in the sacred tradition as handed down through the classical writers.

In the aftermath of pharaonic civilisation fumes of boiled cumin were believed to heal a 'fixed' uterus.[73] Inhaling fumes of Egyptian anise was mentioned by Pliny.[74] One of the usually terse prescriptions is slightly more elaborate when it comes to describing fumigating with myrtle: The man is to be fumigated with it; quench (the fumes) with sweet-beer so that he begins to perspire. Massage him with your hand.[75]

It sounds like the rudimentary instructions to a rather sophisticated treatment. It is interesting that myrtle was used in fumigation in Assyrian medicine.[76]

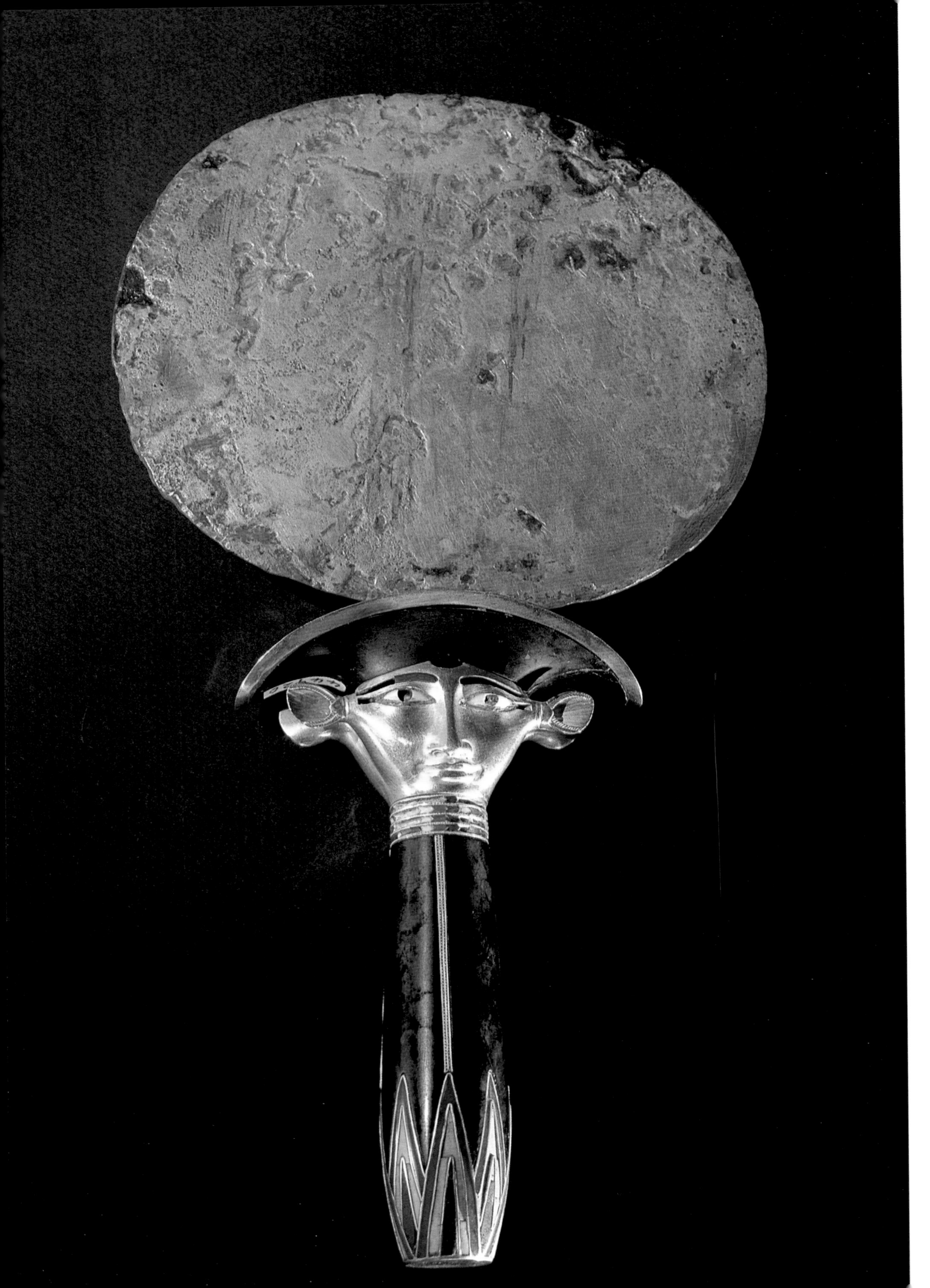

Left: Silver mirror of princess Sathathor-yunet, with a handle in the usual form of a papyrus stem and the double-sided face of cow-goddess Hathor. Silver, gold, electrum, obsidian, stone, and faience. Height 28 cm, 12th Dynasty, 1842–1798 BC. *Egyptian Museum, Cairo*

7 The Art of Cosmetics

Right Votive cosmetic palette of King Narmer, commemorating his success in war. Greywacke, height 63 cm, Early Dynastic Period, c. 3100 BC. *Egyptian Museum, Cairo*

At the dawn of civilisation in Ancient Egypt sometime before 3000 BC, when remains of cosmetic paraphernalia are conspicuous, the very beginning of Egyptian-ness is nowhere more clearly demonstrated than in one such object. The earliest masterpiece in Egyptian art, with a fully developed canon of representation, setting the standard for the next three millennia, is the so-called ceremonial cosmetic palette of King Narmer.

It appears to be the last one in a series of large palettes, up to some 60 cm in height, with sculpted decoration on both sides. The 'recto' has a cavity to hold the substance that was the initial raison d'être for the palette. No doubt the cosmetics placed in the hollow were intended for use in the region of the eye, for such was indeed the earliest recorded item of body paint to be found in Egypt. Numerous finds of less ornate examples than the royal palette, as well as various eye paint containers and grinding stones, testify to the use of eye paint at this early date. However, although we are accustomed to using the word 'ceremonial palette' for the large ornamental specimens, there is no indication of the nature of the ceremony in which they played a part, except for the fact that it must have involved the ruler depicted on the object and that, in the case of the Narmer palette, the setting was the temple, for it was in the temple of the ancient city of Hierakonpolis that the object was actually discovered.

In primitive societies cosmetics have a ritual function, traces of which are reflected even in modern times. The application of face paint and the desire to improve one's appearance and project particular aspects of

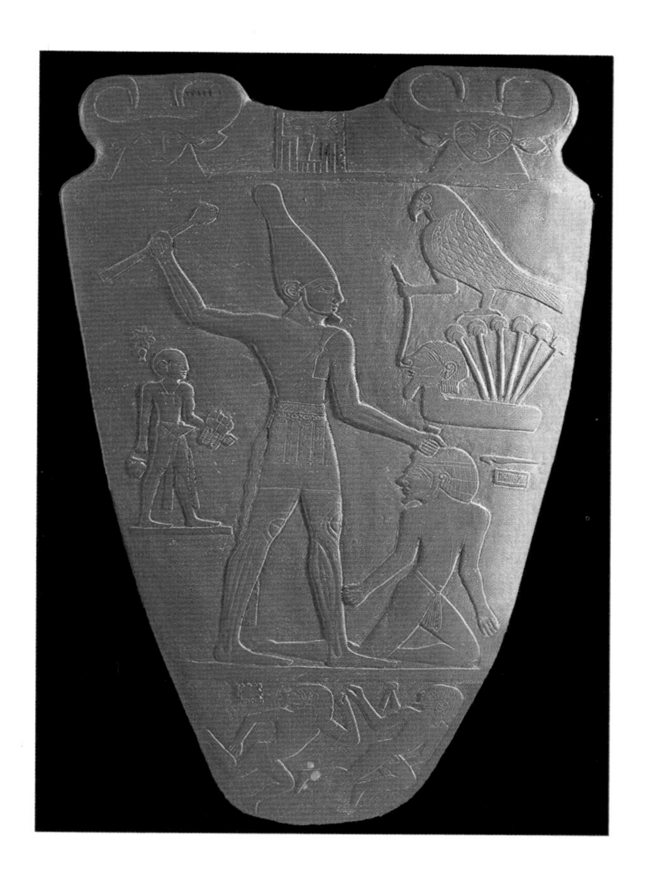

one's personality is basically of a sexual nature. In ancient times the continuation of the species was the ultimate purpose of life, and as in the animal world, humans would emphasise their sex and their sexuality in their behaviour (of which we are rather ignorant) as well as in their appearance (where we are much better informed).

It is the irony of fate that, in spite of more recent approaches to the interpretation of the archaeological remains of town sites, most of our information on the life of the Egyptians derives from objects or monuments prepared

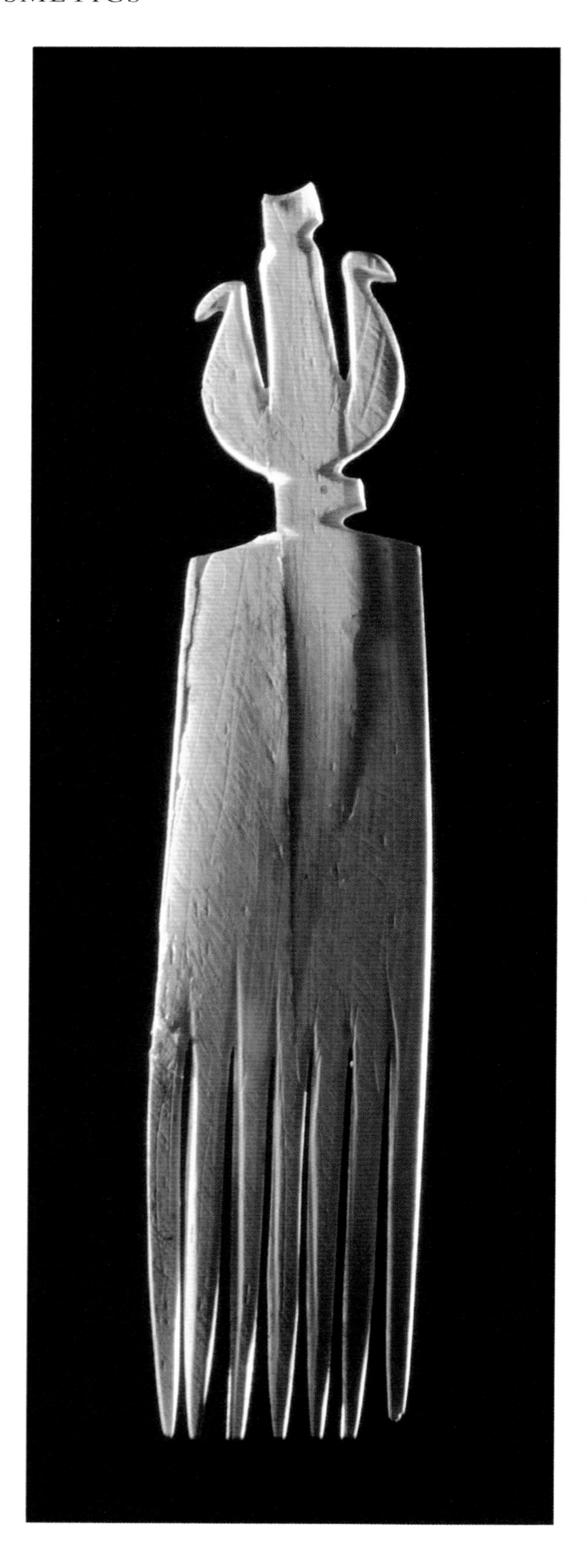

Bone comb with double birds, Height 12.8 cm. Predynastic, c. 3100 BC. *Ashmolean Museum, Oxford (1895.937)*

in connection with their death. In order to understand the life of the Egyptians we have to approach them through their funerary beliefs - which in turn reflect their attitude to life itself.

When we study the texts, pictures and objects which relate to the crucial question of life after death it becomes clear that in historical times the focal point was the process of mummification, purification of body and soul and the eventual rebirth for life in the Hereafter. It is only when we consider the act of regeneration in terms of a replica of birth before life on earth that the combined intentions of funerary equipment and tomb decoration make sense. It is in this context that we must interpret the presence of cosmetic objects among early grave goods as well as representations of them in the sophisticated scenes in tomb chapels of later date.

In a funerary setting cosmetics thus emphasise the sexuality of the deceased in order to enable him or her to undergo the vital process of rebirth in the same manner as the same cosmetics, as well as the perfumed preparations dealt with in the previous chapters, in real life underlined the sexuality of the person in the eyes of the opposite sex. On earth, the end result was intended to be conception and procreation. On the threshold of life in the Hereafter, it concerned the individual's own regeneration and rebirth, enabling him and her to take part in the blissful existence of the gods.

THE IMPORTANCE OF HAIR

On the fringe of the cosmetic arts, though an exponent of its sexual implications, is the question of body hair and the way in which this asset was treated. In most so-called primitive civilisations hair is seen as a symbol of sexuality. Even today, any interference with its natural or conventional appearance touches profound layers of our consciousness. The long-haired lads of the 1960s and the female skinheads of the 1980s would in the views of

Cosmetic palette in the form of a ram. Palettes were used to grind the pigments for eye makeup. Later they were adopted also for ritual purposes. Schist. Predynastic Period, c. 3100 BC. Height 13.4 cm. *Ashmolean Museum, Oxford (1895.855)*

the majority of people be unacceptable, or at least deeply disturbing.

The Egyptians went to extremes in emphasising the significance of hair, for they appear to have made extensive use of wigs and hair pieces. This is apparent in art from the Old Kingdom and on, and actual finds of wigs as gravegoods include these objects in the collection of paraphernalia required for rebirth. These wigs are made from human hair, pleated or curled and set by means of preparations based on beeswax. Wigs in various stages of completion have recently been excavated near the temple of Deir el-Bahari in a room that was obviously a wig workshop. The find includes a model head with black lines drawn to show the outline of a wig's attachment.[1]

In their wigs men and women display the changing fashions throughout the millennia. The general idea was that hair, though kept simple, should be voluminous. By the Middle Kingdom the wig maker had perfected his craft to an art. Literary texts make unambiguous reference to the use of wigs, revealing that wigs were not solely intended for the tomb.

The Tale of the Two Brothers from the New Kingdom contains in its opening section an episode which mirrors the situation of the wife of Potiphar known from the Bible. The wife of the elder brother has set her eyes on the younger brother who lives with the couple. As he spurns her advances, she turns vindictive and tells her husband that it was he who tried to seduce her. The expression used to entice a woman to bed in those days was: 'Don your wig and let us spend a happy hour!' The mere mention of the wig leaves her husband in a fuming rage. An argument of philological interest has hinged on the new suggestion for the word

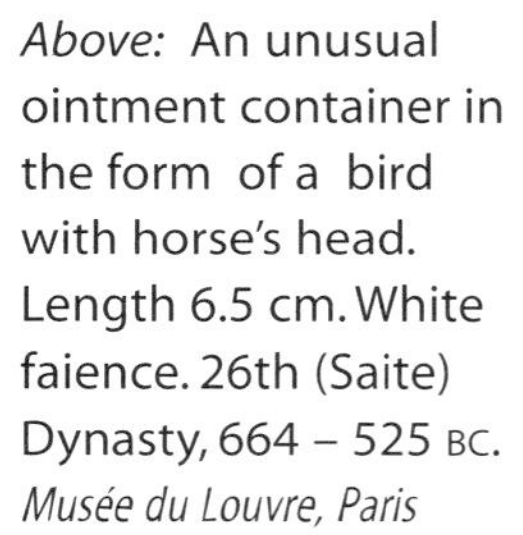

Above: An unusual ointment container in the form of a bird with horse's head. Length 6.5 cm. White faience. 26th (Saite) Dynasty, 664 – 525 BC. *Musée du Louvre, Paris*

Above right: A kohl container, labelled 'genuine kohl' in hieroglyphs, held by a monkey. Height 5.5 cm. Wood. New Kingdom, c. 1570 – 1070 BC. *Musée du Louvre, Paris*

'to don' which was by older translators tentatively rendered as 'remove'. Having the girl equip herself with artificial hair before intercourse gives rare textual substance to abundant pictorial evidence revealing its crucial erotic significance.[2] The situation is reflected in a contemporary love poem:

> My heart remembers your love
> while only half of my temple is plaited.
> I hasten to seek you,
> and my hairdo becomes undone.
> But I shall don a wig
> and will be ready any moment![3]

There are other examples in the Egyptian texts which demonstrate that beautiful hair made the owner sexually attractive and that an immediate effect would be produced by donning a wig, or by just breathing its fragrance, as in the tale of the scented wig in pharaoh's laundry above, p. 91. When it comes to eternity, a notion that was never far from the Egyptian mind, the act of producing a beautiful coiffure for the preliminaries of rebirth was carefully staged, and many tombs exhibit the motif of a hairdressing scene. It serves the purpose of alluding to sexuality of the couple and thus joins the other cosmetic paraphernalia deemed vital for the transformation of the dead.

HYGIENE

The foundation of bodily and mental well-being of the Egyptians was cleanliness. In the Two Brothers story the wife was expected to pour water over her husband's hands when he came home from work. Men and women appreciated wearing new or newly washed linen clothing. A regular shave was part of the ritual of cleanliness, and when we move from the world of laymen into the secluded world of the temple we find cleanliness a condition for entering beyond the gate. The priests went so far as to shave their heads as well as their chins. According to Herodotus, 'the priests shave their whole bodies every other day, so that when they conduct rituals they will be free of lice and other uncleanliness'.[4] A state of ritual purity was required for any-

Below: In this detail of a garden scene Tutankhamun's wife Ankhesenamun is represented wearing an elaborate wig, presenting the king with bunches of lotus and papyrus flowers and mandrake fruit. Ivory panel of a chest. 18th Dynasty, 1336-1327 BC.
Egyptian Museum, Cairo

one officiating in the temple. A series of rites repeated at regular intervals ensured that the deity itself was always in a state of purity (see p. 45). Water was the chief agent here, along with incense which at least would have dispelled any foul odours.

It is not uncommon to find razors as part of the funerary equipment of ordinary people, and it was not a tool used only by men. They were included in women's toilet boxes, and we do not have to guess why. As the jars of eye and face paint they had a part to play in daily life as well as in the ongoing preparations for access to life in the Hereafter. Removing body hair, including that of the pubic region, would have improved hygiene generally, but more specifically it prepared the woman for sexual activities. It left the area soft and brilliant - not unlike the smooth texture of faience with which it was sometimes compared in literature. A seductress is described as having 'smooth skin'. The reader would have interpreted this expression as a sign that the woman had shaved herself and was ready for lovemaking.[5] The Egyptians had also tried out various applications to remove unwanted body hair. Although some of the ingredients belong in the realm of magic, others may have had an effect, such as a remedy consisting of sycamore juice and gum mixed with cucumber, fatty matter, raven's bone and fly excreta.[6]

A clever method of fighting body odour was to place little balls of senetjer resin mixed with porridge in the armpits and wherever odour might emerge. Such remedies are recommended for men and women alike.[7] Pine kernels, antiu resin and alun were also useful.[8]

HAIR CARE

In the Middle East today, soapwort may be used for cleansing, and we must investigate whether the ancient Egyptians did the same. Dioscorides[9] mentions a herb called struthium, which has been translated as soapwort. If this is correct it is of interest that he adds that the Egyptians called it oeno. If they had a name for it, they must have known it. It was then used specifically for washing wool. Hair shampoo based on soapwort was produced commercially in Europe up till 1930. A foamy liquid can be produced by soaking dried root in warm water.

In connection with linen Dioscorides also refers to the use of soap-stone or French chalk for whitening: 'morochtos lithos . . . growing in Egypt which also they who make linen use for whitening of the clothes, it being soft and melting'.[10]

A recent find has given substance to the idea that the Egyptians knew hair shampoos. In the wig workshop mentioned above were also found the waxy remnants of hard soda soap, covered in white fatty crystals. According to the excavators it still retained detergent properties. Because of the context in which it

Two perfume flasks and an eyepaint container. Core-formed glass embellished with coloured threads. 18th Dynasty, 1450-1336 BC.
British Museum, London

was found it would seem natural to take it as a preparation specifically used for washing hair. A preparation made of fat and natron, maybe mixed with the ashes of plants, would in theory have produced a substance which would have served the purpose of cleaning. The Egyptians must have appreciated the cleansing effect of natron in getting rid of fatty matter.

In his major work on ancient technology Forbes[11] mentions the use of potash, soapwort, asphodil and other alkaline plants for washing clothes, but without references. Various parts of *Asphodelus ramosus* (which grows in North Africa) have been used for consumption, for medicine, and for glue, but, according to a modern expert,[12] not as a detergent. Elsewhere[13] Forbes says that there is no proof of cosmetic soap in ancient Egypt, but that the available ingredients would have included natron, fuller's earth and possibly pounded lupins. *Lupinus albus* L. grows wild in Egypt. The seeds are edible. In folk medicine they have long been used as an emollient skin lotion.[14] The ancient writers, too, provide relevant information. Dioscorides[15] says that the Egyptians knew the seeds as brechu. They cleanse the skin, he adds, and when soaked in rain water till they cream they clear the face. Pliny repeats that dried lupin seeds applied as a poultice restore skin on black ulcers; when kneaded in vinegar and applied in the bath they remove pimples; with pearl barley they soothe inflammation; when eaten they freshen the complexion; and if thoroughly boiled in rain water the decoction makes a detergent with which it is good to foment gangrene and human ulcers.[16] So it remains a possibility that the Egyptians, who clearly knew lupin seeds, used them to clear their skin, if not to wash their hair. A 'lupin soap' is once recorded in a modern herbal.[17]

For keeping their hair clean the ancient Egyptians might conceivably also have used a dry shampoo containing ingredients such as orris root and rosemary to name just a few examples from modern herbal hair care. The ingredients would have been available, but so far there is no proof that they used them for that purpose.

One of the medical papyri gives instructions for preventing grey hair. Black hair, in art even rendered with a dark blue tinge, was obviously a sign of youth and good health. Few Egyptians are depicted with grey hair, and when they are, we should perhaps not interpret the white/grey colour as a sign of ageing. Some of the remedies suggested in the papyrus are sympathetic remedies, using the blackness of other animals in the hope of imparting it to their own hair: blood of a black calf or ox or from the horn of a black ox, horn of gazelle, backbone of raven, raven's egg, burnt ass hoof, fat of a black snake, even a tadpole lends its black colour to these experiments.[18] The chosen ingredient is to be boiled with oil and applied to the hair (and in one case to the eyebrow). It should be mentioned that some mummies from as far back as the prehistoric period appear to have had their hair dyed, probably with henna.

The wig workshop at Deir el-Bahari yielded another fascinating substance no doubt used in connection with hair and/or wigs. A dark brown substance proved to consist of bicarbonate of manganese with added quartz grains. The excavators suggest that it might have been applied to the hair to give extra body and shine, or for 'highlighting', and that mixed with fatty matter it would appear to have dyeing properties.[19]

When not imposed for ritual purposes baldness was treated with fat of powerful animals such as lion, crocodile, hippopotamus, ibex, cat and serpent. If these creatures were not available hedgehog bristles provided an acceptable substitute. The tooth of a donkey ground in honey was also recommended.[20] Women, too, could be afflicted by baldness if we are to believe a remedy prepared for a queen Shesh, mother of king Teti of the Sixth Dynasty: leg of hound, hoof of ass and kernel(?) of date are boiled thoroughly with oil and rubbed into the skull.[21] It is a curious

Unguent container in the form of the tilapia fish, regarded in ancient Egypt as a potent symbol of rebirth. Polychrome glass. Length 14.5 cm, 18th Dynasty, Amarna period, c. 1352-1336 BC. *British Museum, London*

coincidence that the mummy of an Eighteenth Dynasty queen shows a bald patch at the top of the head, concealed by an added switch of hair. Remedies to promote hair growth from the plant kingdom include castor fruit rubbed in oil, or a mixture of fatty matter and fir resin.[22]

SKIN CARE

A dry climate like the Egyptian encouraged the use of oils and fats for keeping the skin supple. Oil for external use would be included in one's wages which before the days of notes and coins were always given in kind. The workers engaged in the cutting and decorating of the tombs of the kings in the New Kingdom provide one such example. Thanks to the discovery of numerous accounts and receipts from the workmen's village at Deir el-Medina we are well informed about these matters. Such oils were not perfumed preparations like those dealt with in earlier chapters, but the users had to tolerate the natural smell of castor and sesame oil among others.

Sesame oil (known as neheh) has a characteristic nutty aroma. Although it could be cultivated in Egypt we also know that it was imported from Syria. The army was in charge of bringing the seeds to Egypt, where it was then boiled ('cleaned', as it is called) by the unguent makers and stored in magazines or in the treasury, from where it was distributed. A written requisition was required for this purpose such as: 'To Ramose the scribe. I have come to the overseer of the treasury and he said to his deputy who was there in the treasury in Thebes: "Give this man ten jars of sesame oil." So he said.'

Workers were also paid in an oil called segenen, 'anointing (oil)', which could refer both to the body and the wick of a lamp. The 'sweet' variety was used on the skin. The word persisted in Greek as sagdas or psagdas, which was then a name of a red unguent from Egypt sold in the shop of a certain Peron.[23]

Moringa oil, too, (cf. p. 29) was at times imported, either from the land of Naharina or from Cyprus. It was more precious than sesame, and deliveries are known not just for private individuals, but also for the temple and the palace. For ordinary workers this was too expensive. The oil may be qualified as 'fresh' or 'sweet'. The latter was favoured for cosmetics.

It has been suggested that the contents of two large jars found in the burial of 18th Dynasty princesses had served the purpose of cleansing cream. Analysis revealed that it consisted of oil and lime, possibly chalk. Chalk as a cleansing agent is used in modern preparations for its gently abrasive effect.

Papyrus Ebers is once more helpful in providing recipes reflected in archaeological finds. A prescription for improving the skin specifies 'red' natron, 'northern salt', and honey to anoint the skin.[24] The remedy can be easily tried out at home. Travellers to Egypt who have visited the 'alabaster' workshops near Luxor may add a fourth ingredient listed in another prescription for 'beautifying the body': calcite powder.[25]

The state of perpetual youth so vividly demonstrated in art as the ideal state included fighting a sure sign of ageing: wrinkles. Senetjer resin, wax, fresh balanos oil and cyperus grass is to be ground and mixed with fermented plant juice and applied to the face every day.[26] In all, five prescriptions to combat wrinkles are given, and one of them specifies that the client is a woman '(mix' powdered gum in in (unidentified) liquid. When she has washed her face every day she should anoint her face with it'.[27] The fact that such remedies existed suggests a definite concern with the signs of aging. Our attempts at trying them out is again hampered by the fact that we are not always able to provide a certain translation of all the ingredients. One includes gall of ox, oil, gum, powder of ostrich egg and an ingredient called *bedet*, made into a face wash, or resin, honey and bedet. An ointment consisted of *kebu* water, calcite powder, gum, and green frit, made into a dough and pounded with woman's milk.

This exquisite face with heavy eye make-up is virtually all that is left of a wooden statuette which was devoured by termites.
Painted wood with ebony, alabaster, copper and obsidian inlays, 12th Dynasty, c. 1985-1956 BC.
Fitzwilliam Museum, Cambridge

It would be remiss to discuss female beauty in Egypt without recalling Cleopatra, although her image on contemporary coins suggests that her fame owed more to her intellect than to appearance. But legend has it that Cleopatra bathed in asses milk, and if this is true she must have found out that protein in a fatty emulsion improves the skin.

EYE PAINT

From a cosmetic point of view it is evident that in Ancient Egypt the focus was on the eyes. Eye makeup emphasised the size and shape of the eyes, and the artists immortalised the skills of the beauticians in sculpture, relief and painting. The slow changes of fashion were also felt in this area, and some works of art, especially when in a fragmented state, may be dated by means of the size and shape of the contours of the eye, whether there was a heavy line prolonging the eye, a faintly tapering line, or sometimes no apparent line at all. But where an archaising effect was aimed for, normal criteria for dating can no longer be relied on.

We mentioned above in Chapter 2 the crucial role played by the eye of Horus in symbolising the offer to the deity. The eye has a quite distinct shape, a human eye rather different in shape from the circular eye of a falcon, Horus's usual manifestation. Below the eye are stylised markings of birds' feathers, and the eye itself is made up according to archetypal Egyptian custom with prolonged cosmetic line and the brow following its curve. Such is the shape of this eye, be it in a tiny faience amulet or as a larger object placed on the hands of the king or priest.

Numerous samples of eyepaint have survived, either as raw material or as a dried up paste or powder. There were two main types: green and black.

Green eyepaint was made from malachite, a green carbonate of copper which is found on the surface of copper ore deposits in Sinai and the Eastern desert. It was used by Egyptians in the fourth millennium and until the end of the New Kingdom. In art, green eyepaint is conspicuously absent unless one interprets the copper framing of inlaid eyes in statuary, now oxidised, as the artist's rendering of an ancient cosmetic custom. The most peculiar example of the use of green eyepaint occurs in three statues of Third Dynasty date in the Louvre. The figures are carved out of white limestone. Their wigs retain their black colour, and below their eyes (not on the lids) are broad areas of green paint.

Although it is rarely represented, green eyepaint must have been popular in real life, for it was included as part of the funerary equipment even in quite modest burials. It was kept in shells, segments of reeds, wrapped in leaves or in small vases. The raw material was placed in a small linen or leather bag. When prepared, it was ground on a slab of stone and mixed with a liquid of some sort, probably either water or gum. Such grinding stones, as well as little palettes to which the

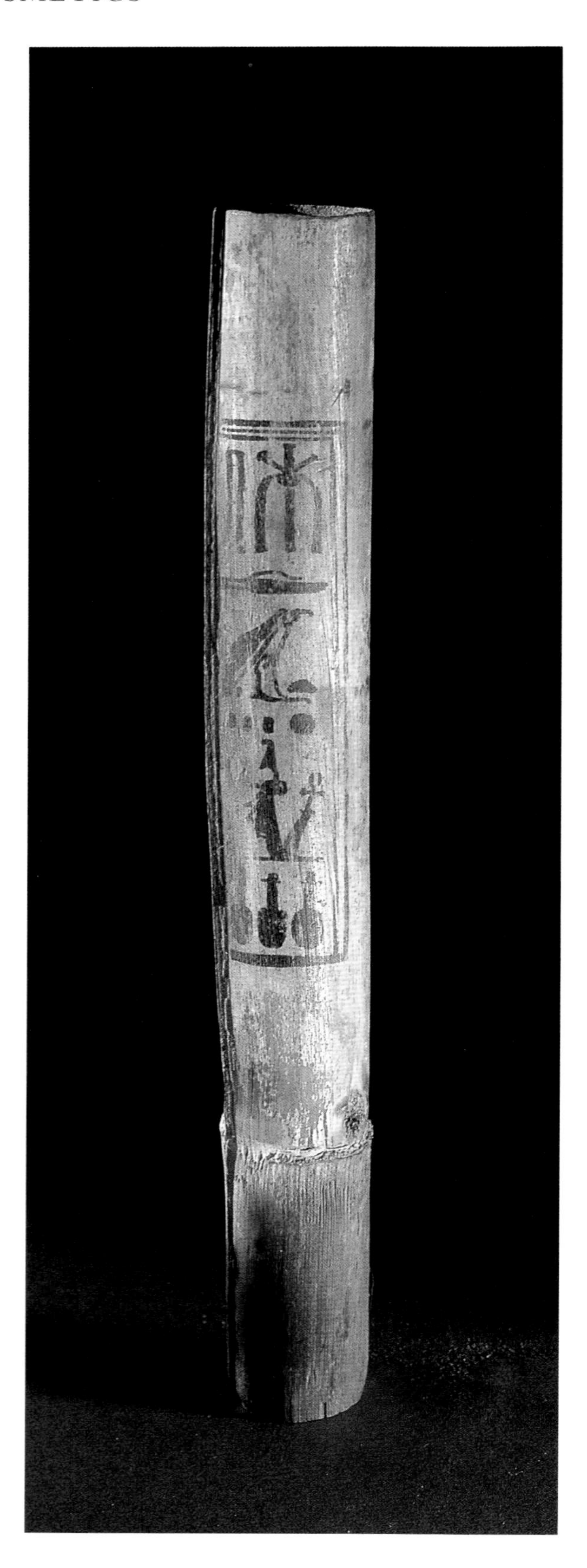

Reed kohl container labelled as 'genuine, very excellent kohl'. Height 15.5 cm. Found in a tomb at Medinet el-Ghurob dating from the reign of Amenhotep III, 1390–1352 BC.
Musée du Louvre, Paris

substance could be transferred, often show green stains. Analyses show that fatty matter was added to facilitate application. We may here quote another passage from the Tale of the Two Brothers. The scheming wife of the elder brother made herself look as if she had been beaten up by the younger brother, and for this purpose she used a mixture of fat and grease. Perhaps she added a little green malachite to achieve the right hue?

Black eyepaint was usually based on galena, a dark grey ore of lead which could easily be extracted from a number of localities in Upper Egypt between Quseir and the Red Sea as well as near Aswan. The ancient Egyptians would have been unaware of the health risks involved in applying lead to the skin. Black eyepaint from modern Egypt (kohl) consists of soot of some sort, applied in its dry state by means of a tear: that is, the kohl stick is passed along the eyelids inside the lashes. In Roman and Medieval times an antimony compound was used, a raw material not found in Egypt itself. In Latin, this was called 'stibium', a word derived from the Egyptian mesdemet, which was a designation for eyepaint in general. The word is sometimes qualified by the adjective 'good' or 'genuine, really good'.

Recent analyses of minute amounts (about 1 mm^3) of the contents of 49 kohl containers in the Louvre dating from 2000 – 1200 BC have revealed that the ancient Egyptians were able to use 'wet chemistry'.[28] The kohl was found to contain substantial amounts of laurionite and phosgenite which on their own have the appearance of a white powder. These do not occur naturally in quantity and must have been produced synthetically by a laborious process of admixing rock salt and/or natron in water and repetitive filtration. The resulting substance was then added to kohl consisting of galena or cerussite (a white mineral).

Such eyepaint was an essential tool in the process of justification and resurrection of a deceased person. Before presenting himself at the tribunal in the 'Hall of Justice' the candidate must purify himself, dress in white garments, make up his eyes and anoint himself. Only then may he enter the realm of Osiris.[29]

The ancient records mention imported eyepaint. This was not strictly necessary, but it must have lent an air of the exotic to the preparations. Such apparently irrational acts of trading goods already available are quite common as a sign of friendly international relations. The Asiatics, the people of Naharina beyond the Euphrates and the inhabitants of distant Punt (probably in the Eritrea region) were the suppliers to the Egyptian court. The Puntites traded all sorts of goods which had arrived from even further away, such as incense from Arabia and spices from India. Both malachite and galena are found in Arabia which could thus well have been the source of the products handled by the Puntites.

The medical papyri contain numerous prescriptions for combatting a variety of eye ailments. Many are in the form of ointments, and some are specifically called cosmetic remedies. Both black and green eye paint enters into the remedies, mixed with fatty matter, honey and minerals.[30]

The circumstances surrounding the acquisition of eyepaint are reflected in a copy of an official letter from the palace in the late New Kingdom. Pharaoh had to have the best, or the suppliers would have to try again. 'Let twice excellent galena suitable for Pharaoh's eyepaint be brought to the place where the Pharaoh is, and have 15 deben galena brought through [this official]. As it was given to the physicians from the Office of Pharaoh's Palace Physicians in order to prepare it, it was found that the galena was useless, as there was nothing in it that was worthy of eyepaint for Pharaoh's use. One single deben galena was it which one found in it [that was suitable?].' The galena is returned and the request is now for 100 deben four times excellent galena.[31]

Eyepaint container covered with a lid. Its residual contents were among those recently subjected to analysis which proved the hitherto unsuspected sophistication of Egyptian chemists. Limestone, height 5.8 cm, Deir el-Medina, 19th Dynasty, c. 1200 BC. *Musée du Louvre, Paris*

In some works of art with inlaid decoration the eyelids and eyebrows are rendered in dark blue lapis lazuli. This need not imply that this material entered into any of the preparations actually used, even if it does occur once for medicinal purposes.[32] Rather it is a question of interchange of colour, a practice which was not uncommon in Egypt. Black and dark blue (as opposed to light blue) were found to be interchangeable, that is to have the same value and used to render the nature of a particular object, as early as in the Old Kingdom both in coloured hieroglyphs and in representations of hair. The often reproduced gold mask of Tutankhamun (see p. 87) has brows and lids inlaid in lapis lazuli. These two precious materials were ideally suited for representing a divine state such as that achieved by the young king after his burial. One may here mention the sun god Re, who is described as having lapis lazuli blue eyes, or even with his eyes 'made green'.

Applying eye paint was part of the daily cult ritual, either as virtual make-up or in the form of a symbolic offering. It is less well known that offerings in the form of live cows would also wear eye make-up. A relief in the Fifth Dynasty temple of king Sahure shows a group of cows being subject to the ministrations of female temple personnel while they wait to end their days in the noblest of fashions: by ritual slaughter. If the deity itself is in the shape of a cow, such as Hathor in one of her manifestations, her eye, too, will be shown as a fully made-up eye.

The colour of the cheeks of Nefertari, favourite wife of Ramesses II, was obviously enhanced with face paint. Wall painting, 19th Dynasty, c. 1295-1186 BC. Valley of the Queens, Thebes

Opposite The strong colour of Nefertiti's lips suggests that the queen liked to apply a thick layer of tint to . her lips. Painted bust, limestone, Amarna period, 18th Dynasty, c. 1352-1336 BC. *Ägyptisches Museum, Berlin*

FACE PAINT

Egyptian art is polychrome. This means that different shades of a given colour are as a rule not used with deliberate effect in a scene, although natural variations of a colour do occur, depending on its source. Hence in representations of women the artist would not find it correct to show such subtle details as, for example, the application of rouge to the cheek bones or any other part of the face. But every rule has an exception, and in this case we only have to turn to the illustrious tomb of Nefertari, queen of Ramesses II in the Nineteenth Dynasty. The wall-paintings in the tomb of the queen show a clear circle on her cheeks of a darker red hue than the remaining part of her complexion. The colour red was usually derived from ochre, which occurs naturally in the Egyptian desert. It is no coincidence that certain modern preparations which came on the market in the 1980s take their inspiration from Egypt. 'Soil of the Nile' was the name of one of them, sold in a pottery jar and marketed with a clear reference to ancient Egypt.[33] Papyrus Ebers is once more helpful, for when we look under remedies used for darkening a burn we find two that include red ochre, though not used as a powder, but mixed with sycamore juice.

The contents of a cosmetic jar dating from the Middle Kingdom proved to contain organic matter (probably vegetable grease) with a 26.8% mixture of red ochre. This could well have served the purpose. Curiously we have a roughly contemporary relief which depicts a woman applying something to her cheek with a piece of cloth or similar. Perhaps the custom of using rouge was far more common than the scarce evidence suggests.

In this connection it is of interest to reflect on the Egyptian word for skin, *inem*, which was already in ancient times confused with the word for 'colour', *iun*. As mentioned earlier, the Egyptians were fond of plays on words, and the word was sometimes used so as to perplex and amuse the ancient reader. In a love poem, for example, the boy desires to see the 'colour' of the girl:

> I wish I were her Nubian slave
> who guards her steps.
> Then I would be able to see the colour [or skin]
> of all her limbs!

LIP TINT

A substance similar to, if not identical with, Egyptian rouge preparations may have been used as lip tint. The one and only example of the use of this remedy is the so-called erotic papyrus, now in the Egyptian Museum in Turin, which shows one of the ladies in an orgy making up her lips with a spatula. In her other hand she grasps a mirror and an elongated container that probably held the tint.

If we look at lips in some wall paintings or coloured reliefs and sculpture we may discern

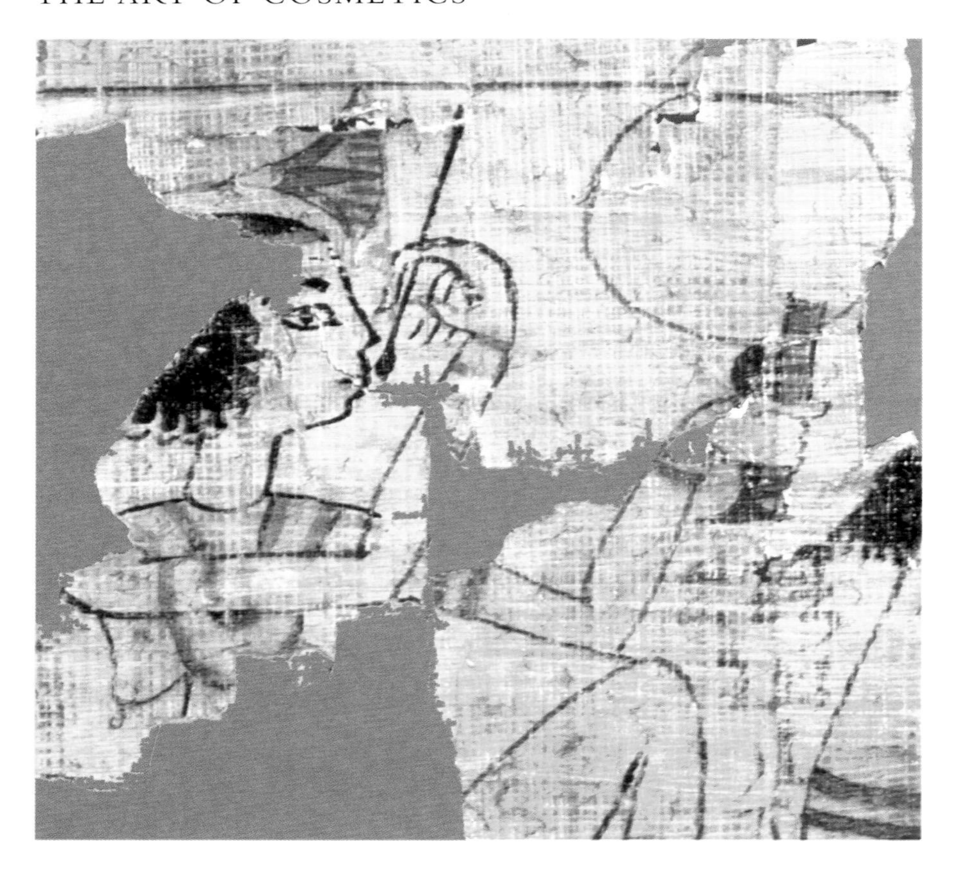

A prostitute with a lotus flower in her wig paints her lips, holding in her left hand a mirror as well as the paint container. Erotic papyrus 55001, 19th Dynasty, c. 1295-1186 BC. *Museo Egizio, Turin*

a slightly darker hue in the lips of women, contrasting with their conventional yellow complexion. This may suggest the use of lip tint, but on the other hand it may just render the actual difference in the shade of skin. The famous bust of Queen Nefertiti (p. 139) does indeed have reddish lips. In the Amarna period, a woman's complexion was rather darker than usual, approaching the red hue of male skin. This was one of several arguments in favour of interpreting the peculiar representations from that period as underlining what we may call 'unisex', or the attitude held by King Akhenaten that the male and female creative principles united in his own fertile body. On the almost peach colour of her skin, the full, red lips of Nefertiti still stand out in her striking physiognomy. The claim made in popular literature that she painted them with cinnabar is pure fiction. But there was one additional source of red in New Kingdom, namely realgar, a sulphide of arsenic. This often occurs in connection with another mineral, orpiment, another sulphide of arsenic and a source of yellow in the Amarna Period and elsewhere. But whether these two minerals were used for cosmetic purposes (rather than as painting pigments) remains to be ascertained by analysis of a substance found in a proper context.

NAIL COLOUR

In Egyptian painting, nails tend to be white, contrasting with the red complexion of men and the yellow skin of women. In painted statuary, nails of fingers and toes are occasionally indicated in red. This may reflect the possible use of henna for dyeing hands and feet (as is customary in Islamic countries today). Indeed, some mummies show such coloration, although the dyeing may have occurred during the process of mummification.

BODY DECORATION

The final paragraph on cosmetics concerns the body, for there is clear evidence that some Egyptians decorated their limbs with various designs. These are generally interpreted as tattoos, that is pigment injected subcutaneously. The proof that this was indeed the case comes from the mummified bodies of Egyptians on which traces of such practice have been detected.

The designs are either a figure or pattern consisting of tiny dots; a cross; or it is the characteristic silhouette of the dwarf god Bes. Such patterns are found only on images of women, and in very definite circumstances.

The dotted design occurs on female figurines of all periods, even of predynastic date. In historical time, from the Middle Kingdom and on, they are often called 'concubine figures'. It consists of rhomboid groups of points dispersed over the woman's thighs. The two strands crossing the chest and a cowroid hip belt also drawn in black may not be tattoos, but a rendering of the garments. The pubic

The tattoo on the lute player's thigh represents Bes, the ubiquitous god believed not only to protect the family but also to be the god of drunkenness.
The design suggests that it is a wine drinking bowl.
Faience, height 4.5 cm, diameter 14 cm, late 18th Dynasty, c. 1400-1300 BC.
Rijksmuseum van Oudheden, Leiden

triangle has also been emphasised with black dots.

In other figures crosses are shown in the abdominal area. Dotted design was also found on mummies of two girls at Deir el-Bahari.

The Bes design is prominent in a wall-painting (now lost?) from one of the houses at Deir el-Medina, copied over 50 years ago.[34] The motif shows a dancing woman playing a double oboe, surrounded by a leafy garland. On her upper thighs are two Bes designs. Bes was the ubiquitous god in the world of women, guarding them during all the stages from conception to childbirth.

A second example of a Bes design on a woman's thigh can be seen in a roughly contemporary tomb also in the Theban area, this time on a girl playing the lyre.[35] As the design is visible on her upper thigh the girl wears very flimsy garments, if any, as does her counterpart from the Deir el-Medina house. An unguent vase in the shape of a pubescent girl holding a large jar (where the unguent was placed) is in itself a major work of art on a minor scale, but in this context it is interesting that the painted design on the girl's neck is in the form of a Bes figure suspended from a string. Perhaps the artist's rendering of an actual necklace? Possibly a tattoo?[36]

The perfect indication of a sexual significance of the Bes tattoo comes in the shape of a decorated faience dish of similar date. (p. 141). It unites most of the items which can be interpreted in this way. A naked female musician squats on a cushion. The extremity of her lute is decorated with a duck's head. A vervet is engaged in fastening (or loosening) her hip belt. She has lotus flowers thrown over her arms, another adorns her head and on top of her wig she is wearing an unguent cone. And on her right thigh she sports an outsize Bes tattoo.

It has been suggested in the past that the Bes tattoo on women's thighs was placed there as a protection against the kind of disease that might befall ladies of a certain occupation. This may be so, but in any case the connection with female sexuality seems to be beyond question.

Epilogue

Fish nibbling a lotus flower. Multiple cosmetic dish, 18 cm long. Egyptian alabaster. 18th Dynasty, c. 1550– 1295 BC.
Metropolitan Museum of Art, New York. (17.190.1966 – Gift of J. Pierpoint Morgan, 1917)

The preceding pages have demonstrated the very high degree of importance attached to perfumes and cosmetics in Ancient Egyptian society – on an everyday level to attract, allure, to treat and to honour, and on a more spiritual level to venerate the gods and to negotiate a passage to the different sphere of the Hereafter.

The elusive art of perfumery was coupled with the lasting esthetic enjoyment of the container in which the precious substance was kept. The characteristic polychrome glass vessels for scented oil, found in all the countries surrounding the Mediterranean, bear witness to the popularity of Egyptian scent which was in turn manufactured from ingredients which had already travelled to Egypt. Impenetrable glass was ideally suited for keeping the oil intact, and the dark blue colour which was predominant blocked out

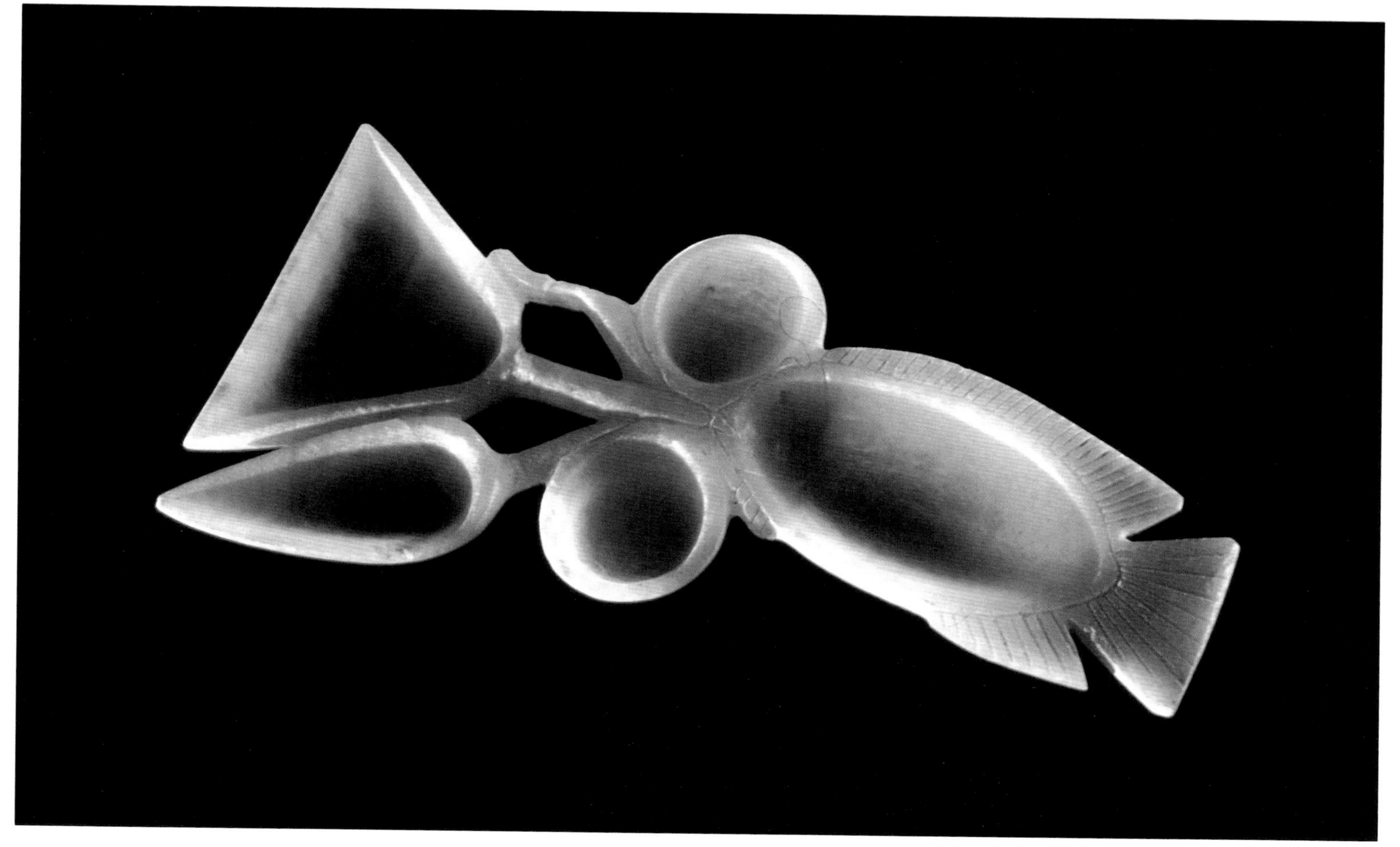

Cosmetic spoon in the form of a young woman in a papyrus thicket supporting a vessel heaped with unguent, which in itself forms the cavity for the scented substance. The lid has not been found. Length 18 cm. 18th Dynasty, c. 1375 BC.
Ny Carlsberg Glyptotek, Copenhagen.

harmful sunlight. Other more elaborate containers and spoons were crafted expressly for the Egyptian market where the symbolic significance of the iconography would be appreciated, especially when it was of an erotic nature (lotus flower and mandrake fruit, duck and vervet).

Scent and cosmetics always had as their prime function the enhancement of the wearer's sexuality as well as restoring his or her vitality and health. According to Pliny, receptacles made of stone were perfect for storing fragrance. In Egypt, the stone employed was usually the softest available, the creamy white calcite, popularly known as alabaster. The jars found in the tomb of Tutankhamun show the extent to which the craftsmen played around with the soft material to create vessels with thin curved arms which have earned them the nickname 'spaghetti vessels'.

The purpose of the wooden shallow containers, or 'spoons', as they are often called, would have been either to contain fragrance in the form of solid paste or dry powder or grains such as incense which would be scooped up from a larger container and dispensed on the fire. We are left guessing here, for the Egyptians drew no pictures of such 'spoons' being used or even displayed. Most of the surviving specimens definitely belong in the context of private users, carrying many of the symbolic references that we meet in the so-called banquet scenes such as scantily dressed women bedecked in jewellery and heavy wigs, secular musical instruments, ducks, vervets and flowers.

The tradition of the importance of fragrance was persistent and survived through the classical writers mainly via Arabic scholars to the Middle Ages and hence to the present day when the knowledge of scent and its effects has seen a revival in many areas of life from local practitioners of aromatherapy to industrial use of scented air conditioning aiming to improve productivity. Modern analysis of active ingredients in plant material, much of which is naturally scented, has gone a long way to affirm therapeutical benefits which were known, though not necessarily understood, by our ancestors.

At the present day, our sense of smell is affected by exposure to the potent scent of distilled perfume from a bottle, hampered by consumption of copious quantities of alcohol and by a varitety of allergies which seem to affect the breathing organs in particular. If by means of dietary measures and environmental precautions we could wipe the slate clean, we would be more likely to appreciate the wisdom of ancient Egyptians as they did.

In order to recreate an impression of the composite scents of Ancient Egypt one must first try and experince the properties of the individual ingredients insofar as this is possible. The general impression of the nature of Egyptian scent would seem to be on the heavy, fruity and spicy side. Many of the recipes quoted by the classical authors include cinnamon, and it is likely that this particular spice can be traced back to more ancient times, whether its equivalent is tisheps or something else. Other favourite ingredients were myrrh and frankincense. Both of these can be bought in some health shops and ethnic markets. By throwing a few grains on glowing embers one can experience the unadulterated pleasure which was once believed necessary for the welfare of the gods, a scent which is at the same time fruity, astringent and purifying. The dried root of *Acorus calamus* L., nowadays more easily available than the 'flower' so appreciated by Pliny, may be subjected to the same treatment, producing a delicate, warm fragrance. The root would probably have been the part of the plant used by the Egyptians, too, as it was imported and not grown locally. Roots keep, but flowers do not.

Pine resin, juniper, lemon grass and mint would yield sharper odours whilst marjoram, a favourite herb in Egypt today, is the source of perhaps the sweetest of all the herbal fragrances. Combining these varied components, of which we have only mentioned the most familiar and easily identifiable, into long-lasting scents that faithfully reflected the taste of the day, was a true art the secret of which was no doubt well guarded.

During the past decades the West has seen a revival of traditional skills and practices particularly in the area of spiritual experiences and healing methods many of which have been derived from the Far East. By staying at the cradle of European civilisation, but going back a few steps further in time, neglected paths remain to be explored and experienced. This book is one attempt to show the way.

Notes

1 The Ingredients

1 Pliny, *Natural History,* XIII, 26.
2 Theophrastus, *Enquiry into Plants,* IX, 7.3.
3 *Ibid.*, IX, 7.3.
4 Theophrastus, *On Odours*, 33.
5 Pliny, *op. cit.* XII, 110.
6 *Ibid.*, XXIV,111.
7 Dioscorides, *On Medical Matters,* I, 19.
8 Alpini, *La Médecine des Égyptiens* (*Medicina Aegyptiorum*), Cairo 1980, pp. 296–7. For this writer see Note 33 in Chapter 3.
9 Cf. the note by É. Chassinat in *Le Mystère d'Osiris au mois de khoiak*, Cairo 1968, pp. 434–5.
10 Pliny, *op. cit.,* XV, 30.
11 Theophrastus, *Enquiry into Plants,* IX, 7.3, 7.1.
12 Dioscorides, *op. cit.,* I, 16.
13 Pliny, *op. cit.,* XII, 104; XII, 106; XXI, 120.
14 Chassinat, *op. cit.*, pp. 425-30.
15 Theophrastus, *On Odours*, 33-4.
16 For a reference to spices shipped from India see Theophrastus, *op. cit.*, IX, 7.2.
17 Dioscorides, *op. cit.*, I, 5.
18 Theophrastus, *Enquiry into Plants,* IV, 4.14; IX, 5.3.
19 Dioscorides, *op. cit.,* I, 12.
20 Chassinat, *op. cit.*, pp. 387-9. Cf. 'tisheps' designating seed pulp, pp. 404ff.
21 Dioscorides, *op. cit.*, I, 13.
22 Herodotus, *History*, II, 86-8; Diodorus, *The Library of History*, I, 91.6.
23 Chassinat, *op. cit.*, pp. 389ff.
24 Alpini, *Histoire des plantes en Égypte*, 112.
25 Cf. V. Täckholm, *Students' Flora of Egypt*, pl. 291, p.786: 'swollen . . . black ellipsoid tubers of *C. rotundus* are collected as a drug.'
26 Pliny, *op. cit.*, XXI, 117.
27 Theophrastus, *Enquiry into Plants*, IX,7.3; *On Odours*, 28.
28 Dioscorides, *op. cit.*, III, 67.
29 Pliny, *op. cit.*, XII, 109; XII, 5-6; XIII, 12.
30 Dioscorides, *op. cit.*, I, 124.
31 *Ibid.*, I, 1.
32 Theophrastus, *Enquiry into Plants*, IX, 7.3.
33 Dioscorides, *op. cit.*, I, 24; I,103; I,104.
34 See Chassinat, *op. cit.*, p. 430.
35 Pliny, *op. cit.*, XIII, 51.
36 Herodotus, *op. cit.*, II, 86.
37 Pliny, *op. cit.*, XXI, 35.
38 *Ibid.*, XIX,165.
39 Dioscorides, *op. cit.*, III, 47.
40 Theophrastus, *op. cit.*, IX,7.3.
41 Dioscorides, *op. cit.*, I, 58.
42 Chassinat, *op. cit.*, pp. 433-4.
43 *Ibid.* p. 431. *Id.*, *Revue de l'Ancienne Égypte*, III, pp. 159-61.
44 Pliny, *op. cit.*, XIII, 5; XIII, 10.
45 Theophrastus, *On Odours*, 27.
46 John 12:3, cf. Mark 14:3.
47 Theophrastus, *Enquiry into Plants*, IX,7.2; *On Odours*, 28.
48 Pliny, *op. cit.*, XII, 42; XII, 43; XIII,16.
49 Theophrastus, *On Odours*, 38, 42.
50 Chassinat, *op. cit.*, pp. 413-25.
51 R. Germer, *Flora des pharaonischen Ägypten*, Mainz am Rhein, 1985, p. 147.
52 Pliny, *op. cit.*, XII, 104-6.
53 Theophrastus, *Enquiry into Plants*, IX,7.1-2.
54 Dioscorides, *op. cit.*, I, 17.
55 Pliny, *op. cit.*, XII, 32.
56 For frankincense and myrrh see A. Lucas, *Ancient Egyptian Materials and Industries*, 4th ed., revised and enlarged by J. R. Harris, London 1962, Chapter 4; N. Groom, *Frankincense and Myrrh. A Study of the Arabian Incense Trade*, New York 1981.
57 e.g. Germer in *Lexikon der Ägyptologie* IV.275. Groom, op. cit., p. 27 suggests 'perfumed bdellium' for antiu (cf. also pp. 24ff.).
58 Chassinat, *op. cit.*, pp. 217-23; *Edfou* II, p. 206.
59 Paszthory suggests galbanum for this ('Laboratorien in ptolemaischen Tempelanlagen', *Antike Welt* 19, 1988, pp. 16-17).
60 Paszthory suggests myrrh (*art. cit.*, p. 16).
61 Paszthory: turpentine resin (*art.cit.*, p. 17).
62 For a full discussion of the word and its implications see N. Baum, 'SNṮR: une revision' in *Revue d'égyptologie* 45, 1994, pp. 17-39.
63 Chassinat, *op. cit.*, p. 217, n. 2.
64 Groom, *op. cit.*, p. 123-4. The author suggests that Pliny's 'scented myrrh', probably from *C. erythraea*, was the antiu obtained by the Egyptians from Punt (p. 27).
65 Dioscorides, *op. cit.*, I, 80.
66 Pliny, *op. cit.*, XII, 35. Pliny describes bdellium from Bactria near India as being shiny and dry. It exudes grease when crumbled, has white spots like fingernails, but is otherwise transparent like wax.
67 Dioscorides, *op. cit.*, I, 92.
68 *Ibid.*, I, 71.
69 *Ibid.*, I, 90; 91.
70 Chassinat, *op. cit.*, pp. 381-7.
71 Dioscorides, *op. cit.,* I, 86.
72 Paszthory, *art. cit.*, p. 12.
73 Theophrastus, *Enquiry into Plants* 9.7.3.
74 Theophrastus, *On Odours* 6.29.
75 O. Steuer, *Myrrhe und Stakte*,Vienna 1933.
76 For various oils see R. Germer in *Lexikon der Ägyptologie* IV, cols. 552-555. For oils used in antiquity specifically for perfumery see Theophrastus, *op. cit.* 14-20.
77 Theophrastus, *Enquiry into Plants* 4.2.6; *On Odours* 16.
78 Pliny, *op. cit.* XII, 100-2.
79 *Ibid.,* XIII, 8, cf. XIII, 5, where it is mentioned next to 'The Mendesian', though not necessarily as an ingredient of it.
80 Theophrastus, *On Odours* 16
81 Herodotus, *op. cit.,* II, 94.
82 Pliny, *op. cit.,* XV, 25.
83 Theophrastus, *Enquiry into Plants* IV, 2.7.
84 Strabo, *Geography* XVII, 1, 35.
85 Dioscorides, *op. cit.*, I, 29-30.
86 Theophrastus, *On Odours* 15.
87 Dioscorides, *op. cit.*, II, 121.

2 Scent in the Temple

1 J. Gwyn Griffiths, *Plutarch's De Iside et Osiride*, University of Wales 1970 (79).
2 *Ibid.,* (52).
3 See also the section on antiu in chapter 1
4 A. Moret, *Rituel du culte divin*, Paris 1902, p. 78, cf. J. D. S. Pendlebury et al., *City of Akhenaten* III, London 1951, p. 234.
5 Pyramid Texts, 376b.
6 *Ibid.,* 179ff.
7 F. le Saout, 'Un magasin à encens du temple de Karnak et le problème du nom de Tyr: Mise au point', *Karnak* VIII, Paris 1987, pp. 325ff. The blocks in question are placed in the Open Air Museum at Karnak.
8 P. Lacau, 'Deux magasins à encens du temple de Karnak', *Annales du Service des Antiquités* 52, 1952, pp.185ff.
9 For titles of such books kept in temple libraries see Grimm in *Beiheft Studien zur altägyptischen Kultur* 3, 1989, pp. 3ff.

10 E. Paszthory, *art. cit.*, pp. 3ff.
11 Chassinat, *op. cit.*, p. 611.
12 For the remaining oils and their use in the funerary cult see below, Chapter 5.
13 S. Cauville & *Edfou* II, pp. 220-4; J. Dümichen, *Geographische Inschriften altägyptischer Denkmäler*, pls. XCI-XCV; id. *Zeitschrift für ägyptische Sprache*, 17, 1879, pp. 97-123; V. Loret, 'Études de droguerie', *Recueil de Travaux*, 16, pp. 134-62; Paszthory, *art. cit.*, pp. 14-15.
14 In the first publication of this text in 1879 (*Zeitschrift für ägyptische Sprache* 17, pp. 97-128) J. Dümichen cautiously translated 'Süssbaumfrucht'; Paszthory, *art. cit.* pp. 9, 14-15 follows Loret's suggestion and renders it as 'carob'; Chassinat, *op. cit.* pp. 404-7, concluded that it must have been an Ethiopian black tree similar to acacia.
15 The word *aref* literally means 'to be contained in (a bag ?)'. Possibly the seeds were first soaked in water and this stage was omitted from the recipe for being too obvious. Otherwise it is difficult to see how seeds from a pod could become liquid.
16 *Sic* Paszthory, *art.cit.*, p. 15.
17 *Edfou* II, pp. 229-30; Dümichen, *Geographische Inschriften*, pl. LXXXIX; id. *Libysche Wüste*, pp. 1-6; Paszthory, *art. cit.*, p. 15.
18 An as yet unidentified plant that occurs in other recipes.
19 Chassinat in *Revue de l'ancienne Égypte* 3, 1931, pp. 8ff with reference to earlier publications; *Edfou* II, p. 227.
20 Often translated 'alkanet', based on references to this plant by classical writers. But see the lengthy discussion by Chassinat in *Revue de l'ancienne Égypte* 3, pp. 147-58.
21 Paszthory, *art. cit.*, pp. 15-6, fig.19; *id., Salben, Schminken und Parfüme im Altertum*, p. 20 and fig. 31. Paszthory interpreted the recipe as specifying cyperus rhizomes, juniper berries, a conifer resin and alkanet as suggested here, but also needles and wood of *Juniperus oxycedrus*. He makes no reference to cinnamon and aspalathos, and it remains unclear what his recreated unguent actually contained. In his translation of the recipe Chassinat takes tisheps to mean styrax rather than our suggested 'cinnamon' and renders our cyperus rhizomes as 'lentisque' (mastic).
22 *Edfou* II, pp. 214-5. Translated and discussed in detail in S. Aufrère, *L'univers minéral dans la pensée égyptienne*, I, Cairo 1991, pp. 330ff. Translated without comment by D. Kurth in *Treffpunkt der Götter*, Zurich/Munich 1994, pp. 115-6. This author takes tisheps to mean carob.
23 Aufrère, *op. cit.*, p. 332 [g] sees in the much disputed tisheps a liquid extract, in this case, when specified as coming from the nedjem tree, liquidambar, a tree that grows in Asia Minor, yielding the balm known as storax. That the Egyptians knew the tree is indicated by the piece of wood found in the tomb of Tutankhamun, see Lucas, *op. cit.*, pp. 437-8.
24 Menen or menenen is a substance else where mentioned in connection with embalming, long thought to be bitumen, but more likely wood tar or wood pitch, or possibly a coniferous oil or resin. For a discussion of this and other suggestions see J. R. Harris, *Lexicographical Studies in Ancient Egyptian Minerals*, Berlin 1961, pp. 173, 234, and, more recently, Aufrère, *op. cit.* pp. 639-42.
25 Aufrère omits this and calls this version of the text inexact.
26 Aufrère n. [aa]: 'gaudron végétal'. Kurth suggests '<In> 2 Kite <Wein> ansetzen' in this place, reading *senu* (a kind of wine) for *sefy*.
27 See Aufrère, *op. cit.*, chapters 10 and 11.

3 Kyphi and Tiryac

1 The kyphi recipes were first studied together by V. Loret, 'Le kyphi. Parfum sacré des anciens Égyptiens', *Journal asiatique* 10, July-August 1887, pp. 76-132. Since then new suggestions have been made regarding the identity of the ingredients (see Chapter 1). See also the long entry on 'kyphi' in Pauly-Wissowa, *Real-Enzyklopädie der klassischen Altertumswissenschaft* (Nikolaus Myrepsius, ed.), Stuttgart 1925.
2 *Claudii Galeni Opera omnia*, ed. K. Gottlob-Kühn, Leipzig 1827, reprinted Hildesheim 1965, pp. 117-9.
3 Sometimes bdellium occurred interspersed with a substance resembling cut fingernails.
4 S. Sauneron, *Un traité égyptien d'ophiologie*, Cairo 1989, index p. 240.
5 *De materia medica,* I, 24. The work was translated by John Goodyer in 1655 and published as *The Greek Herbal of Dioscorides* by R. T. Gunther, New York 1959.
6 E. A. Wallis Budge, *The Syriac Book of Medicines*, I-II, Oxford etc. 1913, pp. 406-7.
7 É. Chassinat (2nd rev. ed. by S.Cauville & D. Devauchelle), *Le temple d'Edfou*, II (1987), pp. 203-4 and 211-2.
8 On the basis of an inscribed pot from the tomb of Tutankhamun containing plant fragments Renate Germer suggests *Chaerophyllum sp.* in her book *Flora des pharaonischen Ägypten*, Mainz am Rhein 1985, p.143. *Osiride*, University of Wales 1970, (80).
9 J. Gwyn Griffiths, *Plutarch's De Iside et Osiride*, University of Wales 1970, (80).
10 Translated as 'hartwort' or *Drachenwurz*.
11 W. Helck in *Lexikon der Ägyptologie*, s.v. 'Kyphi' suggests 'sorrel' for *lanathos*.
12 *Alexander von Tralles*, ed.T.Puschmann, Vienna 1878, reprinted Amsterdam 1963, I, 573 and Pauly-Wissowa, *loc. cit.*
13 Paulus Aegineta, *Epitomae medicae libri septem*, VII. 22; Aetios Amid. XIII, 117.
14 Griffiths, *op. cit.,* 80.
15 See K. Ryholt, *The Story of Petese son of Petetum and seventy other good and bad stories*, Copenhagen 1998, col. 5, 11.27 ff.
16 See P. Derchain, 'La recette du kyphi', *Revue d'égyptologie* 28, 1976, pp. 61-65; W. Erichsen, *Das grosse Papyrus Harris* I, 53a, 4-9.
17 Known from an inscribed potsherd, see J. D. S. Pendlebury et al., *City of Akhenaten*, vol.3, London 1951, p. 175 (no. 306).
18 *Grundriss,* IV, p. 261. For a colour photograph of balls of kyphi prepared according to this recipe see S. Schoske, (ed.), *Schönheit - Abglanz der Göttlichkeit. Kosmetik im alten Ägypten,* Munich 1990, p. 51.
19 There may be a connection between *gnn* and the word *knn*, translated in the present work as 'sweet flag'.
20 Pyramid Texts, 404.
21 Loret, *op. cit.*
22 *Alexander von Tralles, op. cit.*, I, p. 475.
23 *Ibid.,* I, pp. 572-3.
24 *Ibid.*, II, pp. 90-1, 298-301.
25 Papyrus Carlsberg 500 in the Carsten Niebuhr Institute, Copenhagen: *Acta Orientalia* 27, 1963, p. 34.
26 As quoted in Pauly-Wissowa, *op. cit.*
27 See H. Hickmann, *Musicologie pharaonique*, Kehl 1956, p. 81.
28 As quoted in Pauly-Wissowa, *op. cit.*
29 I am indebted to J. R. Harris for acquainting me with this rare pamphlet.
30 The same may be said concerning a sample presented to the public during an exhibition of ancient scents in the galleries of the National Museum in Copenhagen in the autumn of 1998. The 'kyphi' displayed in a plastic container among Egyptian artefacts was based on a combination of ancient recipes, including among other things mastic, myrrh, honey and date extract, but leaving out the otherwise characteristic raisins and cinnamon. (Information kindly provided by the modern 'kyphi' maker, cand. scient. Joel Katz.)
31 An Arabic translation of *De Materia Medica* by Dioscorides, completed in 990 AD by Abu Abd Allah el-Natili in Samarkand; 11th century copy, Universiteitsbibliotheek, Leiden.
32 *Medicine of the Prophet*, transl. by P. Johnson, Islamic Texts Society, Cambridge 1998.
33 Galen, *op. cit.*, pp. 119ff.
34 Avicenna, *Canon of Medicine* vol. V, 'Special Prescriptions and Theriacs', in J. Sontheimer, *Zusammengesetzte Heilmittel der Araber,* Freiburg 1845, pp. 5, 15-17, reprinted 1996 by the Institute for the History of Arabic Islamic Science at the J. W. Goethe University, Frankfurt, as vol. 9 of *Islamic Medicine.*

35 L. Cogliati Arano, *The Medieval Health Handbook: Tacuinum Sanitatis*, London and New York 1976 (XLI); P. Willett Cummins, *A Critical Edition of Le régime très utile et très proufitable pour conserver et garder la santé du corps humain*, Chapel Hill 1976, pp. 44ff.
36 Galen, *op. cit.*, pp. 107-8, cf. p.119.
37 Prosper Alpin, *La Médecine des Égyptiens*, Cairo 1980, Book IV, Chapters VIII-XIII.
38 Cf. chapter 2, n. 24.
39 Alpin, *op. cit.*, p. 309.
40 Budge, *op. cit.*, p. 409.
41 Alpin, *op. cit.*, p. 263.
42 I am indebted to Mr Mohsin el-Naggar for this information.

4 Recipes for Luxury

1 L. Bass, 'The bronze age shipwreck at Ulu Burun, Turkey. 1985 campaign', *American Journal of Archaeology* 92, 1985. See also *National Geographic Magazine* Vol. 172, No. 6, December 1987, pp. 693ff.
2 C. Shelmerdine, *The Perfume Industry of Mycenaean Pylos (Studies in Mediterranean Archaeology* 34, 1985).
3 See E. Ebeling, 'Mittelassyrische Rezepte zur Bereitung von wohlreichenden Salben', *Orientalia* 17, 1948, pp. 129ff; 299ff.
4 Pliny, *op. cit.,* XII.78.
5 *Ibid.* XXII.118.
6 *Ibid.* XIII.20.
7 Theophrastus, *On Odours* 34. 38.
8 Pliny, *op. cit.,* XII.109.
9 Theophrastus, *op. cit.,* 37.
10 *Ibid.* 28, 31, 42, 44; *Growth of Plants* 6.17.2.
11 Pliny, *op.cit.* XIII.4,17.
12 *Ibid.* XIII,8.
13 Dioscorides, *op. cit.*, I.72.
14 Pliny, *op. cit.,* XIII.17.
15 *Ibid.* XIII.7, cf. Lucas, p. 88.
16 Pliny, *op. cit.,* XIII,4.
17 *Ibid.* XIII.5-6.
18 Athenaeus, *The Deipnosophists* XV. 688ff.
19 Dioscorides, *op. cit.,* I.71; I.39.
20 Pliny, *op. cit.,* XIII.8.
21 Dioscorides, *op. cit.,* I.16.
22 *Ibid.* I.17.
23 *Ibid.* I.18.
24 Lucas, p. 89.
25 Theophrastus. *On Odours* 44.
26 Pliny, *op. cit.,* XIII.8.
27 Dioscorides, *op. cit.*, I.62.
28 Pliny, *op. cit.*, XIII.12.
29 *Ibid.* XV.31; XII.12; XIII.17.
30 Theophrastus, *On Odours* 27; 42.
31 Dioscorides, *op. cit.,* I.1; 66.
32 Pliny, *op. cit.*, XXI. 40.
33 Theophrastus, *op. cit.,* 29. Pliny implies that other ingredients could be mixed in (*Natural History* XIII.14).
34 Pliny, *op. cit.*, XXI.40, 42; XIII.5.
35 Theophrastus, *Enquiry into Plants* IX.7.4.
36 Theophrastus, *On Odours* 32-4; 38.
37 Dioscorides, *op. cit.*, I.124.
38 Pliny *op. cit.*, XII.109.
39 Papyrus Ebers 774.
40 Pliny, *op. cit.*, XII.109; XIII.12; XIII.5.
41 *Ibid.* XIII.17.
42 Theophrastus, *On Odours* 25, 26, 27.
43 Dioscorides, *op. cit.*, I.65, I.124.
44 Shelmerdine, *op. cit.*, pp. 26-31.
45 Theophrastus, *On Odours* 31, 42, 50, 55.
46 Dioscorides, *op. cit.*, I.58, I.68.
47 Pliny, *op. cit.*, XXI.61.
48 *Ibid.* XXI, 163, cf. XII.10.
49 *Ibid.* XIII.5.
50 *Ibid.* XXI.37.
51 Theophrastus, *Enquiry into Plants* IX.7.3; *On Odours* 30.
52 Pliny, *op. cit.*, XIII.6.
53 *Amarakinon*: Dioscorides I.68; Pliny, *op. cit.*, XIII.14; *sampsuchinum*: Dioscorides, *op. cit.*, I.58; Pliny, *op. cit.*, XIII.10.
54 Dioscorides, *op. cit.*, I.14.
55 Theophrastus, *On Odours* 38, 42, 55.
56 By the respective translators of the Loeb edition of Pliny and Dioscorides (Goodyer).
57 Dioscorides, *op. cit.*, I.69.
58 Theophrastus, *On Odours* 30, 35; Pliny, *op. cit.*, XIII.13; Dioscorides, *op. cit.*, I.68, 69.
59 Theophrastus, *On Odours* 31, 42.
60 Dioscorides, *op. cit.*, I.12, 13.
61 Theophrastus, *Enquiry into Plants* IX 4.4; 5.
62 Dioscorides, *op. cit.*, I.74; Pliny *op. cit.*, XIII.15.
63 Pliny, *op. cit.*, XXI.36.
64 *Ibid.* XV.37; Theophrastus *Enquiry into Plants.* VI.8.5.
65 Dioscorides, *op. cit.*, I.48; Pliny, *op. cit.*, XIII. 9.
66 Pliny, *op. cit.*, XIII.10, 11.
67 *Ibid.* XIII.9.
68 *Ibid.* XIII.9, 18.
69 Shelmerdine, *op. cit.*, pp. 25ff.
70 Theophrastus, *On Odours* 25; Pliny, *op. cit.*, XIII.9; Dioscorides, *op. cit.*, I.53.
71 Theophrastus, *On Odours* 25, 50.
72 *Ibid.* 31, 33.
73 *Ibid.* 45, 51.
74 Pliny, *op. cit.*, XIII.17.
75 *Ibid.* XIII.4.
76 Dioscorides, *op. cit.*, III.40.
77 Pliny, *op. cit.*, XIII.18.
78 *Ibid.* XIII.17.
79 Theophrastus, *On Odours* 29.
80 Dioscorides, *op. cit.*, I.77. On the subject of myrrh and stakte see also O. Steuer, *Myrrhe und Stakte*, Vienna 1933.
81 Theophrastus, *On Odours* 38, 42, 44.
82 See Ebeling, *op. cit.*, pp. 132ff. for the identity of these ingredients.
83 Papyrus Anastasi IV.15ff.: A. H. Gardiner, *Late Egyptian Miscellanies,* Brussels 1937, p. 51. Translated by R. Caminos, *Late Egyptian Miscellanies,* London 1954, p.200.
84 Dioscorides, *op. cit.*, II.91.
85 *Ibid.* II.92.
86 Pliny, *op. cit.*, X.55; cf. Paszthory, *op. cit.*,p.49: Commagene, named after a locality in Anatolia, consisted of goose fat with nard and cinnamon. Cf. also Theophrastus, *Enquiry into Plants* IX.7.2 where a perfume named *komakon* is mentioned as being an ingredient in exquisite perfumes. Its place of origin appears to be Arabia, but the pas sage is not entirely clear.
87 For the significance of unguent cones see below, Chapter 5.
88 H. Carter & A. C. Mace, *The Tomb of Tut. Ankh.Amen* II, pp. 206-10.
89 *Journal of the Chemical Society*, 1926, p. 2615-9.
90 Carter & Mace, *op. cit.*, III, p. 147, pl. 89A.
91 *Ibid.* p. 147, pl. 89A.
92 *Ibid.* p. 146, pl. 78B.
93 Carter's notes are now kept in the Griffith Institute, Oxford.
94 Carter & Mace, *op. cit.*, I pl. 14 (visible on the extreme right of this overall view of the chamber).
95 *Ibid.* III, pl. 18.
96 *Ibid.*, pl. 48.

5 Scent for Love and Rebirth

1 For a translation of most of the texts of which extracts are quoted below see e.g. W.K. Simpson (ed.), *The Literature of Ancient Egypt*, Yale University 1972.
2 Already in the Middle Kingdom such servants had specific titles: 'he who anoints dignitaries in his master's house', see E. S. Thompson, 'The anointing of officials in Ancient Egypt', *Journal of Near Eastern Studies* 53, 1994, p. 25.
3 For a recent study of unguent cones see N. Cherpion, 'Le "cône d'onguent"', *Bulletin de l'Institut français d'archéologie orientale* 94, 1994, pp. 79-106 with a reference on pp. 86-7 to the suggestions of this writer.
4 For the shape of the cones see E. Maraite, 'Le cône de parfum dans l'Ancienne Égypte' in Fs Vandersleyen, Louvain-la-Neuve 1992, pp. 213-19.
5 B. Bruyère, *Rapport sur les fouilles de Deir el-Médineh* (1924-25), Cairo 1926, pp. 69-72, quoted by Cherpion, *op. cit.*, p. 83.
6 W. Westendorff, 'Bemerkungen zur "Kammer der Wiedergeburt" im Tutankhamungrab', *Zeitschrift für ägyptische Sprache* 94, 1967, pp. 139-50.
7 M. L. Ryhiner, *L'offrande du lotus dans les temples égyptiens de l'époque tardive,* Brussels 1986, pp. 31, 43, 53.
8 A vivid description of the life of a man

with extraordinary olfactory skills is given in Patrick Süskind's novel *Das Parfüm*.

9 W. A. Emboden, 'Transcultural use of narcotic water lilies in ancient Egyptian and Maya drug ritual', *Journal of Ethnopharmacology* 3, 1981, p. 58.
10 P. Leiden XXIV.7-11, ed. by F. Ll. Griffith ands H. Thompson, 1904, reprinted 1974.
11 Dioscorides, *op. cit.*, IV. 76.
12 R. Germer, *Flora des pharaonischen Ägypten*, Mainz am Rhein 1985, p. 169.
13 Emboden, *loc. cit.*
14 Dioscorides, *op. cit.*, IV. 76.
15 M. Zohary, *Plants of the Bible*, Cambridge 1982, p. 189.
16 C. Desroches-Noblecourt, 'Poissons, tabous et transformation du mort. Nouvelles considé-rations sur les pèlerinages aux villes saintes', *Kemi* 13, 1954, pp. 32-42.
17 Papyrus Rylands IX 8/15-18, see S. E. Thompson, 'The anointing of officials in ancient Egypt', *Journal of Near Eastern Studies* 53, 1994, pp 15ff.
18 H. Altenmüller, 'Das Ölmagasin im Grab des Hesire in Saqqara (QS 2405)', *Studien zur altägyptischen Kultur* 4, 1976, pp.1-29.
19 *Edfou* II, p. 210, cf. the old translation in J. Dümichen, *Der Grabpalast des Patuamenap in der thebanischen Nekropolis*, Leipzig 1885, p.28.
20 J. M. Kruchten, *Les annales des prêtres de Karnak* (Orientalia Lovaniensa Analecta 32), Leuven 1989, p. 159.
21 See J. van Dijk, 'Hieratic Inscriptions from the Tomb of Maya at Saqqara: A Preliminary Survey', *Göttinger Miszellen* 127, 1992, pp. 23-32.
22 É. Chassinat, *Le Mystère d'Osiris au mois de khoiak*, Cairo 1968, pp. 611-13.
23 *Ibid., passim.*
24 *Edfou* VI, p. 166; Chassinat, *op. cit.*, pp. 611ff.; Aufrère, *op. cit.*,pp.337ff.
25 Aufrère reads '1 hin', or 0.5 l.

6 Fragrant Remedies

1 See the extensive bibliography in J. E. Nunn, *Ancient Egyptian Medicine*, London 1996.
2 M. A. H. Ducros, 'Essai sur le droguier populaire arabe de l'inspectorat des pharma cies du Caire', *Mémoires de l'Institut d'Égypte* XI, Cairo 1930.
3 Dioscorides, *op. cit.*, I.52.
4 Theophrastus, *On Odours* 59.
5 Papyrus Ebers, 527.
6 Berlin papyrus No. 3038, 151.
7 Papyrus Chassinat, 123, see W. Till, *Die Arzneikunde der Kopten*, Berlin 1951, p. 122
8 Dioscorides, *op. cit.*, I.59.
9 *Ibid.* III.75.
10 Papyrus Hearst, 113.
11 A. Leroi-Gourhan, *La momie de Ramsès II* (ed. L. Balout & C. Roubet), Paris 1986, pp.162ff.
12 Dioscorides, *op. cit.*,I.45,46.
13 *Ibid.* I.74.
14 Papyrus Ebers, 687.
15 Dioscorides, *op. cit.*,II.86.
16 *Ibid.* I.91.
17 Pliny, *op. cit.*,XIX.161.
18 Papyrus Ebers, 770.
19 Papyrus Ebers, 258.
20 *Ibid.*, 142
21 Dioscorides, *op. cit.*, III.67.
22 Papyrus Hearst, 44.
23 Papyrus Ebers, 249.
24 Berlin papyrus No. 3038, 163e.
25 Dioscorides, *op. cit.*, I.61.
26 *Ibid.*, II.124.
27 Papyrus Edwin Smith 21,9-22,10.
28 Papyrus Ebers, 473.
29 Dioscorides, *op. cit.*, I.65.
30 *Ibid.*, I.66.
31 Theophrastus, 'On Odours' 36.
32 Papyrus Ebers, 85.
33 Dioscorides, *op. cit.*,I.105.
34 Alpini, *op. cit.*, 318.
35 Dioscorides, *op. cit.*,I.62.
36 Pliny, *op. cit.*,XXI.126.
37 Papyrus Ebers, 475.
38 Alpini, *op. cit.*, 248, 316.
39 Dioscorides, *op. cit.*,I.68; I.58.
40 Theophrastus, *On Odours*, 35.
41 Dioscorides, *op. cit.*,I.72.
42 *Ibid.* I.71.
43 *Ibid.* I.48.
44 Papyrus Ebers, 471.
45 Papyrus Chassinat, 219, see W. Till, *Die Arzneikunde der Kopten*, Berlin 1951, p. 127.
46 Dioscorides, *op. cit.*,I.53.
47 Pliny, *op. cit.*,XXII.59; XX.246; XX.73; XXVII.17; XXI.122.
48 Theophrastus, *On Odours* 35.
49 Alpini, *op. cit.*, 318.
50 Dioscorides, *op. cit.*,III.40.
51 Papyrus Ramesseum V No. XIII.
52 Papyrus Hearst, 180.
53 Papyrus Ebers, 672.
54 *Ibid.*, 254.
55 *Ibid.*, 142.
56 *Ägyptische Urkunden aus den königlichen Mu-seen. Koptische Urkunden*, I, Berlin 1904, p. 113.
57 *Ibid.* 9, see Till, *op. cit.*, p. 113.
58 Papyrus Chassinat, 96, see Till, *op. cit.*, p. 120.
59 Papyrus Ebers, 363.
60 *Ägyptische Urkunden . . . Koptische Urkunden*, 114-5, see Till, *op. cit.*, p. 122.
61 Papyrus Hearst, 223; 234.
62 Berlin papyrus No. 3038, 131.
63 Papyrus Hearst, 161.
64 Berlin papyrus No. 3038, 142.
65 Papyrus Ebers, 574.
66 *Ibid.*, 690.
67 Pliny, *op. cit.*, XX.121, 138; XXI.123, 127.
68 Papyrus Hearst, 235.
69 Papyrus Ebers, 175.70;
Berlin papyrus No. 3038, 142.
71 Berlin papyrus No. 3038, 40.
72 Papyrus Hearst, 87.
73 Papyrus Chassinat, 125.
74 Pliny, *op. cit.*,XX.187.
75 Berlin papyrus No. 3038, 76.
76 R. Campbell Thompson, *The Assyrian Herbal*, London 1924, p. 166.

7 The Art of Cosmetics

1 *Études et travaux* 10, 1978, pp. 83ff.
2 The interpretation of this passage in the Tale of the Two Brothers was convincingly argued by P. Derchain in his article 'La per-ruque et le cristal', in *Studien zur altägypti-schen Kultur* 2, 1975, pp. 55ff.
3 Papyrus Harris 500, 5, 12–6, 2, adapted to Derchain's suggestion, cf. n. 2.
4 Herodotus, *op. cit.*, II.37.
5 Derchain, *op. cit.*, pp. 69ff.
6 Papyrus Hearst 155.
7 Papyrus Ebers 711; Papyrus Hearst 32, 151.
8 Papyrus Ebers 708; Papyrus Hearst 31, 150.
9 Dioscorides, *op. cit.*, II.193.
10 *Ibid.*,V. 152, cf. R. J. Forbes, *Studies in Ancient Technology*, IV, p. 82.
11 Forbes, *loc. cit.*
12 M. Grieve, *A Modern Herbal*, London 1992, p. 503.
13 Forbes, *op. cit.*, III, p. 180.
14 Ducros, *op. cit.*, p. 29.
15 Dioscorides, *op. cit.*,II, 132-3.
16 Pliny, *op. cit.*,XXII, 154ff.
17 Grieve, *op. cit.*, p. 503.
18 Papyrus Ebers 451, 459, 454, 458, 457, 453, 460, 461, 456
19 *Études et travaux* 10, pp. 119ff.
20 Papyrus Ebers 465, 466, 470.
21 *Ibid.*, 468.
22 *Ibid.*, 251, 473.
23 Athenaeus, *The Deipnosophists*, XV, 689–90; Clemens Alexandrinus, *Stromateis* II, 64, 2.
24 Papyrus Ebers 714.
25-7 *Ibid.*, 715, 716, 717.
28 *Nature* 397, pp. 483–4, 11 February 1999 and *CNRS Info* 371, February 1999, pp. 3–4.
29 Book of the Dead, rubric to spell 125.
30 H. von Deines, H. Grapow & W. Westendorf, *Grundriss der Medizin der alten Ägypter* IV, 2, pp. 56-7.
31 Published in *Journal of The American Research Center in Egypt* 6, 1967, pp. 135–8.
32 Papyrus Ebers 390.
33 A somewhat similar concept was marketed as 'California Glow'.
34 *Revue d'Égyptologie* III, 11938, pl. III.
35 N. de G. Davies, *Seven Private Tombs at Kurnah*, pl. 28.
36 Excellent colour photograph in *Arts of Asia*, November-December 1983, p. 78.

Bibliography

Chassinat, É., 'Quelques parfums et onguents en usage dans les temples de l'Égypte ancienne' in *Revue de l'Égypte ancienne* 3, 1931, pp. 117–67.

Cherpion, N., 'Le "cône d'onguent" ' in *Bulletin de l'Institut français d'archéologie orientale* 94, 1994, pp. 79–106.

Dioscorides, *The Greek Herbal of Dioscorides, Englished by John Goodyer 1655,* Gunther, R. T. (Ed.), New York 1955.

Egypt's Golden Age: The Art of Living in the New Kingdom 1558-1085 BC (Museum of Fine Arts), Boston 1982, pp. 184-226.

Forbes, R. J., 'Cosmetics and Perfumes in Antiquity' in *Studies in Ancient Technology*, III, Leiden 1955, pp.2–24.

Galen, *Claudii Galeni Opera Omnia*, ed. K. Gottlob-Kühn, Leipzig 1827, Hildesheim 1965.

Germer, R., *Flora des pharaonischen Ägypten*, Mainz 1985.

Hepper, F. N., *Pharaoh's Flowers*, London 1990.

Hughes, G. R., 'The Cosmetic Arts in Ancient Egypt' in *Journal of the Society of Cosmetic Chemists,* vol. 10, no., May 1959, pp. 159–76.

Loret, V., 'Le Kyphi, parfum sacré des anciens égyptiens' in *Journal asiatique* 10, July–August 1887, pp. 76–132.

Lucas, A., *Ancient Egyptian Materials and Industries,* 4th ed. revised by J.R. Harris, London 1962, pp. 80-5

Manniche, L., *An Ancient Egyptian Herbal*, London 1989, pp. 44 ff.

Manniche, L., 'Ancient Egyptians. Pioneers in Natural Cosmetics' in *Cosmetics & Toiletries*, U. S. A., June 1994, pp. 65-70

Manniche, L., 'Cosmetics in ancient Egypt', in *British Museum Magazine* 11, Autumn 1982, pp. 8–9.

Nunn. J. E., *Ancient Egyptian Medicine*, London 1996.

Paszthory, E., 'Laboratorien in ptolemäischen Tempelanlagen' in *Antike Welt* 19, 1988, pp.2–20.

Paszthory, E., *Salben, Schminken und Parfüme im Altertum*, Mainz am Rhein 1992 – *Antike Welt* 21, 1990, pp. 1-764.

Pliny the Elder, *Natural History*, Vols. 1–5 transl. by H. Rackham, Vols. 6–10 transl. by W. H. S. Jones, Cambridge, Mass. 1966 and 1969

Schoske, S. (ed.) *Schönheit – Abglanz der Göttlichkeit. Kosmetik im alten Ägypten*, Munich 1990

Theophrastus, *Enquiry into Plants*, Vols. 1 and 2, transl. by A. F. Hort, Cambridge, Mass. 1916, 1926.

Vartavan, C. de and Amorss, V. A., *Codex of Ancient Egyptian Plant Remains,* London 1998.

Wallert, I., *Der verzierte Löffel*. Ägyptologische Abhandlungen vol. 16, Wiesbaden 1967.

Winand, J. et al., *L'art du parfum,* Paris 1993.

Acknowledgments

The author and the photographer are indebted to the staff of the Louvre, in particular Catherine Bridonneau, for answering numerous queries and providing facilities for photography, and to Christiane Ziegler, convervateur général of the Egyptian Department, for permission to publish illustrations of the objects.

Quotations reprinted by permission of the publishers and the Loeb Classical Library from

Herodotus: *History*, II, LCL 117, translated by A. D. Godley, Cambridge, Mass.: Harvard University Press, 1981;
Pliny the Elder: *Natural History* X ,Vol. 3, LCL 353; XII, XIII, XV, Vol. 4, LCL 370; XIX,Vol.5, LCL 371, translated by H. Rackham; XX–XXII,Vol. 6, LCL 392 translated by W. H. S. Jones, Cambridge, Mass.: Harvard University Press, 1966, 1969;
Theophrastus: *Enquiry into Plants*,Vol. 1, LCL 70,Vol. 2, LCL 79, translated by A. F. Hort, Cambridge, Mass.: Harvard University Press, 1916 and 1926.
Theophrastus: *De causis plantarum*, LCL 471, translated by Benedikt Einarson, Cambridge, Mass.: Harvard University Press, 1976. © The President and Fellows of Harvard College 1976.

Acknowledgment is made to the following for permission to reproduce illustrations:

Ägyptisches Museum, Berlin
Ashmolean Museum, Oxford
British Museum, London
Calouste Gulbenkian Museum, Lisbon
Christie's, London
The David Collection, Copenhagen
Egyptian Museum, Cairo
Fitzwilliam Museum, Cambridge
Griffith Institute, Oxford
Hermitage, St Petersburg
Metropolitan Museum of Art, New York
Musée du Louvre, Paris
Musées Royaux d'Art et d'Histoire, Brussels
Museo Egizio, Turin
Norbert Schimmel Collection, New York
Pushkin Museum of Fine Arts, Moscow
Rijksmuseum van Oudheden, Leiden
Topkapi Palace Library, Istanbul
Universiteitsbibliothek, Leiden

Ancient Egyptian Terms

Alkanet	*nesti*
Almond	*awent*
Aspalathos	*djalem*
	djeba
Balanos	*ished*
Camel grass	*shut Nemty*
	kema Kush
	kek Nehsw
Castor oil plant	*degem*
Cinnamon	*tisheps*
Conifer resin	*sefet*
Cumin	*tepenen*
Cyperus sedge	*giu* , *shebin*
Dill	*imset*
Fat	*adj*
Fir	*ash*
Frankincense	*senetjer* , *antiu*
Gum	*kemyt*
Henna	*henu*
Juniper tree	*wan*
berries	*peru wan* , *peresh*
Kyphi	*kapet*
Ladanum	*ibr*
Lotus	*seshen*
Mandrake	*reremet*
Medjat	*medjat*
Mint	*nkepet* , *akay*
Moringa oil	*bak*
Myrrh	*khery*
Olive	*djedtu*
Persea	*shawab*
Pine tree	*ash en khaset imentet*
seeds	*peru shenu*
	mereh nar
tree	*qed*
'Sacred oils'	*hekenu*
	seti heb
	sefet
	nekhenem
	tuat
	hat en ash
	hat en Tjehenu
	madjet
Sesame	*iku*
oil	*neheh*
Sweet flag	*kenen*
	sebi nedjem
Wood pitch	*menen*

Index

Ab (resin) 29
Abhal (brathy, juniper) 21
Abies cilicica 28, 108
Acacia 39, 108, 114, 123–5, 145
oil 114
Acetone 88
Achaia 71
Acidity 25
Acorus calamus 15, 23–25
Adj ('fatty matter') 43
Aegina, island of 23
Ahm (antiu) 27
Akakia (extract of acacia seeds) 39, 115, 124
Akay (mint) 22
Akhenaten 31, 33, 35, 61, 62, 65, 140
Alasia 83
Aleppo 29, 122
Alexander the Great 8
Alexander from Tralles 56
Alexandria 16, 47, 56, 77, 101
Alhagi maurorum 14
Alkanet 23, 71, 79, 80, 95, 123, 146
All-heal 72, 81
Almond oil 30, 66, 67, 122
Aloe 123
Alpini, Prospero 14, 18, 57, 58, 119, 123
Alun 130
Amaracinum 74, 76
Amaracum 22, 74
Amaracus 74, 75
Amarakinon 74, 75, 83, 121, 148
Amarakon 74, 75
Amarna 31, 33, 35, 61, 62, 65, 81, 133, 138, 140
Amenemhat III 109
Amenemhat IV 120
Amenemhet 109
Amenherkhopeshef 39
Amenhotep II 18, 117
Amenhotep III 10, 34, 64, 76, 81, 92, 94
Amomon 75
Amomum 75, 76, 81
Amulets 91, 98, 135
Amun 7, 18, 28, 36, 38, 53, 54, 83, 88, 92, 94, 96, 102, 106, 110
Anaesthetic 121
Anastasi 148
Anatolia 85, 148
Andromachus 57, 58
Andropogon schoenanthus 15, 16
Anethum graveolens 18, 115
Angina 118
Anhydrite 33, 70,71
Anise 125
Ankh-imy (henna ?) 19
Ankhesenamun 61, 90, 130
Anointing 8, 35, 36, 45, 68, 79, 95, 96, 116, 118, 121, 124, 135, 137
Antelopefat 117, 123
Anthemis tinctoria 116
Antidote 47–49, 50, 55, 57–59
Antimony 137
Antiphanes 63
Antirheumatic 122
Antiseptic 119, 122
Antiu 7, 26, 27, 29, 36, 38, 39, 41, 42, 45, 55, 85, 95, 96, 109, 110, 117, 124, 130, 145
Anus, heat in the 117, 123
Anxiety 33, 57,58, 115
Apemum 102
Aperioum 102
Aphrodisiac 56, 101
Apium graveolens 115
Apollonios Mys 66
Apousi 80, 123
Arabian 77, 81, 144
Arabs 10, 56
Arakhou 18, 117
Aramaic 50
Arar (arkeuthos) 21
Aristolochia 58
Aristotle 10, 33
Arkeuthos 21, 52
Armenia 75
Aromatherapy 1, 3, 9, 18, 30, 53, 74, 113–16, 119, 122, 123
Aromatics 45, 81, 111, 114
Arsenic 140
Arundo donax 24
Arw 21
Ascalon 19, 71
Ash (fir tree Abies cilicica) 23, 28, 108, 118
Asia 12, 15, 27, 80, 118, 122, 137
Aspalathos 14, 15, 44, 123
Asphalt 58
Asphodelus ramosus 132
Asphodil 132
Ass 133–135
Assyrian 61, 125, 150
Asthma 49
Astringent 14, 39, 42, 44, 71, 73, 77, 79, 118, 122, 124
Aten, the sun disc 24, 27, 31, 33, 35, 58, 61, 65, 82
Athenaeus 8, 66
Athens 8, 63, 65
Athribis 27
Atropine 102
Aui-sha 27
Avicenna 57, 147

INDEX

Baboon 70, 71
Babylon 15, 81
Bactria 145
Bak (moringa) 30
Balanites aegyptiaca 30, 65
Balanos 29, 30, 65, 68, 75, 77, 81, 122, 134
Baldness 85, 134
Balm 67, 146
Balsam 67, 75, 77, 85, 86, 122
Balsamarium 67
Balsamum 67, 69, 122, 123
Balti fish 72, 142
Barley 110
  flour 102, 124,
  pearl 133
Basil 115, 124
  oil 115
Bastet 82
Bath 63, 95, 99, 113, 121, 133, 135
Bazaar 56, 59
Bdellium 28, 48, 52, 145, 146
Bedet 134
Beer 92, 94, 102, 124, 125
Beeswax 85, 86, 129
Behen-oil (moringa oil) 30
Belching 114
Bergamot 75
Bes 81, 141, 142
Bible 8, 23, 77, 129, 149
Bicarbonate of manganese 134
Bite, serpent 49, 57, 58, 67, 77
  scorpion 116
Bitumen 45, 52, 58, 108, 111, 146
Black 88, 106, 111, 133
Bladder 118
Blisters 116
Blood 44, 83, 114, 116, 133
Body decoration 141
Boil 78
Bois de Rhodes 14
Bois de roses 14
Bone 27, 34, 36, 43, 124, 130, 138
Boswellia 26, 28
Bowels 118
Bowl, drinking 141
  incense 26, 34, 57, 59
  unguent 71, 85
Brathy 21,23
Breasts, inflamed 124
Breath, 'sweet' 29
  disguising bad 55
Breathing fragrance 91, 113, 130
Brechu (seed) 133
Bruyère, Bernard 96
Burial 21, 34, 35, 86, 94, 98, 99, 108, 109, 111, 124, 128, 135, 136, 138
Burns 121

Calamus aromaticus 23
  odoratus 24
Calamus verus 23
Calcite 63, 86, 106, 109, 134
Calycotome villosa 14
Camel grass 15, 16, 55, 67, 76, 77, 79
Camomile oil 115, 116
Canopus 19, 71
Carbonate of copper, green 138
Cardamom 16, 81
Carob 38, 145, 146
Carpobalsamum 75, 77
Carter, Howard 84, 86
Cassia 16
Castor fruit 134
  oil 30
Cat excrement 55
  fat 134
Catfish 55
Cat-thyme 81
Cedar 17, 119, 120
Celery 115, 118, 124
  oil 115
Censing 10, 47, 48, 53, 55
Cerussite 137
Chalk 132, 135
Champollion, Jean-François 95
Cheops (Khufu) 108
Chest, diseases of the 51, 114, 125
  unguent 120
Chicory 123
Children 53, 92, 98, 105, 106, 109, 118, 125
Childbirth 141
Chios 29, 61
Christthorn 71
Chroma 74
Cici oil 31
Cilicia 23, 30, 63, 71
Cinnabar 23, 79, 140
Cinnamominum (cinnamon oil) 77
Cinnamomum camphora 17
  cassia 16
  verum 17
  zeylanicum 17
Cinnamon 16, 17, 39, 41, 44, 49, 54, 55, 57, 59, 63, 65, 68, 72, 73, 75, 75, 79, 81, 85, 111, 116, 122
  oil 77, 116
Circulation 116
Clary sage 80, 123
Clay 57
Cleanliness 130
Cleansing 34, 52, 116, 130, 132, 135
Cleopatra 63, 135
Comb 8, 128
Commagene 77, 85, 148
Commiphora africana 28
  erythraea 28
  gileadensis 67
  opobalsamum 67
Conception 92, 97, 128, 141
Cone, unguent 85, 92, 95, 96, 98, 105, 130, 142
Container, cosmetic 39, 63, 66, 67, 76, 82, 86, 88, 106, 125, 132, 133, 137, 140; see also Bowl, Dish, Flask, Jar, Spoon
Convolvulus scoparius 14
Convulsions 122
Copts, Coptic 12, 17, 22, 28, 56, 114, 122. 123
Coriander 19, 71, 79, 124, 125
Corinth 63, 71
Cos 74
Costus 58, 75, 76, 81
Cough 51, 125
Cow 138
Cow-goddess Hathor 5, 126
Crete 14, 61
Crocinum (saffron perfume) 23
Crocodile 22, 55, 134
Crocus sativus 23, 50, 59, 68, 79, 81
Cucumber 130

Cumin 116, 117, 124,125
Cumin oil 116, 117
Cyclades 18
Cymbopogon schoenanthus 15
Cyperos 18, 79
Cyperus grass (sedge) 17, 134
Cyperus longus 17, 18
rotundus 18
Cypress 33, 78
Cyprinum (henna perfume) 19, 71, 73
Cypros 19, 63, 71
Cyprus 7, 19, 29, 30, 61, 63, 72, 74, 78, 134
Cytisus lanigerus (broom) 14
Cyzicus 63, 71, 74

Dakhla 41
Damocrates 47,48
Daphnitis 16, 77
Dar shishahan 14
Darius 8
Darsisahan 14
Dasam 17
Decoration, body 141
Deer 55
Degem 108
Deir el-Bahari 25, 36, 37, 95, 129, 134, 141
Deir el-Medina 134, 141
Delirium 58
Delos 63, 66
Dementia 58
Demten (mastic) 55
Dendera 11, 37, 41, 44
Depression 102, 115,116
Detergent 132, 133
Diaphoretic 16
Diarrhoea 124
Diaxylon 14
Digestive problems 118
Dill 18, 117-119
oil 117
Diocles 22, 74
Diodorus 116, 119, 144
Diorite 109
Dioscorides Pedanius 8, 12, 19, 21, 24, 26, 29, 31, 41, 49, 50, 65, 102, 103, 106, 113, 119, 121, 123, 132
Dish, cosmetic 72, 73, 141, 142; see also Bowl, Spoon
Distillation 10, 19, 71, 99
Diuretic 16, 119, 121
Djahi 28
Djalem 15
Djeba 15
Djed en qed 29
Djefti 83
Djerem 15
Donkey 55, 117, 118, 134
Dorcas gazelle 64
Dough 135
Dreckapotheke 55
Drinon 71
Drunkenness 92, 141
Duck 33, 54, 66, 106, 142
Dung, gazelle 122
Dwarf 62, 141
Dye, dyeing 23, 45, 71, 73, 74, 79, 80, 95, 96, 116, 134, 141
Dysentery 123
Dyspepsia 25

Ear complaints 56, 117, 123
Ebers, Papyrus 113, 134
Ebony 76, 120, 134
Edfu 27, 29, 31, 35, 37, 38, 41, 43, 45, 51, 52, 54, 99, 106, 108, 110
Edwin Smith, Papyrus 113
Egg, ostrich 135
raven's 133
Egyptian' perfume, 'The 64
Elettaria cardamomum 16
Embalming 111, 116
Emmer wheat 124
Emollient 133
Entian 58
Epagomenal days 110
Epheres 109
Ephesos, Rufus of 47, 48
Ephesus (Ephesos) 47, 48
Epilepsy 56
Eritrea 18, 137
Erotic 91, 94, 97, 99, 102, 121, 130, 140
Erysisceptrum ('red sceptre') 14
Ethiopia 26, 28, 30, 38, 80
E-ti (henna) 73
Euboea 18
Euphorbia 59
Euphrates 7, 81, 137
Excrement, animal 55, 122, 130
Exhalation 33, 52, 53
Eyebrows 134, 137
Eye complaints 124
Eye of Horus 29, 34
Eye paint 63, 86, 109, 132, 135, 137, 138

Face, blackened 106
treatment of the 102, 116
paint 127, 130, 138
wash 135
Farouq', 'tiryac of 58
Fats 10, 12, 31, 108, 134
Fayum 31
Feast 43, 44, 92, 94, 95, 97, 99, 102, 104, 109, 110
Feet, steeped in unguent 63
dyeing of 141
Fennel 14
Fenugreek 79, 118
oil 118
Fertility 46, 94, 97, 106, 140
Ferula 28, 83
Fetet 29
Fever 118, 119, 121
Fig 116, 146
Filtration 137
Fingermarks, thieves' 86
Fingernails, painted 141
Fir chips 124
oil 108, 110, 118
resin 28, 134
Fish 50, 72, 99, 104-106, 133, 137, 142
Fishing 102-106
Flask, ointment 8, 97, 125
Flatulence 25
Fly excreta 130
Forbes, R. J. 11, 132, 133
Fowling 102, 104, 106
Fractures, treatment of 118
Frankincense 10, 25, 26, 30, 47, 50, 53, 55, 57, 108, 111, 124
Fumigation 21, 47, 49, 51, 113, 125

Fumitory 59
Funeral 72, 99, 110, 111

Gaiuma resin 111
Galbanum resin 28, 66, 67, 122
Galena (ore of lead) 136, 137
Gall of ox 135
Gangrene 133
Gar-nu (antiu) 27
Gar-pekher (antiu) 27
Gati (scent) 83
Gazelle 8, 55, 64, 122, 133
Genen of niuben-tree (sweet flag ?) 24, 55
Gerard, John 120
Ges-fek 108
Gilukhepa or Kirgipa 81
Giu 'of the oases' (cyperus grass ?) 17
Gizir (cassia) 17
Gnn 24
Goodyer, John 14
Goose fat 31, 85, 119, 124
Grape, wild 81
Greece 16, 31, 47, 61, 65, 73, 79
Gums 12, 25, 65

Haemorrhage 114
Haemorrhoids 118, 121
Hair care 130
Hair, importance of 12, 129
Hairdressing 130
Hair, lock of 91
Hair loss, inducing 121
Hair remedy 85
Hallucinogenic (mandrake) 102
Hands, anointed 63, 68, 79, 80
  dyed 141
Harris I, Papyrus 54
Hartwort 146
Hat-en-tjehenu 108
Hathor 5, 15, 37, 41, 43, 78, 95, 126, 138
Hatshepsut 25, 28, 36,37, 53, 92, 105, 117
Head, adornments 129, 134, 142
  anointed 95, 97,
Headache 56, 75, 117–119, 121, 122, 124
Hearst, Papyrus 113
Heart remedies 58, 110, 114, 130
Heb-sed (royal jubilee) festival 108

Hedeosmos (mint) 22
Hedgehog 134
Hekenu 15, 37, 39, 41, 43, 108
Heliopolis 31, 53
Heliotrope 83, 123
Hemayt (fenugreek ?) 118
Henbane 59, 102
Henna 19, 63, 71, 73, 81, 118, 134, 141
Henna oil 118
Henu (henna?) 19, 71
Herodotus 21, 30, 116, 130
Herpes 124
Hesire 108, 110
Hierakonpolis 127
Hip belt 141, 142
Hippopotamus 122, 134
Hittites 81, 83
Hodveg (cyperus grass) 18
Homer 79
Hoof of ass 133, 134
Horemheb 74, 115
Horn, deer 55
  gazelle 133
Horus 7, 27, 29, 34,36, 41, 51, 110, 135
Humour 89, 102
Hunting 86, 97, 104
Hyacinth 98
Hygiene 130
Hyksos 113
Hyoscyamine 102

Iber scent 109
Ibex 134
Ibis 43
Ibn Botlan 57
Ibn Qayyim al-Jawziyya 57
Ibn Sina (Avicenna) 57
Idhkir 16
Iinbu scent 83
Iker (sweet flag) 24
Iku (sesame) 31
Illyria 71
Imset (dill) 18, 117
Incense 7, 24–6, 33-9, 41, 43, 47, 49, 50–5, 56, 83, 92, 94, 95, 108–11, 130, 137
India 10, 16, 17, 23, 24, 28, 59, 67, 75, 137, 144, 145

Indigestion 25
Inektun herb 55
Inem (skin) 140
Inflammation 102, 118, 121, 122, 124, 133
Infusion 79, 121
Inhalation 99, 102, 113, 114, 125
Inhasaasenen 27
Ini, ship's captain 61
Intoxication 53, 92, 94, 101
Ipuky, sculptor 99
Iran 15
Iraq 13, 59, 103
Irinon, iris oil 69
Irinum, iris perfume 68, 69, 71
Iris 12, 19, 63, 68, 69, 71, 118
  albicans 19
  florentina 19
  oil 71, 118
Isis 7, 56
Islam 57, 69, 79, 141, 147
Istanbul 13, 41, 56, 103, 152
Itasin (fenugreek) 118
Ity 44
Iun (colour) 140
Iuncus odoratus 16
Ivy 102

Jamb, door 36, 47
Jar, ointment 6, 63, 70, 74, 115, 117, 137, 138, 141
Joints, pains in the 118
Judaea 19, 52, 58, 67, 71
Jujube (Ziziphus lotus) 81, 83
Juniper 10, 17, 21, 45, 49, 51, 52, 111, 116, 117, 119, 124
  oil 119
Juniperus communis 119
  excelsa 21
  oxycedrus 21
  phoenicea 21
Justinian 56

Kadjawar 83
Kalamos (sweet flag) 16
Kapet (kyphi) 47, 55
Kapt (fumigation) 49
Karcom (saffron) 23

Karnak 36, 38, 53, 95
Kebu water 134
Ked (Aleppo pine ?) 122
Kedem (city) 7
Kedria (juniper oil) 116, 119
Kedros (juniper oil) 21
Kenen (sweet flag ?) 24
Keni ('embrace') 94
Ken-enet (sweet flag) 24
Khaemwast 61
Khatti (land of the Hittites) 83
Khebeb vessel 40, 42
Khery 28
Khet-des (myrtle) 122
Khet en qed (resin of Aleppo pine) 29
Khet nedjem (cinnamon) 17
Khoiak, month of 106, 110, 144
Ki-risawi (antiu) 27
Kiki (castor-berry) 30
Kirgipa (or Giluhkepa) 81
Knn 24
Kohl (pigment) 116, 122, 137
Kom Ombo 44
Krinon (lily) 68
Kupar (kyphi) 50,51
Kush 15
Kypairos 72
Kypeiron 14
Kypeiros 17, 18, 72
Kyperos 72
Kyphonion 56
Kyphi 10, 14, 17, 21, 23, 24, 29, 33, 41, 46, 57, 59, 64, 111, 122, 124
Kypros 72

Labellum vessel 79
Laboratory 29, 37, 41, 51, 86, 99, 108, 110
Ladanum 81
Lanathos (sorrel ?) 52
Lapis lazuli 45, 137, 138
Laurel 16, 58, 79
Laurionite 137
Lawsonia inermis 19, 71
Laxative 116, 118
Lead 72, 136,137
Lebanon 15, 28, 108
Leeks 18
Leg of hound 134
Legs, swollen 115, 124
Lentiscus 29, 50
Lesbos 85
Leucas 71
Levant 7, 28
Libân (gum resin) 26
Libium (juniper) 21
Libya 15, 18, 67, 108, 110
Lice 130
Lilium candidum 68, 120
Lily 19, 21, 22, 68, 69, 120, 124
  oil 120
Limbs, decorated 141
  swollen 115,
  stiff 122, 124,
Linen 95,96, 99, 109, 130, 132, 136
Lion 55, 86, 88, 134
Lips 138, 140
Lip tint 138, 140
Liquidambar 83
Liver 48, 51, 56, 58
Loins, pains in the 122
Loret, Victor 14, 55, 56
Lotus 12, 22, 49, 62, 76, 78, 80, 81, 97, 102, 104, 108, 110, 111, 117, 121, 130, 140, 142
  oil 121
  scent 106
Lovage 118
Lovemaking 92, 94, 130
Lump of fat, scented 85, 96
Lung 48, 51
Lupin 133
Luxor 54, 92, 135
Lydia 56

Maa-maa . . . astiu (antiu) 27
Macedonian iris, white 71
Maceration 45, 51, 68, 69, 71, 73, 75, 78–80, 106, 114, 115, 118, 121
Madjet 30, 37, 43, 45, 81, 83, 106, 110
Magic 8, 34, 35, 36, 100, 106, 108, 130
Make-up 129, 135
Malachite 135, 136
Malgatta 83
Mandragora officinarum 100
Mandrake 100–103
  oil 121
Manetho 52
Manganese, bicarbonate of 134
Marjoram 22, 56, 74, 75, 79, 81, 83, 85, 115
  oil 121, 122
Marrow 116
Massage 113, 114, 116, 118, 119, 125
Mastic 29, 47, 50, 52, 54, 56, 78
Matet (celery ?) 115
Matricaria (camomile ?) 116
Maya (overseer of the treasury) 110, 121, 149
Medjat 15, 29
Megaleion 76,77, 81, 121, 123
Megalos 76
Megalus 76
Mehendi (oil of Lawsonia inernis) 19, 71
Melanthelaion (camomile oil) 116
Memphis 61, 83, 104, 115
Mendes 63, 65, 66
Mendesian', perfume, 'The 30, 65, 67, 77, 122
Mendesium 65
Menen (embalming tar, oil or resin) 45, 108, 111
Menstruation 115, 118, 121, 122, 124
Mereh nar (pine kernels) 21, 23
Merenra 6
Merhet (unguent) 108, 110
Mesdemet (stibium, eyepaint) 137
Meshib (antiu) 27
Mesopotamia 28, 79
Metopion (galbanum perfume) 66, 67, 122, 123
Metopium 29, 30
Milk 134, 135
Mimusops laurifolia 100
Min unguent, secret 45, 110, 111
Mint 22, 51, 54, 75, 111
Mirror 5, 53, 120, 126, 129, 140
Mitanni 81
Mith (wild celery) 115
Mitylene 74
Moringa oil 7, 30, 83, 108, 111, 116, 117, 135

Moringa oleifera 30
pterygosperma 30
Moringa shells 80
Mouth', 'Opening of the 22, 45, 108,109
Mucus 125
Mumia (bitumen of Judaea) 58
Mummification 7, 21, 29, 116, 119, 128, 141
Mummy 10, 17, 18, 22, 80, 94, 98, 110, 111, 115–117, 123, 134, 141
Muscatel 123
Muscles, treatment of injured 122
Mycene 7, 61, 73, 79, 80, 123, 124
Myrobalanos 59
Myrobalanum 30
Myrrh 17, 25–9, 33, 47, 49–53, 57–9, 63–5, 67, 68, 71–3, 75–7, 79, 83, 116, 122, 127
unguent 81
Myrtinum (myrtle unguent) 77
Myrtle 78
oil 122
Mys, Apollonios 66

Nabataea 15
Naharina 28, 81, 83, 134, 137
Nail colour 140
Nam-tar (mandragora ?) 102
Nar (iris) 19, 69
Narcotic 100, 121, 149
Nard 8, 10, 18, 23, 59, 74, 76, 79
Nardinon 23
Nardostachys 23
Narmer 127
Narona 71
Natron 132, 133, 135, 137
Nebamun, scribe of the granary 92, 94, 95, 105
Nebamun, sculptor 99
Neck, pain in the 118
Nedjem ('sweet tree') 38, 39, 41, 42, 45, 108, 111
Nefer 92, 105
Nefertari 138
Nefertiti 61, 138, 140
Neheh (sesame oil) 31, 134
Nekfitir (scent) 83
Nekhbet 34
'Nemti, herb of' (camel grass ?) 15
Nenib tree 29, 41
Nervous disorders 118
Nesmen (obscure ingredient of a sacred unguent) 108, 109
Nesti plant 45
Nicolaus, unguent-maker 56
Nisyrus 14
Niuben 24, 55
Nkepet (mint) 22
Nose, polyps in the 118
Nostrils, anointing the 118
Nubia 15, 101, 102, 140
Nudj (unguent ingredient) 36, 110
Nuhi-heri tree 28
Nut, black 30
Nut, sky-goddess 76
Nymphaea caerulea 97, 100
lotus 22, 97, 100

Obsidian 65, 86, 109, 134
Ochre 117, 124, 138
Oeno (soapwort) 132
Olive 18, 31
oil 19, 31, 67, 71, 72, 75, 77, 79, 122
Omphacium (green olive oil) 31, 67
'Opening of the Mouth' 22, 45, 108,109
Opium 58, 59
Opobalsamum 67, 81, 83
Opopanax resin 83
Oregano 74
Origanum 22, 75
Orikanon 22
Orpiment 140
Orris root 21, 25, 69, 118, 133
Osiris 7, 27, 29, 34, 43, 56, 91, 96, 106, 110, 137
Ostrich 55, 134
Ox 15, 18, 31, 37, 43, 44, 83, 85, 86, 88, 116, 124, 133, 134

Pain 16, 58, 102, 116, 118, 119, 122, 124
Painkiller 101, 102, 121
Palestine 61, 79
Palette, cosmetic 80, 127, 129, 136
Palm tree, date 89
trees, doum 25
Palm shoots 85
tops 69
wine 116
Pamphylia 71
Papyri, medical 17, 55, 56, 113, 116, 119, 133, 137
Papyrus Ebers 113
Edwin Smith 113
Harris I 54
Hearst 113
Parthey, G. 55, 56
Parthia 80
Patchouly 23
Pearl barley 133
Peas 125
Peker (Chaerophyllum sp.?) 51, 111
Peresh (kyphi) 21, 108
Perfume 9, 10, 12-14,18, 21, 22, 28, 30, 31, 46, 55, 61, 63, 64, 74, 80, 81, 83, 97, 115, 119, 121, 123, 128, 134
Perga 71
Peron, merchant 135
Persea tree 101
Persia 8, 13, 23, 29, 41, 67, 79
Perspiration 121, 125
Peru shenu (pine kernels) 22
Petese 53, 147
Phaselis, town in Lycia 80
Philae 15, 23, 47, 51, 54
Phoenicia 10, 21, 66-68, 80
Phosgenite 137
Phrenitis 124
Phthiriasis 116
Pigment 129, 140, 141
Piles 116
Pimples 133
Pine kernels 23
oil 122
Pinus halepensis 29
pinea 23
Pistacia atlantica 61
lentiscus 29, 50
terebinthus 29, 61
Pitch, wood 108
Plasters 114, 118
Pliny the Elder 8, 10, 12, 14, 15, 18, 19, 21, 24, 26, 28, 30, 61, 63, 65, 68, 71, 81,

85, 106, 114, 116, 120, 122, 124, 125, 133
Plutarch 16, 33, 52, 53, 55, 56, 59
Poem 91, 92, 98, 101, 102, 106, 130, 140
Poison 55, 57, 58, 82, 101
Pollen 80, 86, 115,116, 123
Polyp 118
Pomegranate 57, 78, 92
Poppy 99
Pork fat 85, 123
Porridge 124, 125, 130
Potash 132
Poultice 113, 114, 116, 118, 122, 124, 133
Precious 22nd Khoiak Unguent', 'The 110
Pregnancy 30
Prostitute 140
Protein 135
Psagdas (red unguent) 134
Psammetik 107
Psoriasis 122
Ptah 39
Pudenda 94
Puns 97, 102
Punt 7, 10, 17, 25, 28, 36,37, 137
Purification 33, 45, 53, 61, 128, 137
Purslane 1243Pylos 61, 79, 123
Pyramid Texts 12, 34, 55

Qasab al-zoreira (sweet flag) 23, 24
Qed (wood of Aleppo pine) 29
Quince 72

Radish 116
Raisins 48, 49, 52, 54, 56, 59, 117
Ramesses II 7, 38, 61, 80, 81, 113, 115, 123, 138
Ramesses III 31, 39, 54
Ramesses IV 54
Ramesseum 113
Ramose 134
Raven 130, 133
Razor 130
Realgar (sulphide of arsenic) 140
Reben (liquid seed extract) 39
Reed 15, 24, 136
Regimen sanitatis 57
Rekhmire 24
Reremt (mandrake) 101, 102
Resin 25, 28, 29, 45, 86
Retenu 28, 83
Rheumatism 16, 116
Rhizome 18, 45, 69, 111, 146
Rhodes 14, 18, 23, 63
Rhodinon (rose perfume) 79
Ricinus communis 30
Romans, Rome 8, 22, 47, 48, 78–80, 124, 137
Roots 18, 25, 63, 69
Rosa gallica 79
ricardii 79
Rosemary 133
Rose 14, 15, 77, 79
oil 122
Royal', perfume, 'The 80
Rue oil 123
Rufus of Ephesus 47, 48, 50, 55

Sacred Unguents', 'The Seven 108, 109
Saffron 23, 48, 50, 52, 58, 63
Sagdas (red unguent) 134
Sage 79
oil 80, 123
Sahure 138
St John's wort 14
Salt 30, 68, 72, 75, 77, 79, 80, 86, 123, 124, 135, 137
Salvia sclarea 80
Sampsuchinon 22, 83, 115, 121
Sampsuchinum (marjoram perfume) 74, 75
Sampsuchon 74
Sampsuchum 74, 75
Sampsucum (sweet marjoram) 22
Sangar (Sakarya in Turkey) 83
Santorin (or Thera, now Thíra) 18
Sappho 79
Saqqara 34
Sawdust 124
Sbin (cyperus grass) 17
Scabritias 116
Scabs 119
Scala 12, 17
Scalp massage 118
Schoenus (Andropogon schoenanthus ?) 15
Schoinos 15, 16, 24
Scopolamine 102
Scorpion 55, 116
Scroll 26, 36, 47, 98, 102, 106, 113
Sedative 24, 99, 100, 101,102, 122
Sedge (Cyperus grass) 17
Seduction 92, 129, 130
Sef wan (juniper oil) 21
Sefet (fir resin oil) 28, 108, 118
Sefy bitumen 45, 108
Segebyn 7
Segenen oil 134
Sekhet 104
Senenmut 117
Senet 111
Senetjer 28, 51, 96, 130, 134
Serichatrum (shrub) 81
Serpent 49, 57, 58, 134
Sesame oil 31, 71, 110, 134
Sesamum indicum 31
Seseli 52, 57
Seshen (lotus) 22
Seven Sacred Unguents', 'The 108, 109
Sexuality 92, 97, 100, 106, 121, 127, 128, 130, 141, 142
Shampoo 132, 133
Shaving 130
Sheba 67
Shebet (mastic) 55
Shebi nedjem ('sweet rush') 24
Shebin (cyperus grass) 17
Shell 30, 39, 63, 70, 80, 86, 114, 136
Shena berries 21
Shesh 134
Skin care 134
Soap 132, 133
Soap-stone 132
Soapwort (Saponaria officinalis) 132
Sokaris 111
Solid perfume 123
Spikenard 23, 48, 52, 81
Spoon, cosmetic or incense 43, 48, 49, 64, 85, 88, 89
Stakte 30
Sun disc, see Aten
Suppository 117, 123
Susinum (lily perfume) 22, 68, 69

Sweet flag 23, 24
Sycamore 45, 124, 130, 138
Synthetic eyepaint 137
Syracuse 76
Syria, Syriac 10, 14, 15, 21, 24, 29-31, 50, 58, 65, 74, 101, 102, 118, 122, 134, 146
Syrup 124

Tadpole 25, 133
Takhsi 83
Tampon 115
Tapeworm 119
Taquinum sanitatis 57
Tar 46
Tashere 92
Tattoo 141, 142
Tefnet 96
Tekhu seeds 42, 108
Tepenen (cumin oil) 116
Terebinth 29, 61
Teti 134
Thebes 7, 24, 30, 58, 74, 83, 94, 95, 102, 104, 113, 116, 134, 138, 141
Theophrastus 8, 12, 14, 18, 21, 24, 29, 31, 63, 66, 68, 69, 71, 76, 79, 81, 106, 114, 118, 122, 123
Thighs, tattoo on 141, 142
Thmuis 66
Thorn (aspalathos) 14
Thoth 27, 34
Throwstick 97, 105
Thyme 75, 81, 123, 124
Tigris 101
Tilapia fish 104, 133
Tiryac 47, 57, 59, 113
Tisheps 17, 24, 41, 43, 45, 110, 111, 116
Tit en qet (pine resin ?) 39
Toe remedy 124
Toes, painted 141
Toilet 130
Toiletries 151
Toothache 102, 122
Tooth, donkey's 134
Toxic 30
Tralles, Alexander from 56
Trance 101
Trees 21, 25, 28, 31, 36, 37, 55, 101, 108, 118
Trefoil 14, 15
Triacle 57
Trigonella foenum-graecum 118
Tua 108, 109
Tumours 114
Tunip (city in the Levant) 7
Turkey 47, 58, 61
Turpentine 28, 67, 145
Turquoise 45
Tutankhamun 4, 21, 26, 28, 30, 31, 46, 54, 61, 84, 86, 90, 97, 100, 106, 109, 110, 121, 124, 130, 138
Tuthmosis III 7, 24, 36, 73, 83, 109
Tuya 10
Tyre (Lebanese town) 7

Ulcers 119, 122, 133
Ulu Burun (Turkish town) 61, 64
Unas 34, 35
Unguent cone 96, 97, 104, 142
Urinary disorder 124
Uterus 115, 123, 125

Valerian 23, 86
Vermifuge 16
Vervet 142
Vinegar 102, 123, 124, 133
Vomiting 123
Vulva 114, 118, 121, 122

Wan 21
Washing 130, 132, 133, 135
Wawat, land of 28
Wax 85, 111, 116, 124, 132, 134
Weariness 118
Werekh unguent 110
'Wet chemistry' 137
Wig 80, 85, 92, 96, 98, 104, 106, 129, 130, 130, 132, 134, 136, 140, 142
Wildcat 82
Willow 124
Womb 98, 106
Wool 122, 132
Wound 7, 114, 122, 124
Wrinkles 134
Wukhizzi 83

Xylobalsamum 75

Ziziphus lotus 19, 81, 124,145